READER'S DIGEST
compendium of
puzzles &brain teasers

READER'S DIGEST
compendium of

puzzles
&brain
teasers

Published by
The Reader's Digest
Association Limited

LONDON NEW YORK
SYDNEY MONTREAL

*

Reader's Digest Compendium of
Puzzles & Brain Teasers
was edited and designed by The Reader's
Digest Association Limited, London.

First edition Copyright © 2000
The Reader's Digest Association Limited,
11 Westferry Circus, Canary Wharf, London
E14 4HE.

www.readersdigest.co.uk

Copyright © 2000 Reader's Digest
Association Far East Limited.
Philippines Copyright © 2000 Reader's
Digest Association Far East Limited.

Printed in Belgium

ISBN 0 276 42449 2

Reader's Digest Compendium of Puzzles & Brain Teasers
was commissioned, edited, designed and produced by:
Book Creation Services, 21 Carnaby Street, London
Managing Director: Hal Robinson

Editor	Alison Moore
Assistant Editor	Martin Griffiths
Art Editor	Jill Adams
Senior Designer	Keith Miller
Designers	Beatriz Waller, Ann Thomson, Claudia Randall, Eno
Copy Editor	Charles Phillips
Puzzle Editors	Ken Russell, Philip Carter
Picture Researcher	Elizabeth Loving
Consultant	David Bodycombe

For Reader's Digest

Editor	Jonathan Bastable
Art Editor	Joanna Walker
Editorial Assistant	Jenny Rathbone
Proofreader	Barry Gage

Reader's Digest General Books

Editor	Cortina Butler
Art Director	Nick Clark
Executive Editor	Julian Browne
Development Editor	Ruth Binney
Publishing Projects Manager	Alastair Holmes
Style Editor	Ron Pankhurst

Contributors
Tony Augarde, David Bodycombe, Brainwarp, Erwin Brecher,
Guy Campbell and Paul Moran, Philip Carter, Brian Greer, Aileen Hall,
C.J. Jones, Don Manley (Quixote), Chris Maslanka, Michael Mepham,
Anna Nilsen, Jeffery Pike, Probyn Puzzles, Puzzlemakers, Ken Russell,
Justin Scroggie, Alan Simmons, Thinks.com Ltd

12–57 mind mazes

An array of 3D and perceptual puzzles to keep your neurons on their toes.

Visual conundrums
14–19 Spot the differences, spot the sames and other visual challenges to get you started.

Into the labyrinth
20–21 A wander round some mazes and labyrinths – the myths, the folklore and the strange geometry.

Maze puzzles
22–33 Be amazed by this selection of labyrinthine puzzles. There is always a way out.

Colours and shapes
34–41 Shape and colour-linking, sorting and arranging – find out how good you are at combining vision and logic.

Tricky tangrams
42–45 Come to the shape of things. Chinese tangrams have been played for thousands of years. Test your ability to build up the bigger picture.

Missing cubes
46 Maths or logic? – you decide.

Sokoban
46–47 An introduction to the Japanese game of warehouse clearance and removal men.

Engineering puzzles
48–51 Weighing and weighing up – a little applied physics will see you through these puzzles.

Battleships
52–53 A true test of diagrammatic logic. Seek out and destroy the enemy ships.

Optical illusions
54–57 Images and puzzles which encourage you to question the solid world around you.

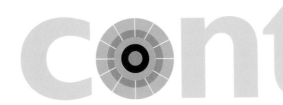

contents

58–109 word power

Anyone who has ever uttered a sentence or written a word will enjoy these puzzles.

Word puzzles assorted
60–65 Under starter's orders with this selection of anagrams, synonyms, oxymorons and other posers.

Doing a cryptic crossword
66–67 A useful guide to understanding the warped logic of crossword setters. Even the most experienced cruciverbalist might learn something.

Crosswords
68–83 Crosswords come in all shapes and sizes – here you'll see them in their many different guises.

Acrostics
84–87 Four pages of simple and double acrostics to test your general knowledge and ingenuity.

Lexiconfusion
88–89 How good is your vocabulary – 75 questions to test all levels of ability.

Linking puzzles
90–91 Can you bridge the gap with these puzzles, which require you to link letters and words?

Wordsearches
92–97 Enjoy these familiar wordsearch puzzles, but beware – some contain tricky twists.

The tricks of the tongue
98–99 Word games are as old as speech, and new verbal amusements are being coined all the time.

Triple word score
100–101 Scrabble problems for old hands and neophytes alike.

Orthography starts with O
102–103 Find out if your spelling's up to scratch.

Beat the clock
104–105 A time challenge in which your goal is to complete a wide array of puzzles in less than an hour.

Play on words
106–109 Juggle words as you cut, paste and rearrange to reach the solutions.

110–137 smart solutions

Fill in grids and solve devious codes. You will need to do some deductive reasoning to finish this chapter.

Logic problems with grids
112–115 Use the grids to help work out the answers in this first section of logic problems.

Logic problems without grids
116–117 Now you've had some practice, try some logic puzzles without grids.

Games puzzles
118–121 A series of puzzles based on popular and familiar games.

Cipherword puzzles
122 Substitute letters for numbers to fill in the grids and find the missing words.

In a safe place
123 Pit your wits and crack the safe with these visual and spatial puzzles.

The Clambake Kid
124 Read the tale of The Clambake Kid and see if you can work out how he broke free from jail.

Matchstick mayhem
125 Try your hand at these popular puzzles, but be careful not to burn your fingers.

Undercover writing
126–127 Codes and how to break them. Learn the lessons of the Enigma machine and Rosetta stone.

Codes
128–133 Two pages of cracking code puzzles.

Chuck Diamond P.I.
135 Fancy yourself as a private detective, or a Sherlock *manqué* – then help Chuck solve the case.

In for a penny
136 These visual challenges all involve coins. Master their secrets to increase your self-worth.

138–175 figure it out

Numbers won't bite, so don't be afraid to take on these mathematical challenges.

Riddlemarithmetic
140–143 Bewildering problems that need a careful approach.

Natural sums
144–145 A selection of real-life problems with numerical solutions.

Creation by numbers
146–147 From a tiger's stripes to a grain of snow, the surprising mathematics of nature.

Figure skating
148–151 See how fast you can do it.

Graphic dilemma
152–153 Graphs and charts made fun.

Mathematical mazes
154–155 Complete the sums to finish the mazes.

A sporting bent
156–157 Forecast the winners and losers in these league tables.

One of our numbers is missing
158–161 Study the sequences and find the missing number – X marks the spot.

Time travel
162–163 A selection of problems all based around the theory of time.

Square deals
164 Traditional number squares – some with a difference.

Pyramid games
165 Use a logical approach to fill in the bricks on each pyramid.

Something to add
166–169 Arithmetical problems involving grids, dates, jugs and money.

Nonograms
170–171 Fill in the squares to reveal the picture.

Cards, dice and dominoes
172–175 Take your place at the table. It's time to shuffle the pack.

176–191 think sideways

To complete these lateral thinking puzzles you'll need an alternative approach and an open mind.

First steps
178–181 A few gentle exercises to get you into the lateral way of thinking.

Double it up
182–183 A selection of two-player games – but is it a level playing field?

Thinking round corners
184–185 What makes a lateral thinker? Can the principles of lateral thinking change the world?

On the rebuses
186–187 These are pictures of hidden words, a kind of charades on paper.

Riddle-me-re
188–189 Riddles are the oldest word-tease of all. See how you cope with some new-minted ones.

Picture this
190–191 An attempt to bewilder and confuse – can you solve these visual lateral puzzles?

192–219 train your brain

A wide range of puzzles – language and numbers, spatial awareness, visual acuity and memory tests.

Next in line
194–196 Visual tasks that require you to find the next in a sequence.

Creative thinking
197 A fun and alternative approach to answering questions – there is no right or wrong.

Mother tongue
198–199 Explore some of the dustier corners of the English language.

Trial by numbers
200–201 These numbers are weapons to joust with: the sharp-edged 7, the pointed 4.

Visual analysis
202–203 Pit your wits against this range of visual and spatial puzzles.

Let's get technical
204–205 Complete these challenges to prove there's an engineer inside you somewhere.

Cerebral pentathlon
206–209 An Olympic challenge for brain athletes.

Mental agility
210–211 Climb ropes, crawl through tunnels, swing across rivers – all in your mind.

Remember, remember
212–213 What is memory, how does it work, and what can you do to improve it?

Memory trays
214–215 Two trays of items to recall in this traditional parlour game.

Total recall
216–219 Stories and tasks that test your ability to retain detail in your short-term memory.

220–251 tricky trivia

Dozens of variations on the general knowledge quiz. Fingers on buzzers…

From A to Z
222–223 Alphabetical questions on literary characters, living things and authors.

Identity parade
224–225 Do you know that face?

Ask the family
226–229 Colour coded questions for everyone.

At the movies
230–231 The world of showbiz under the spotlight.

Natural born teasers
232–233 From dinosaurs to doctors and maths to mammals – how much do you know?

Gridlock
234–235 Can you answer the questions correctly and complete the grids?

Mother Earth
236–237 Questions on the green planet. All the answers are somewhere beneath your feet.

A starter for ten
238–239 Why are quizzes so popular, and how should you go about organizing your own?

It's a classic
240 Rounds for concert goers and art fiends.

X marks the spot
241 Follow the trail of questions to find the treasure.

Rule Britannia
242–243 Questions on the sceptered isle.

Tell me a story
244–245 What do you know about books and the people who write them?

History is bunk
246–249 Prepare to engage with these posers on headlines, battles, world events and famous leaders.

The sound of music
250–251 Musical teasers, old and new, each based around a theme.

Four thousand years ago, when the peoples of Europe were scratching a living from the soil with wooden ploughs and stone axes, the scribes and priests of Babylon were using puzzles to teach mathematics to boys.

Puzzle pioneers

We do not know what form those Babylonian puzzles took. It is reasonable to suppose that some of them were ancestors of the kind of problems you will find on page 168 of this book.

The earliest known puzzle is barely 2000 years old. It is the *loculus Archimedis* or Archimedes' box, also known as the *ostomachion*, and it was a cross between a jigsaw and a tangram. It had 14 pieces which could be rearranged to form a square (for comparison, see the visuospatial awareness puzzles on page 258). The same pieces could be put together to form interesting images – the manuscripts mention an elephant. (For the Chinese version of this idea, see the puzzles on pages 42-45.)

Puzzles can be as diverse as life itself. If you were to plot the natural history of the puzzle, you would have to draw a huge family tree in which some ancient branches become extinct, while others evolve and give rise to entirely new species.

Crosses, cubes and saws

The crossword, for example, is a 20th-century invention, the brainchild of a newspaperman named Arthur Wynne. The Adam-and-Eve of every Down-and-Across appeared in the New York *World* in 1913. The hardest clue in it reads 'The fibre of the gomuti palm', and the answer is (of course) 'doh'.

The crossword was only ever intended as a bit of fun. Many other puzzles were conceived with didactic intent. The first jigsaws depicted maps: they were invented in the 18th century by John Spilsbury, an engraver, to help children learn geography. Rubik's cube was designed to help architecture students think in three dimensions. Nobody, least of all Mr Erno Rubik himself,

expected this hexahedral *jeu d'esprit* to turn into a global craze.

Puzzling is good for you

It is no accident that some puzzles began as mere games, and others as tools of learning. The best puzzles are both: mental fitness demands at least 20 minutes' hard exercise every day, and puzzles provide this.

Puzzles also develop the three elements of intelligence: analytical, creative and practical (the puzzles in this book stretch all of them). Puzzles are a means of conquering boredom and depression. They are what psychologist Mihaly Csikszentmihalyi has called a 'flow-producing activity': they open you up to a feeling of personal discovery, self-control and satisfaction.

And puzzling is great fun. The mental benefits are, in the end, a by-product of the enjoyment. Having fun is not a luxury or a waste of time. As the poet Heinrich Heine wrote: 'Anyone who regards games simply as games and work as work has understood little of either.'

Chapter by chapter

The puzzles in the *Reader's Digest Compendium of Puzzles & Brain Teasers* are gathered into seven chapters. Each one tests a different skill.

All the puzzles are graded with a level of difficulty. If you are uncertain about a particular kind of challenge, do try some of the level 1 puzzles. You might be surprised to find that you enjoy them, and are soon tackling levels 2 and 3.

Mind mazes contains perceptual puzzles: spot-the-differences, tangrams and optical illusions. They require a good eye and a sharp mind.

Word power tests the many forms of linguistic ability with crosswords, anagrams and synonyms, word ladders and verbal conundrums.

Smart solutions is about logic and deductive reasoning. You should bring a detective's mind and a code-breaker's skills to these puzzles.

Figure it out explores numbers and arithmetic. Many people are daunted by maths, which is strange. We all perform complicated calculations every minute of the day as we use money, judge distances, cook or count. Maths is as natural and instinctive as speech.

Think sideways exercises the least-used parts of your mind. Flexibility and suppleness are an important part of mental fitness.

Train your brain looks at intelligence and memory. How does your brain react to a challenge; can you see the patterns in shapes, words and sequences?

Tricky trivia probes your knowledge, and your ability to retrieve that knowledge on demand.

The answers are at the back of the book. Usually the answer to a puzzle is self-explanatory once you see it. Where this is not the case, we have included an explanation of the means by which the solution was reached.

Making the most of your book

This book comes with an acetate sheet and a dry-wipe pen, which allow you to use the book without writing directly onto the page. The sheet can be wiped clean with a tissue. New acetates and pens can be bought at stationers'. You are also free to photocopy any pages if you wish.

As you use the book, you may come up with alternative methods or solutions to the puzzles. If you do, or if you have any other comments about the puzzles, please e-mail us at: gbeditorial@readersdigest.co.uk

We will be glad to hear from you.

A word of advice before you begin.

Resist the temptation to turn straight to the answers when you tackle a puzzle. The solutions are easy to find in the back of the book, but they are also lurking in the back of your brain. Look for them there.

All the answers are within your grasp.

mind

In every waking moment your mind is drawing maps and pictures of the world. Without a highly developed sense of spatial awareness, we could not cross a road, lift a teacup,

mazes

or recognize a familiar face. The puzzles in this chapter test those powers: how good are you at processing the images that bombard your brain?

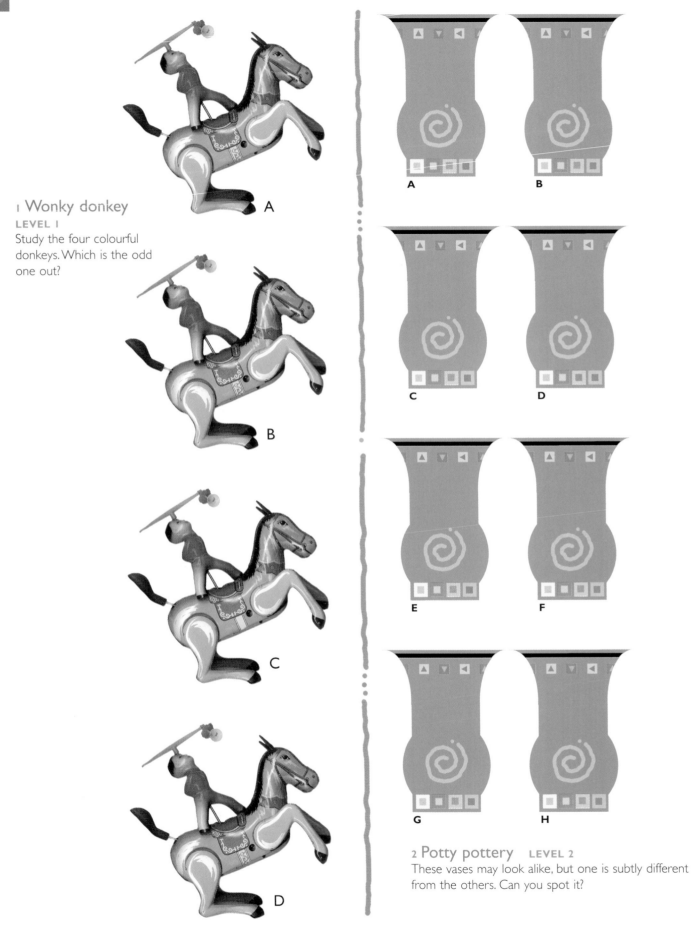

1 Wonky donkey
LEVEL 1
Study the four colourful donkeys. Which is the odd one out?

2 Potty pottery LEVEL 2
These vases may look alike, but one is subtly different from the others. Can you spot it?

3 Hitching a lift   LEVEL 2

Examine the two country scenes below. How many differences can you spot
between A and B? Give yourself 10 minutes to complete the puzzle.

4 Spot the dog

LEVEL 1

Study the eight dogs to the right. They may look similar, but only two are identical. Can you spot which two?

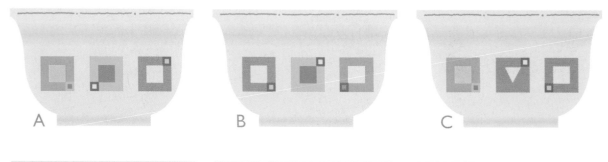

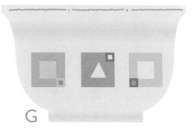

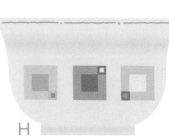

5 Soup's up! LEVEL 1

Ruth wants to buy two identical soup bowls for her husband Don. Can you help her to identify the only two above that match?

6
Life's a beach
LEVEL 1
Mull over this beach scene for 30 seconds. It may look idyllic, but something's not right. Can you spot the interloper?

A

B

C

D

E

F

G

H

I

7 Scene of the crime LEVEL 2

Charlie the cat burglar is up to no good again! Unfortunately for Charlie things don't work out quite as he had planned. Can you arrange scenes A–I in the correct order to show how Charlie learns that crime truly does not pay?

8 The impossible room LEVEL 2

How observant are you? Take a look at the room below; look a bit closer – things are not quite as they seem. In fact, we've found more than 20 things wrong with this room – how many can you spot? Give yourself 15 minutes to complete the puzzle.

MINI MAZE

Maze-like designs are found in every civilization the world over. These pocket-sized labyrinth games were discovered in the Indus valley in India.

Mazes are an ancient human fascination. Abstract spiral designs found on a rock tomb in Sardinia, Italy, are estimated to be have been carved nearly 4000 years ago. But the central maze myth is the tale of the labyrinth at Knossos in Crete. It was built by Daedalus, father of Icarus, to contain the minotaur – which was half-man, half-bull. The beast lived on human sacrifices, and was slain by one of its intended victims, the Athenian hero Theseus. In medieval times, labyrinths were believed to be able to entrap evil spirits. Sailors would take a turn round one to exorcise them before setting off on a voyage. Modern mazes still exert a kind of magic. Walking a good maze is like picking a lock from the inside; it is a twisted geometric mystery ripe for unravelling.

Into the labyrinth

JERUSALEM ROADS

The design on the floor of Chartres Cathedral (below) in France is one of many mazes in Christian tradition. The faithful would traverse the winding pattern on hands and knees as an act of penance. This task was set for those who could not make the pilgrimage to the Holy Land, and so such mazes were known as *chemins de Jérusalem*. The centre of the maze was called *ciel* – paradise.

MINOTAUR IN THE MIDDLE

It may be that the story of Theseus and the minotaur (above) is a folk memory of the cult of the bull and of the labyrinthine palace buildings of ancient Knossos. But the real power of the myth comes from its deep symbolism. There have been many interpretations of the story, but to the modern mind the dark maze with the monster at its heart looks like a picture of the subconscious mind – the wild and dangerous instincts that humanity strives to contain or destroy.

ROYAL AMUSEMENTS

Mazes were often a feature of formal gardens in the 18th century. But the classic circle-in-a-square hedge maze at Hever Castle (below) is a modern puzzle. It was planted in 1905, near the house where Henry VIII wooed Anne Boleyn.

A PATH TO GOD

The medieval Christian labyrinth (copied here on the exterior of the Watts Chapel in Surrey, England) has seven concentric rings – a symbolic number – and is an elaboration of the form of the cross. Its twists and turns are often taken to represent the long and circuitous journey of the believer to God.

STEP FORWARD

Not every maze is a symbol – some are just puzzles, like this big foot at a playground in Bickton, England. There have been modern mazes made of cars; there are mazes shaped like ships or snowflakes; there are mazes based on mirrors, flags, and bridges. It seems almost anything can be made into a maze.

9 Lost in squares

LEVEL 1

Can you find your way
to the middle of the
mystical maze below,
starting at the arrow?
Give yourself 5 minutes
to complete the puzzle.

10 Maddening maze LEVEL 1

Here's another intricate pathway to confound and confuse you. Once again start at the arrow and follow your feet to the centre of the maze. Try to complete the puzzle within 5 minutes.

These mazes are a test of colour perception as well as sense of direction. You may only travel from a pink block to a yellow one, from a yellow block to a blue one, from a blue block to a green one and from a green block to a pink one on your way to the destination.

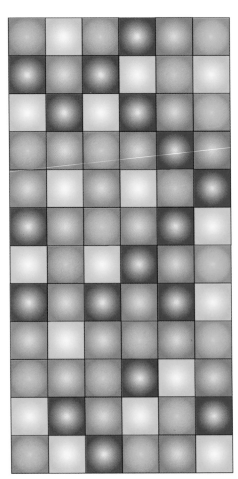

11 Disco lights LEVEL 2

Cross the bridge maze from bottom to top. You do not have to start at a pink square but you must follow the correct colour sequence. Diagonal moves are disallowed.

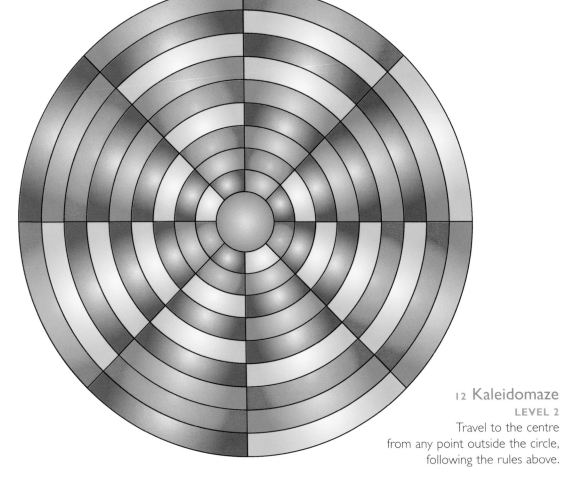

12 Kaleidomaze
LEVEL 2
Travel to the centre
from any point outside the circle,
following the rules above.

13 Tiny circles   LEVEL 2

Round and round the maze does go,
find the centre, off you go. (Start at
the arrow to the left of the maze.)

14 Spy relay LEVEL 2

A group of highly trained female operatives plan to steal some top-secret government papers. Each is sent a strip of photographs showing the route she should take, with the instruction not to turn back. At the point where the routes cross, they hand the papers to the next in the chain. The last spy puts the papers in a secret hideout somewhere on her route. In order to find the top-secret papers, match the photographs to the routes and mark each one on the acetate sheet. The first three spies hand the papers from one to the other at the point where their paths cross. Now work out the order in which they pass the papers along the chain to discover the parcel's secret location.

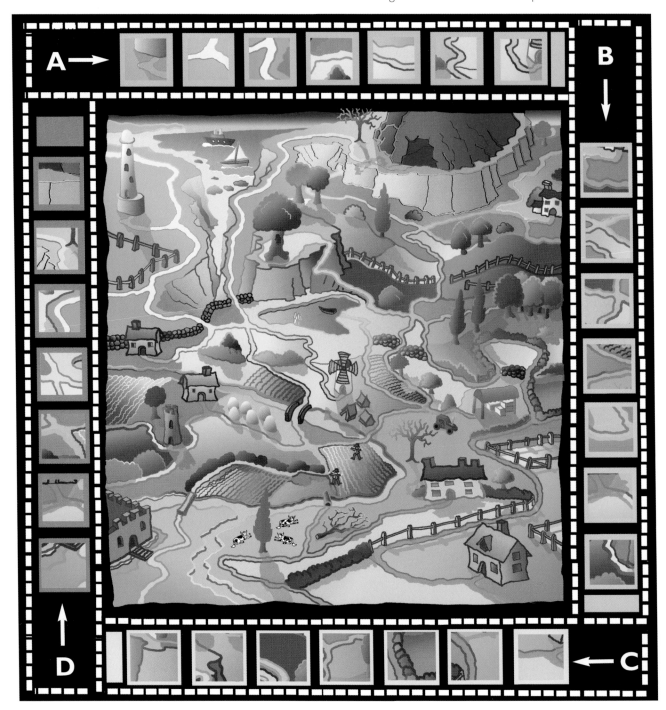

15 The tomb of the pharaohs   LEVEL 3

When Egyptologists first discovered the pyramids, the resting places of the pharaohs, they moved breathlessly from room to room in search of riches. Egyptian pyramids had only a few chambers, but our burial monument is filled with rooms. Starting somewhere in the large ground floor chamber, you play the role of the explorer, gathering the three icons in order (), then taking them to the very top room of the pyramid. You are not allowed to enter any room in the pyramid more than once, except the large ground floor room where you started. If you wish, you can use the acetate sheet to mark out your route as you go.

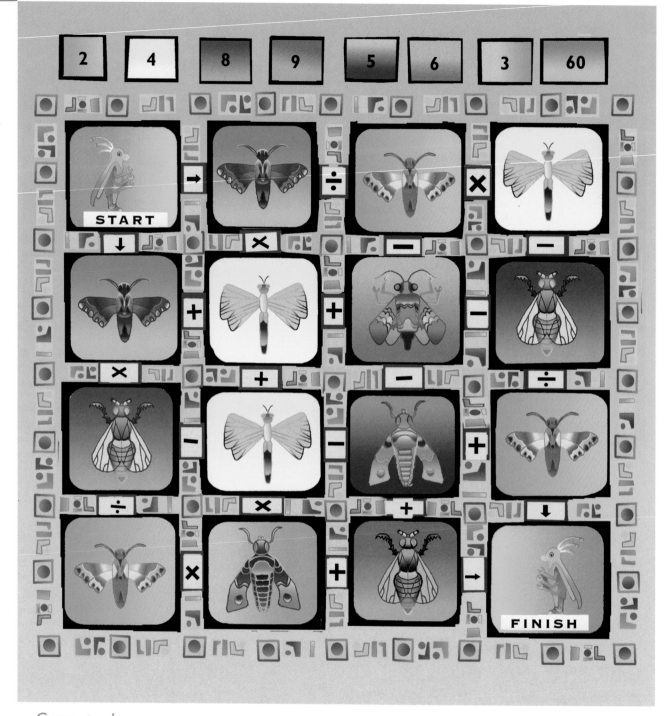

16 Computer bug LEVEL 2

A nasty virus has entered your computer network. To exterminate it, you must track the highest scoring route and the lowest scoring route from start to finish, using the acetate sheet to track your journey. Each monitor has a numerical value, which you can identify by checking the colour-coded number bar at the top (the start and finish boxes have no values). Start by choosing which direction to take. Carefully decode the relevant monitor and write down the number. Move to the next monitor. Having decoded the new monitor, apply the relevant mathematical operator (+, −, ÷ or x) between the two monitors to get an accumulated score, keeping a record of your score as you progress. You may enter each monitor only once.

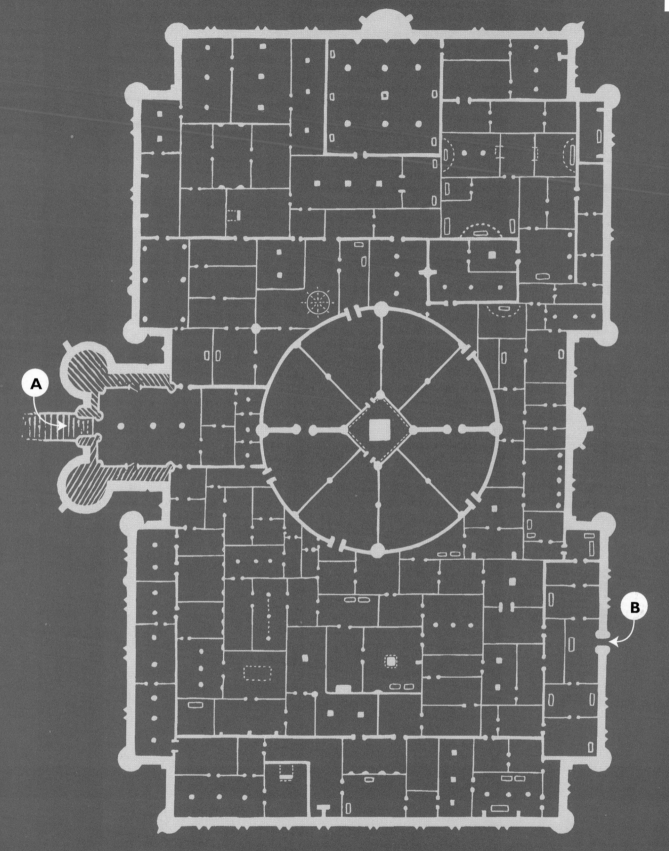

17 Escape plan   LEVEL 2
Hans the burglar entered the palace through the front door (A) and
proceeded to the central atrium, where he took a statuette from its plinth.
He made his escape through the open window (B) at the back of the
building. Can you trace his route through the open doors from start to finish?

18 Paradise and purgatory LEVEL 2

You are trapped in a strange dream-like world. In order to escape, you must ring the bell in the cloud in the sky – but beware of getting stuck in purgatory! Follow the object trail by selecting one of the three crystals in the group adjacent to the Start position on the opposite page. Find its identical partner somewhere on these two pages, then choose another object from that group and see where it leads you. The matching pair may be in a crystal or in a bubble, so look carefully before you move on. Draw your routes on the acetate sheet to find the best path, and time your journey to see how quickly you can escape (it is possible to escape the maze by picking five pieces only).

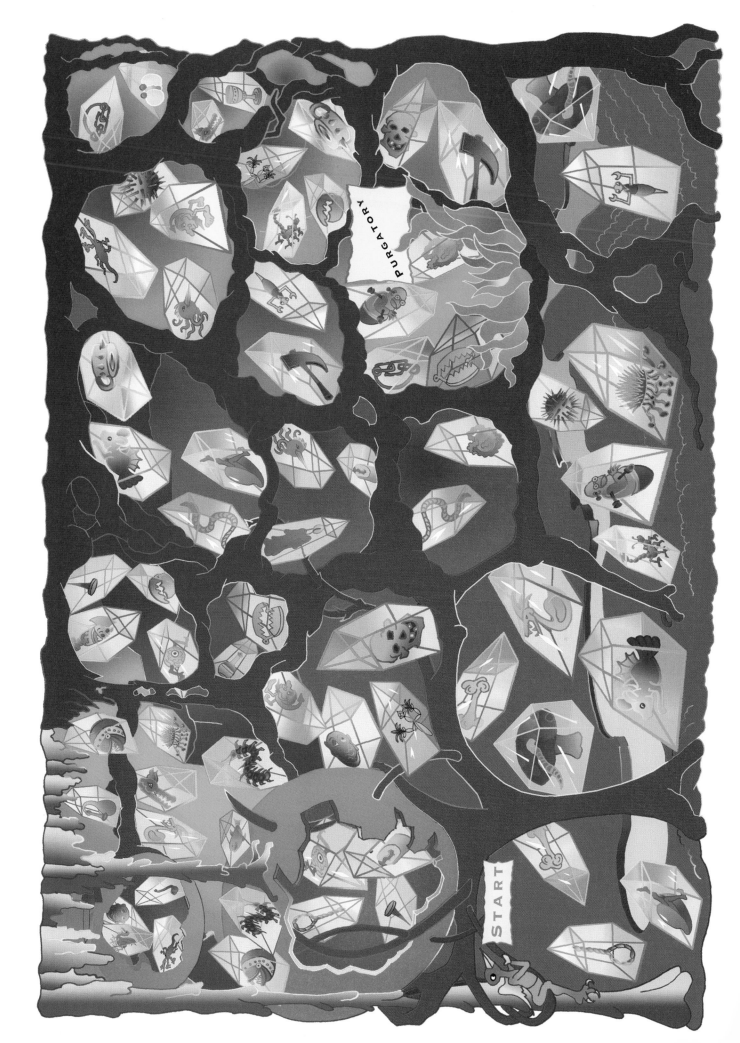

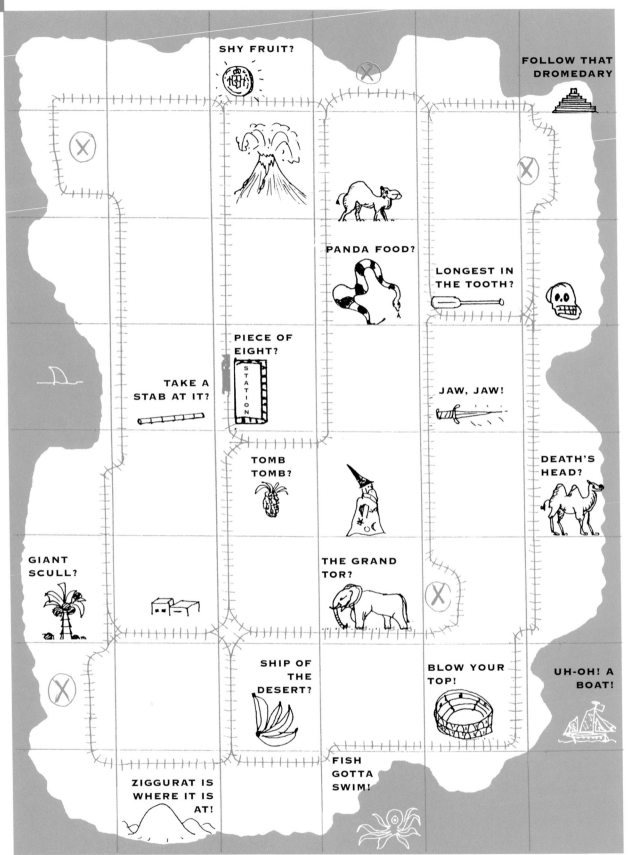

SHY FRUIT?

FOLLOW THAT
DROMEDARY

PANDA FOOD?

LONGEST IN
THE TOOTH?

PIECE OF
EIGHT?

STATION

TAKE A
STAB AT IT?

JAW, JAW!

DEATH'S
HEAD?

TOMB
TOMB?

GIANT
SCULL?

THE GRAND
TOR?

SHIP OF
THE
DESERT?

BLOW YOUR
TOP!

UH-OH! A
BOAT!

FISH
GOTTA
SWIM!

ZIGGURAT IS
WHERE IT IS
AT!

19 Treasure Island express LEVEL 2

Pirate Black Bart's treasure is buried on Deadlock Island.
As usual, X marks the spot – but which one?
Begin at the square containing the station. The word clue
there will lead you to a picture answer in another square.
Now destroy all the track in that square, and use the word

clue in that square to find the next picture answer.
Carry on solving clues and destroying track until the
trail of clues and answers runs out. Now return to the
station and board the train. If you have destroyed the
right bits of track, there will be only one X you can
reach by train. And that's where the treasure is.

20 The Kempe Castle kidnappers LEVEL 2

Professor Keslake had no sooner found a way to turn iron into gold than he was kidnapped and taken to Kempe Castle. The next day, a poacher, Bert Baggs, was caught in the grounds. He was blindfolded, taken to the Castle and put into a cupboard while the kidnappers checked his story. Luckily they released him unharmed. Baggs (in fact an undercover spy) went to the police and told them exactly what he remembered after waking up in the cupboard. From Baggs's statement and the floor-plan, can you work out which cupboard Baggs woke up in, what route he was led and where the Professor is hidden?

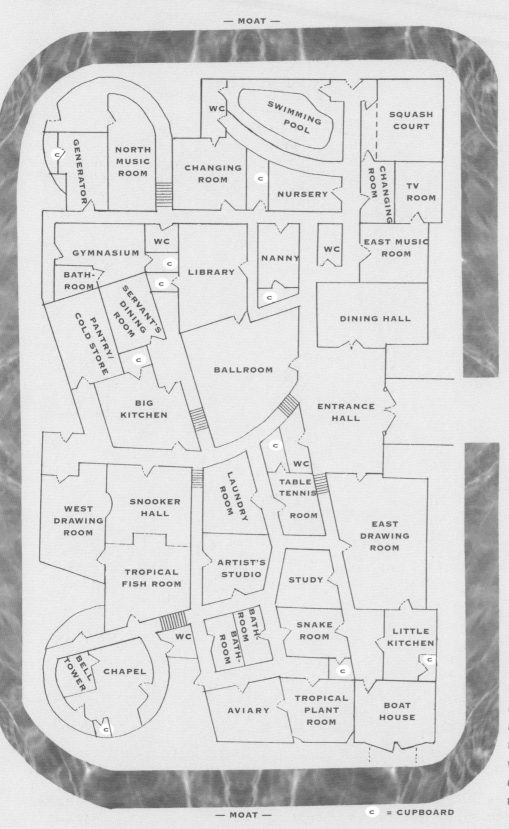

— MOAT —

— MOAT —   Ⓒ = CUPBOARD

'When they took me out of the cupboard, I was in a really warm place. There was a low humming sound. We went through a door on the right and turned left down a corridor. After a while we turned left again. I could hear an odd but distant sound – like balls being hit. We turned left – again! – and then right. Some water was running beside me. Then I nearly fell down some steps.

'We went right, into another very warm room. There was a strange smell, like strong food. We went through another door, and I could hear muffled sounds, like cutlery on plates, I think. We left that room, turned right. As I walked I could definitely smell food and hear balls being hit – though it sounded clearer than last time. The corridor curved to the left, and I was guided up some more steps. We turned left into another room. It was very echoey. I slipped and felt a wooden floor under my hands. Then we went into another room, which was quite different – the sound was muffled, there was carpet, and a musty smell.

'We took a door to the right out of that room, then turned left and left again. I smelt sweat. A flute was being played close by, and there was the hum of an engine or a motor. We turned left, then took a left into another room. There they took off my blindfold. The lights were off, but I saw – just for a moment – the cupboard where they are hiding the professor.'

In each of these puzzles the aim is to draw lines linking the circles of like colours. Sounds easy? The difficult part is making sure that none of the lines crosses any other.

22 Relate eight LEVEL 1

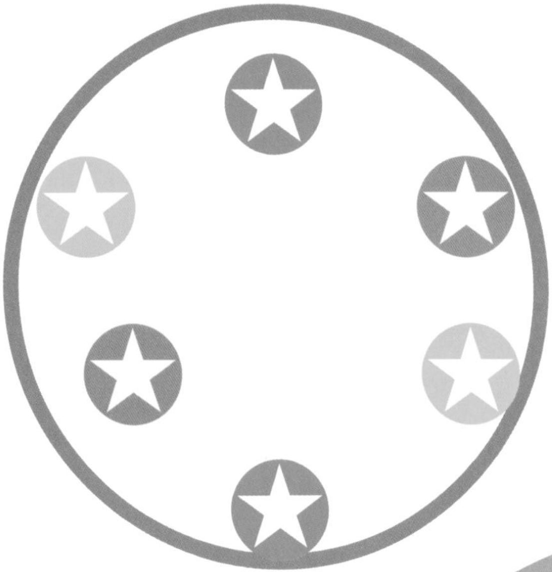

21 Connect six LEVEL 1

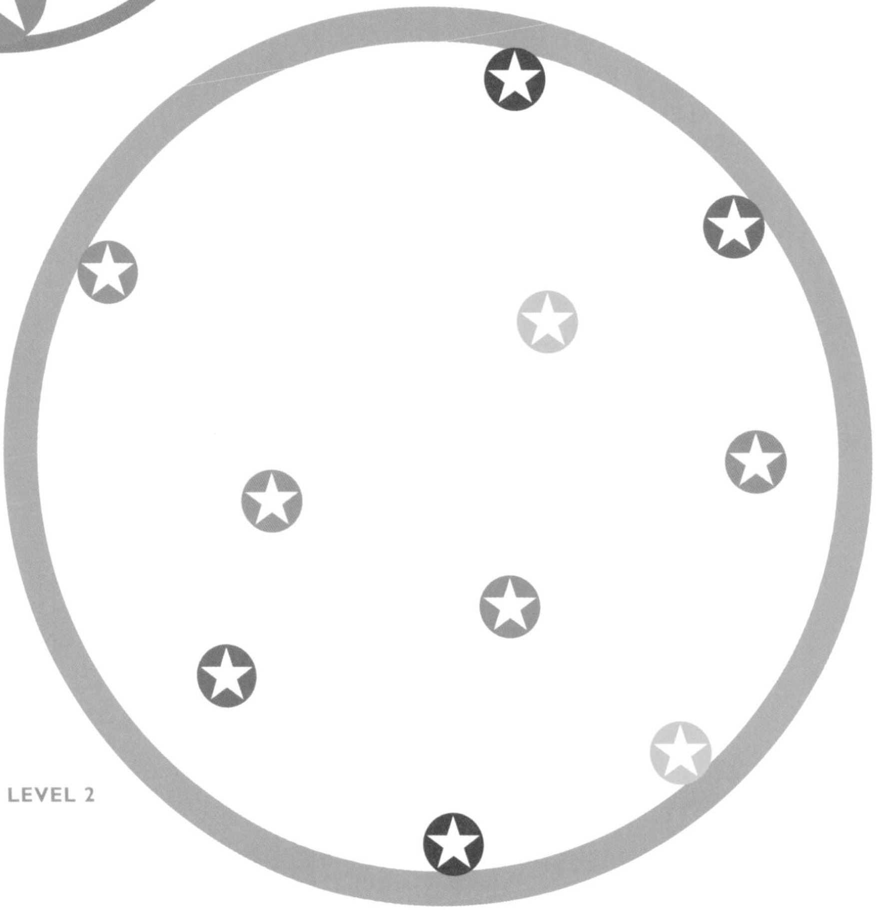

23 Five to five LEVEL 2

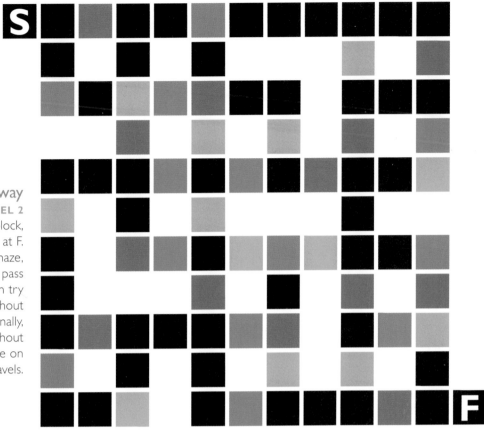

24 Three-way freeway
LEVEL 2

Trace a route from block to block, starting from S and finishing at F. The first time you try the maze, find a way that does not pass through any pink squares. Then try the puzzle again, this time without touching any green squares. Finally, pass through the maze without encountering a blue square on your travels.

25
Constellation
LEVEL 2

Follow the black lines from S to F. To make it more difficult, you may only move from one shape to the next if they have the same shape and/or colour.

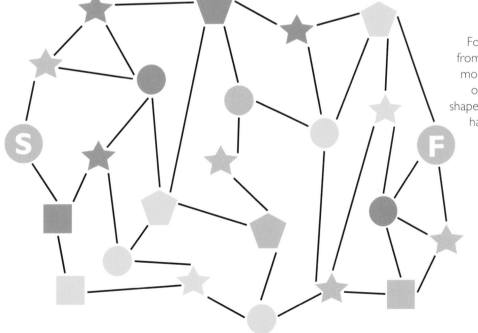

Pairing up is the name of the game with these multicoloured puzzles. Test your ability to match like with like.

26 Fit the pieces   LEVEL 1
How might these six shapes be paired to form three perfect squares?

27 Lock together   LEVEL 2
Can you find the three perfect circles that can be made by matching these spindly shapes?

28 Hex-agony   LEVEL 3
Rearrange these six pieces to form two perfect hexagons.

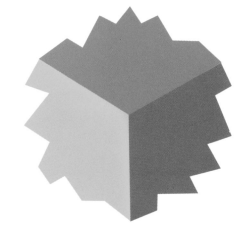

29 Time for colour
LEVEL 2
Can you colour all the white areas of this clock in such a way that no two bordering areas are the same colour? You may use a maximum of four different colours.

30 Band width 1 LEVEL 2
Here are three views of a single cube that has one or more black rubber bands stretched around it. Can you work out how many bands there are?

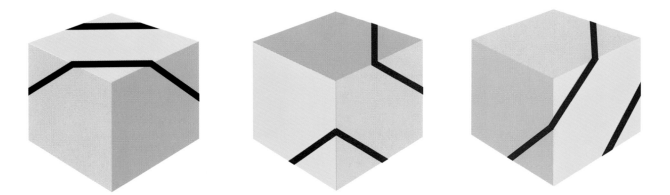

31 Band width 2 LEVEL 3
As in the puzzle above, the object is to determine the number of rubber bands stretched around a single cube seen from three angles.

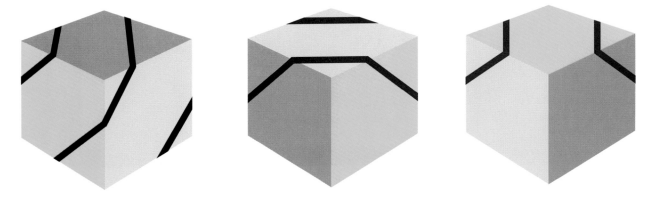

Colours replace letters in these bright variations on the familiar wordsearch puzzle. Here's a chance to show how well you can spot and match patterns.

32 Bee's-eye view   LEVEL 2
How many times can you find the above sequence in the large pattern? The sequence may be rotated but not reflected.

33 Psychedelic chess   LEVEL 3
How many times can you find the sequence below in the large square? In this puzzle, the sequence may be rotated and/or reflected.

34 Know the ropes

Have a close look at the ropes below. How many of these loops will form a knot if the rope is slowly pulled taut? (Where one rope passes under another, the bottom rope has been 'cut away' slightly to aid visualization.)

LEVEL 1: Knots 1–3

LEVEL 2: Knots 4–6

LEVEL 3: Knots 7–9

Each of these puzzles can be arranged so that one colour forms an uninterrupted loop running through all four squares. Can you find it? You may rotate each square about its centre but may not move it otherwise.

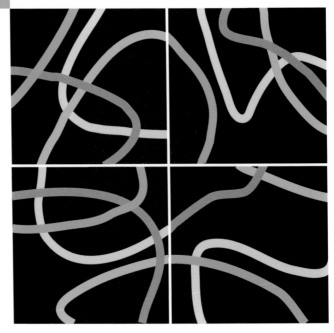

35 Loop the loops 1
LEVEL 1

36 Loop the loops 2
LEVEL 1

37 Rotation vexation LEVEL 2

Each of these circles can be rotated about its centre but not moved from its position. Can you rotate the circles in such a way that all the adjacent segments between touching circles are of the same colour? If you do it correctly, you will find 12 pairs of matching segments.

39 Flag jigsaw 2 LEVEL 2

In this case you see the flag of Malaysia. Which of the four jigsaw pieces fits the gap?

38 Flag jigsaw 1 LEVEL 1

Shown here is the incomplete flag of Guyana. Which of the four jigsaw pieces will fit the hole?

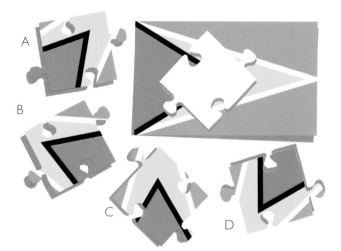

T angrams are an ancient Chinese game of shapes. They are believed to take their name from their creator, a man called Tan. In Chinese tangrams are called *ch'i ch'iao t'u* – 'ingenious puzzle figure of seven pieces'.

To make your own tangram, take a thick piece of card and draw on it a four-by-four grid pattern – like the one below. Then cut out seven pieces, as indicated in the diagram above left. The example above right shows how you might make up a tangram of a boat.

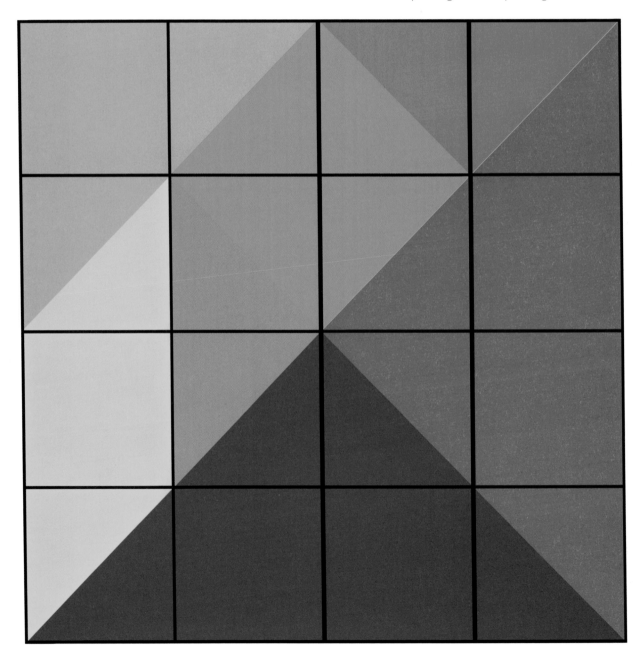

Abstract art

Arrange the seven shapes to produce the tangrams shown on this page. You may find it easier to solve these puzzles if you first make a set of tangram pieces out of card, as shown on the opposite page. In each case, you must use all seven shapes and you must not overlap any pieces.

40 On the campsite   LEVEL 2

42 Farmer Giles's barn
LEVEL 2

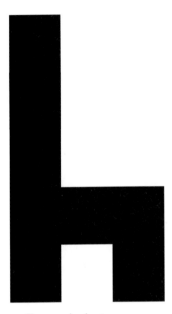

41 Formal chair
LEVEL 2

45
Light my fire
LEVEL 2

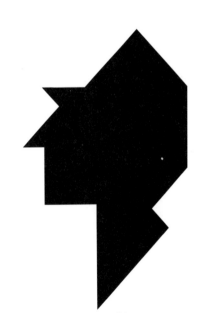

44 Bust in profile   LEVEL 2

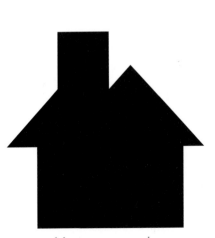

43 Home sweet home
LEVEL 2

Trial by tangram

You've proved your tangram skill by solving the puzzles on page 43; now try your hand at these more difficult designs. Once again, no overlapping is allowed.

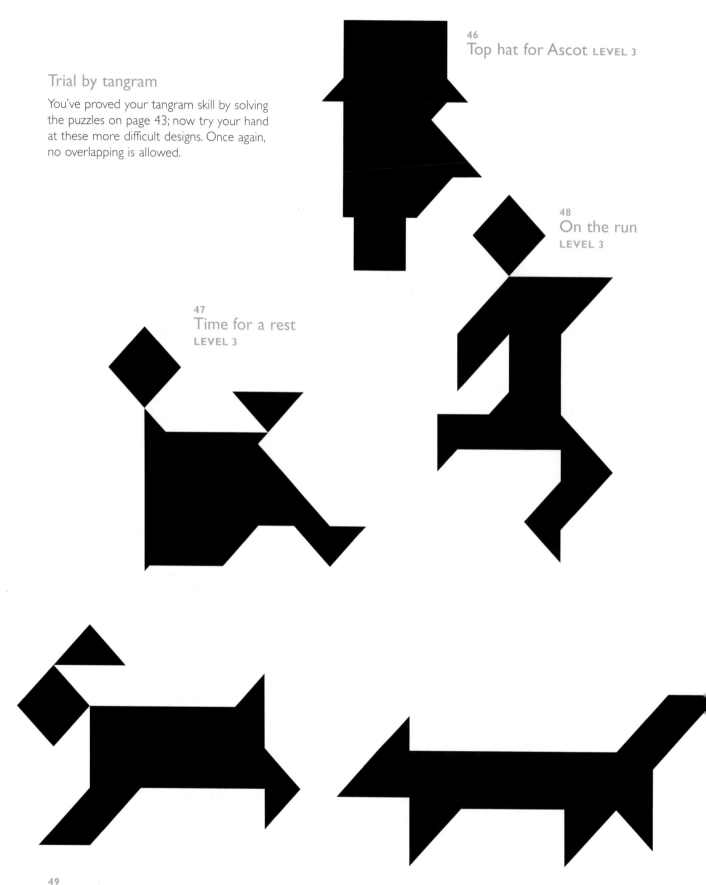

46
Top hat for Ascot LEVEL 3

48
On the run
LEVEL 3

47
Time for a rest
LEVEL 3

49
Rabbit flees from a fox LEVEL 3

50
Tangrams count   LEVEL 3

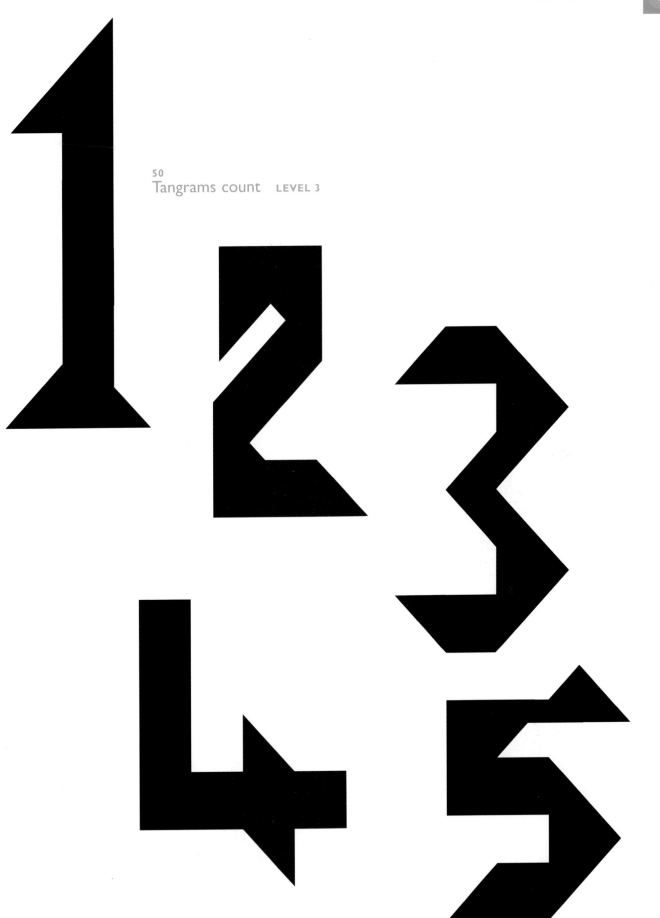

51 A chip off the old block
LEVEL 1

How many small cubes are missing from
the larger cube? You can assume
that any hidden cubes
are present.

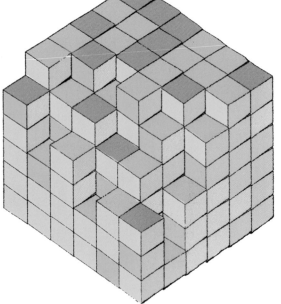

52 Cube-odd   **LEVEL 2**

This cuboid is made from a number of smaller
1 x 1 x 2 cuboids. How quickly can you
determine how many there are? You
can assume that any hidden
cuboids are present.

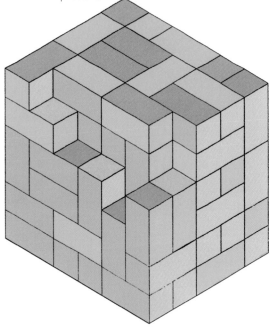

These traditional Japanese
puzzles are great fun. To play,
you'll need a few coins and a chess
pawn or similar token. Place the
coins on the circles and the pawn
on the X. You are a sokoban
(warehouse worker), and it's your
job to move the crates (coins)
out of the warehouse. To do this,
follow these simple rules.

✔ 1   You **CAN** push a single crate
(horizontally or vertically)

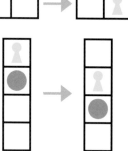

✘ 2 You may **NOT** push two crates at once.

✘ 3 You may **NOT** pull a crate.

To move from one side of a crate to the other,
you have to pass all the way around it through
empty squares. Note that if you push a crate into
a corner you will never be able to get it out
because of rule 3. Once you've cracked our
warehouse puzzle, try creating your own puzzles
then test them out on your family and friends.

53 Warehouse clearance   LEVEL 2

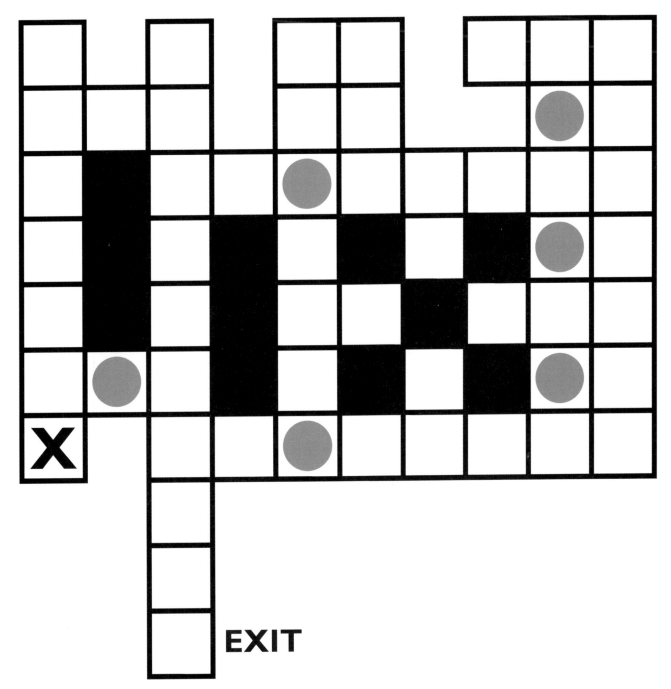

The mechanical mind-benders on this page require a mathematical approach. They may prove tricky, but you should find that the more you do the easier it becomes to solve them. Give yourself 40 minutes to turn them over and weigh them up.

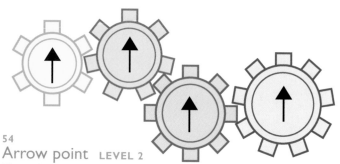

54 Arrow point LEVEL 2

The yellow, red, green and blue cogs have six, seven, eight and nine teeth respectively. What is the least number of complete turns of the yellow cog that will result in all the arrows once again pointing straight up?

55 Classicist's pastime LEVEL 2

The yellow, red, green and blue cogs have six, seven, eight and nine teeth respectively. Bearing in mind that the letter 'O' is a perfect circle, and that the letter 'Y' reads correctly three times every revolution, how many complete revolutions of the yellow cog will result in the word 'TROY' being spelt out perfectly again?

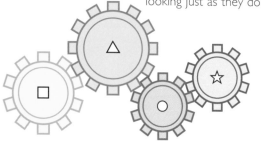

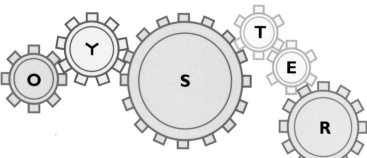

56 Fisherman's delight LEVEL 3

These cogs, from left to right, have eight, nine, sixteen, six, six and twelve teeth respectively. The rules for the 'O' and 'Y' are the same as Classicist's pastime (left), and the 'S' reads the same upside down as it does right side up. How many complete turns of the first cog will spell out 'OYSTER' perfectly once more?

57 A revolutionary problem
LEVEL 2

The square, triangle, circle and star cogs have ten, twelve, ten and ten teeth, respectively. How many complete revolutions of the yellow cog will result in all the patterns looking just as they do now?

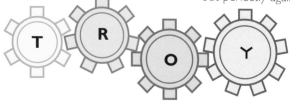

58 Leonardo's teapot LEVEL 3

This remarkable document, discovered under a trattoria in Bologna, shows that Leonardo da Vinci occasionally had thoughts of a nice cuppa while inventing bicycles and flying machines. Can you work out which way to turn each handle, A and B, in order to deliver the renaissance man's tea break?

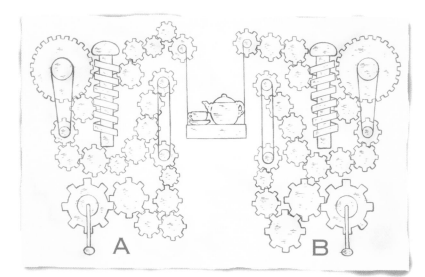

With the exception of puzzle 59, the rules for all these weights and scales problems are identical. The object is to make each set of scales balance by placing all the supplied weights in the pans – one weight per pan. The weight of the rods and pans can be ignored, and the stripes on each rod are of exactly the same length. The last puzzle is more complex, so we have helped you along by placing the first weight correctly. Allow yourself 40 minutes to complete this weighty collection of problems.

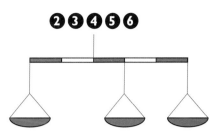

59 LEVEL I
Which three weights, placed singly in each of the pans, can balance this set of weighing scales?

60 LEVEL 2

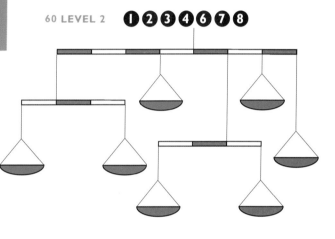

61 LEVEL 2

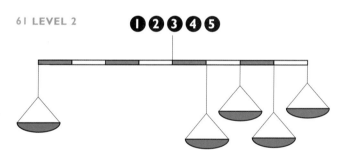

62 LEVEL 2

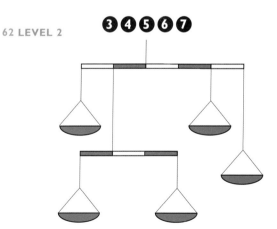

63 LEVEL 3

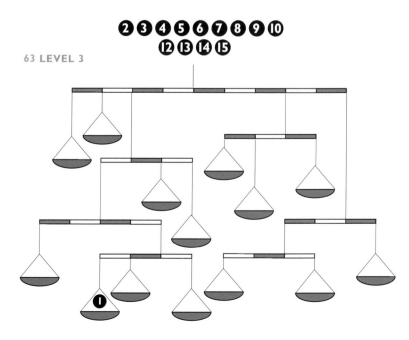

You need a practical mind to solve these puzzles. They test your ability to apply a few of the principles of physics and engineering to real-life situations.

64 In the tub LEVEL 2
A piece of metal is placed in a plastic bowl that is floated in a bath full of water. The metal is then taken out of the bowl and dropped in the water. Does the water level rise, fall or remain the same?

66 Temperature conversion
LEVEL 2
What temperature in Celsius is equal to 77°F, and what temperature in Fahrenheit is equal to 15°C ?

67 Sands of time LEVEL 2
You have two egg timers, one of which is a 4 minute glass, the other a 7 minute glass.

How is it possible to measure 9 minutes with just these two glasses?

4 minutes   7 minutes

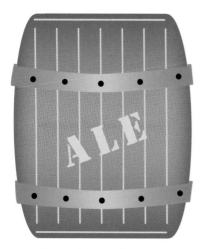

65 Barrel brawl LEVEL 2
The two brewery workers were arguing over whether a barrel of beer was more or less than half full. Without any measuring devices whatsoever, how could they settle the argument?

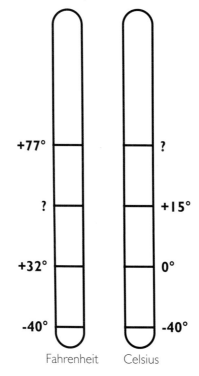

Fahrenheit	Celsius
+77°	?
?	+15°
+32°	0°
-40°	-40°

68 Thick as a plank LEVEL 2

You are asked to mend a hole in a floor exactly 2 ft wide and 12 ft long. All you have available is a board 3 ft wide and 8 ft long.

How can you accomplish the task by making just one cut to divide the board into two pieces?

The hole must be entirely covered, no two parts of the board may overlap and the board may not overlap the edge of the hole.

8 ft

3 ft

BOARD

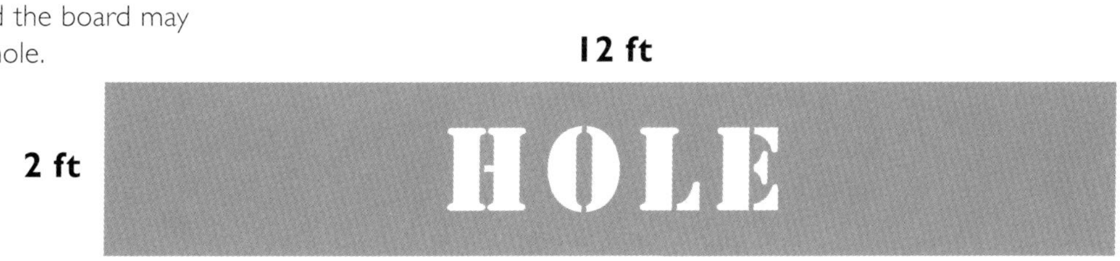

12 ft

2 ft

HOLE

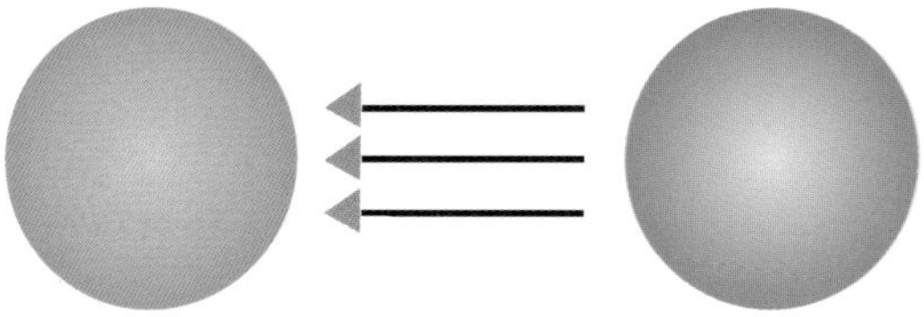

69 Collision course LEVEL 2

A pink rubber ball is suspended freely in outer space completely motionless. A green rubber ball approaches it on a direct collision course at 8000 km/h.

What happens when the green ball hits the pink ball? (The green and pink balls are of the same mass.)

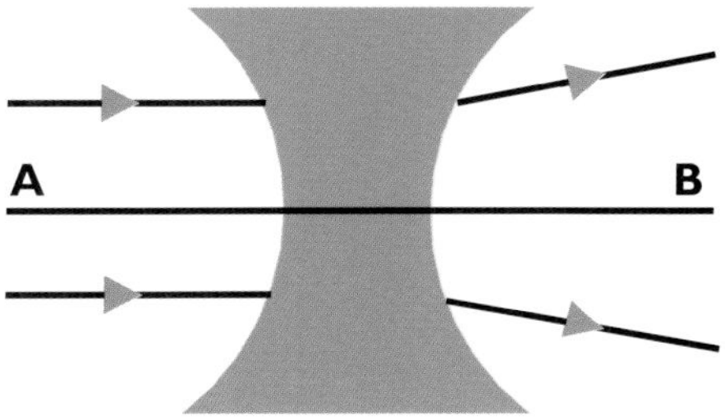

A B

70 Focal point
LEVEL 2
Where on line AB is the focal point of this double concave diverging lens?

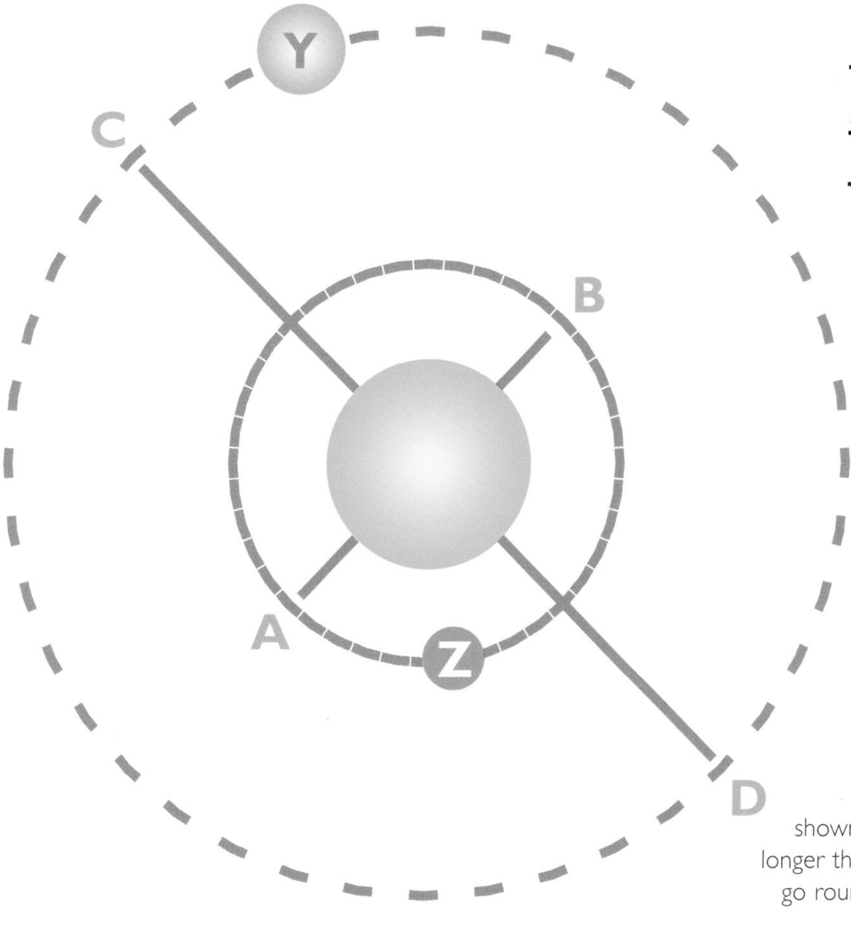

71 Planetary motion LEVEL 3

The orbits of two planets Y and Z are shown around their sun. Line CD is four times longer than line AB. If planet Z takes 2 months to go round the sun, how long does planet Y take?

Battle stations

Battleship puzzles test your diagrammatic logic. As in the pencil-and-paper game of Battleships, you have one battleship (four squares long), two cruisers (three squares each), three destroyers (two squares) and four submarines (one square). Each ship runs horizontally or vertically in the grid. In these puzzles you are also told the number of ship segments that lie in each row and column – indicated by the numbers along the edges of the grid. It is given that no ship is next to any other ship, not even diagonally. Here's an example of a completed puzzle to give you the idea:

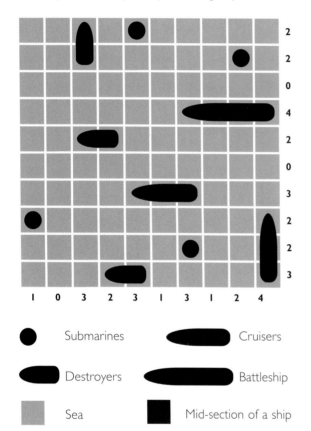

										2
										2
										0
										4
										2
										0
										3
										2
										2
										3
1	0	3	2	3	1	3	1	2	4	

● Submarines   ⬬ Cruisers

⬬ Destroyers   ⬬ Battleship

⬛ (grey) Sea   ⬛ Mid-section of a ship

A few solving hints to start you off:

- Rows and columns with 0 must contain all sea.
- A solid black square indicates the middle section of a ship.
- Deducing where sea is can be just as important as working out where a piece of ship is.
- If there are still two pieces of ship to fit in a certain line, but there are only two empty squares left, you know those squares must contain pieces of ship.
- Try to position the larger ships first – there are only so many places they can go.

If you'd like further explanation of the principles involved, turn to the answers section for a detailed solution to the first puzzle.

72 LEVEL I

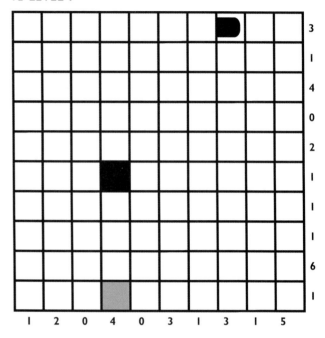

										3
										1
										4
										0
										2
										1
										1
										1
										6
										1
1	2	0	4	0	3	1	3	1	5	

73 LEVEL I

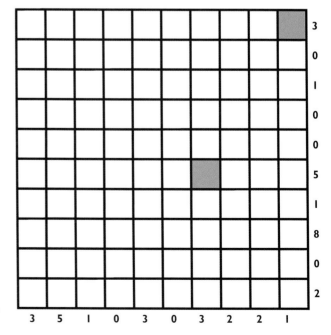

										3
										0
										1
										0
										0
										5
										1
										8
										0
										2
3	5	1	0	3	0	3	2	2	1	

74 LEVEL 1

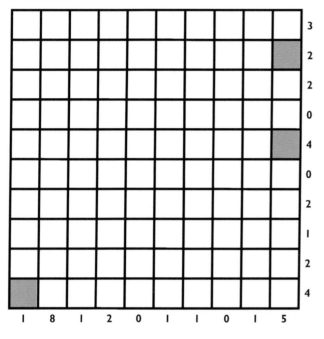

75 LEVEL 2

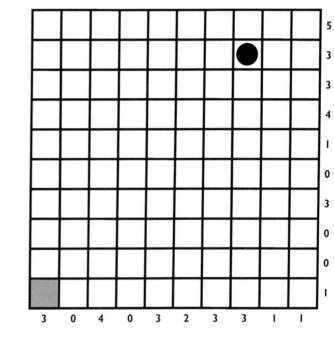

76 LEVEL 2

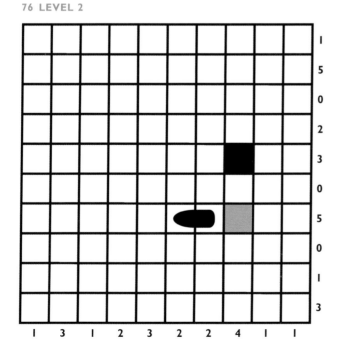

77 LEVEL 3

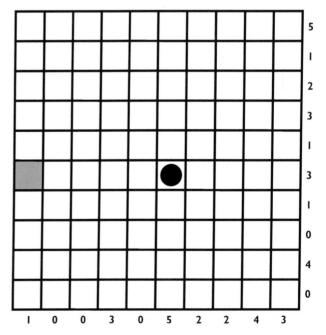

Is seeing believing? On the next four pages you will find a collection of optical illusions — some simple, some extremely elaborate. Just see how easy it is to deceive the human eye.

78 The green man

The 16th-century Italian painter Giuseppe Arcimboldo pioneered the technique of metamorphic art. Look at the painting below (*Market Gardener or Joke with Vegetables*). On first sight it is a standard arrangement of vegetables. Now turn it upside down — what do you see?

79 Trident tested

This is one of the most familiar optical illusions in the world. At first glance it looks like a three-pronged implement, but look closer — all is not as it seems.

80 Impossible triangle   LEVEL 1

Look at the triangle to your right. How would you describe the positioning of the ball? Is it nearer the top or the bottom of the triangle?

81 Line weight
LEVEL 1
Which of the lines between the arrow heads is the longest?

82 Upstairs downstairs

Dutch artist Maurits Cornelius Escher, who died in 1972, is famous the world over for his intriguing and seemingly impossible images, in which the known world is turned upside down and mathematical ideas of perspective are challenged. He produced this lithograph, entitled *Relitivitat*, in 1953. Can you make head or tail of it?

83 Spaced out

LEVEL 2

Here's an optical illusion puzzle for you to try. The parts of a five letter word are all here, but they have been mixed up. What does the word say?

84 Elegance and strength

Can you see the double-headed images in this haunting painting by
Salvador Dali? If you're puzzled, the title of the painting, *Swans
Reflecting Elephants*, may help you to spot the optical illusion.

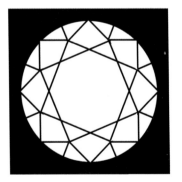 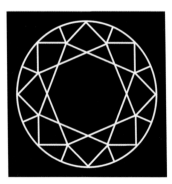

85 Shape up LEVEL 1

Cross your eyes so that a third image appears between the other
two. You should find that this extra image 'shimmers' – this is
because your brain cannot work out whether to use the white or
black image.

While you are looking, turn your attention to the left-hand diagram
only. What is the minimum number of different colours you would
need to colour in all the white areas so that no two areas that
share a border are the same colour?

86 Odd fellows LEVEL 3

There is a kind of illusion hidden in these
shapes? Can you see which two wedges are
the odd ones out?

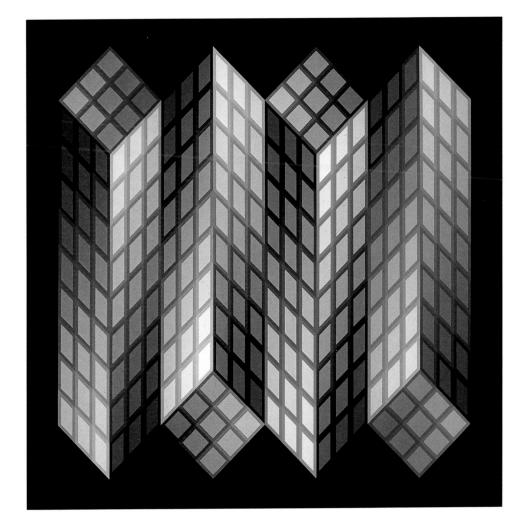

87 Looking-glass skyscrapers

In 1969 the Hungarian-born painter Viktor Vasarely produced this startling picture, *Toroni-Nagy*, that challenges accepted ideas of dimension and shape. The image flickers between concave and convex depending on your viewpoint (looking at the small 3x3 squares at the bottom may help you capture the illusion).

88 Shoot that poison arrow LEVEL 3

This puzzle, based on a well-known optical illusion, invites you to match up the arrow flights with their arrowheads. If you pick the correct six, they will spell out an appropriate word.

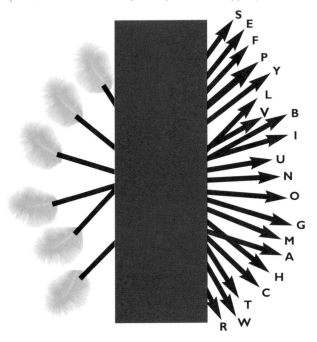

89 Pick up sticks LEVEL 2

This final mind-maddening mind mazes puzzle gives you a last chance to test your visual skills. Remove each stick one at a time, and only when there's no stick on top of it. Can you deduce the sequence of the sticks?

Words are what makes us human: we are the talking apes. And the first pun surely followed hard on the heels of the first word, so when you tackle the anagrams, acrostics and crosswords in this chapter, you are playing a game that is as old as speech itself.

22

23

1 Anagram mountain

Take a word, mix it up a bit, and what you have is an anagram. Here, by way of a warm-up, are some single-word anagrams. Start at the top and try to find your way down.

LEVEL 1
TVA
TEXN
PRYAT
DUESOX

LEVEL 2
BILEQUO
IDLEARCH
TOMCRUISE
BEGFREERUB

LEVEL 3
IUSEVICTORY
DEHORNNODROD
IMBORINGRANTS
ARICHBOGUTOPIA

Who's who?

In each of these sets of anagrams, you are given words of increasing length to find. If you notice that many of the answers have an uncanny association with the anagram itself, that's just a coincidence.
Or is it?

2 World leaders

LEVEL 1
1 Array as feast   (6, 6)
2 Try blind law   (5, 6)
3 This Jones pal   (6, 6)
4 I rat nobly   (4, 5)
LEVEL 2
1 Eyes shrink, grin   (5, 9)
2 Mobile unionists   (6, 9)
3 So brainy norm   (4, 8)
LEVEL 3
1 Kinder fall on voters   (8, 1, 9)
2 Endless insobriety trip   (9, 5, 7)

3 Writers and poets

LEVEL 1
1 Vouch to rig   (6, 4)
2 Emerge angrier   (8, 5)
3 Corrupt males   (6, 6)
LEVEL 2
1 An old, large ape   (5, 5, 3)
2 Brain-rot speaks   (5, 9)
3 Someone snigger   (7, 7)
4 I am a weakish speller   (7, 11)
LEVEL 3
1 Declarations: Hurry on!   (3, 6, 5, 5)
2 And hairs in enchantress   (4, 9, 8)

LEVEL 3
LEVEL 2
LEVEL 1

4 Stop and go anagrams

The groups of eight letters in each of these lights can form anagrams. In the easy (green) lights, your challenge is to find one eight-letter anagram that can be formed with those letters. In the medium (amber) lights, you have to find two different eight-letter words, and in the difficult (red) lights there are three eight-letter words to find – and maybe more! Each letter in each light is used once only.

5 Odd one out   LEVEL 3

Find the odd one out in all of the following:

1 aging, frump, steam, spied, valet
2 mail, dine, annoy, asset, sinned
3 ethereal, withered, brethren, furthest, untether
4 wind, row, elope, tear
5 rated, ulcer, edits, trade, easel, crate, armed, sited, merit, taper, dream, react, lease, remit, cruel
6 friends, end, woe, warpath, quashed, apt, ant, remarry, use, red, sampled, magnate, ape, ear, swooped
7 defamation, deputation, persuasion, mendacious, numeration, precarious
8 pile, slim, balustrade, amen, neat, participle, temperable, naturalism, cane, dear, stalagmite, beastliest, item, bale, confidante, site, cognisance
9 algorithms, artichokes, alpenstock, admonished, avouchment, abridgment
10 gun, boy, pay, rob, sin, new

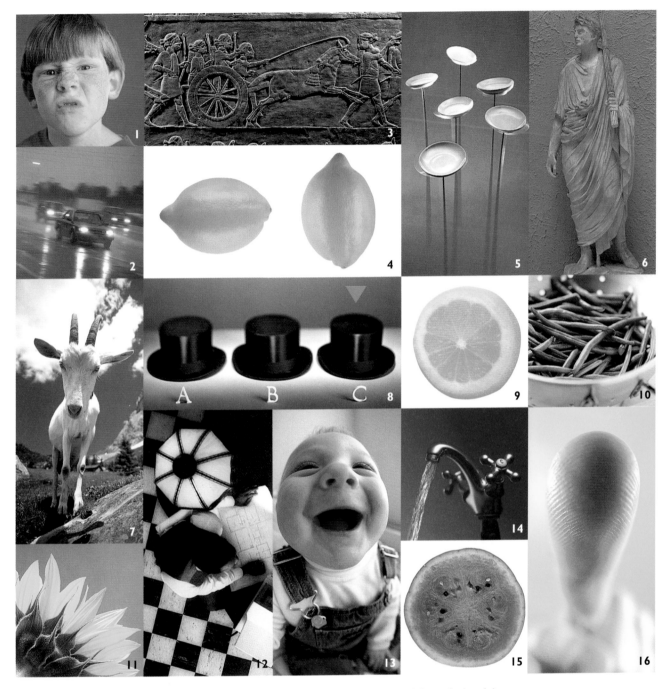

6 Mixed doubles   LEVEL 2
Within this group of 16 pictures you should
be able to find eight pairs of anagrams. Deduce
the anagram concealed in the picture
and find its partner.

Ring the changes
Rearrange the letters in each circle to find a word.

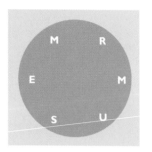

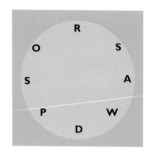

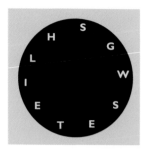

7 LEVEL 1   8 LEVEL 2   9 LEVEL 2   10 LEVEL 3

Jigsquare 1
11 LEVEL 2

Place the jigsaw pieces into the frame to form a square with valid English words reading across each row and down each column. To help you, we have supplied clues to all the words. However, these are not in any particular order.

MEDAL
DRY
FLATTEN
WISE MEN
ICE ARENA
SWAMP
NERVOUS
BLUE

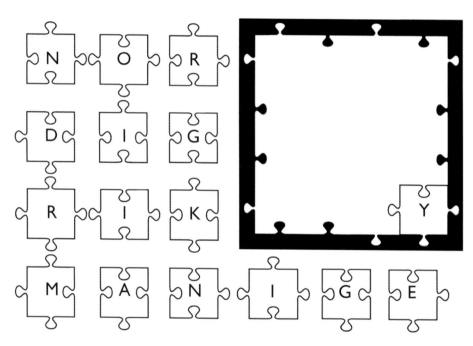

Jigsquare 2
12 LEVEL 2

SONG
PIECE OF STONE
KNIFE
CURVE
LIKE
SMALL CHILD
DECORATIVE BALL
MUSICAL INSTRUMENT

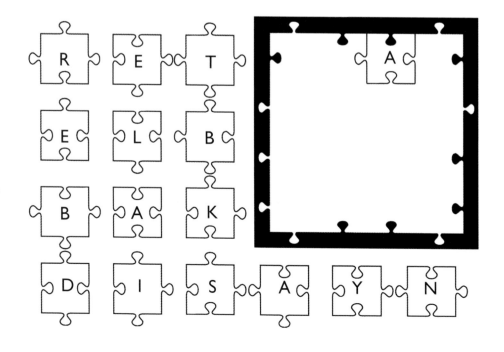

1 IRIPJUTE
2 PINOLES
3 GOTPENNA
4 FIRSTASH
5 UNLETQUIP

13 Hiawatha's secret

This is a three-part puzzle.

LEVEL 1 Solve the anagrams to the left and write the solutions into the corresponding squares.

LEVEL 2 Establish the connection between the words you have solved.

LEVEL 3 Using your knowledge of history, work out how the Native American fits the pattern. (A clue: there is a helpful anagram hidden in the letters that fall on the highlighted squares. You should have solved all of these in the first part of the puzzle.)

Alpha dice

The dice blocks have a six-letter word written on them, but unfortunately you can only see three sides. Try to solve the clues based on the letters you can see and enter the answers in the grid below. The letters in the first column will form a new word.

1						
2						
3						
4						
5						
6						
7						
8						
9						
10						

14 LEVEL 1

CLUES

1 Save
2 Hand tool
3 Earnings
4 Public sign
5 Sufficient
6 Quiet
7 Ditch
8 Essential gas
9 Required
10 Simpler

16 LEVEL 2

CLUES

1 Element, symbol C
2 Acquire
3 Lump of gold
4 Higher-ranking
5 Top priority
6 Small
7 Yarn
8 Foreign places
9 Country
10 Salad plant

15 LEVEL 2

CLUES

1 Courteous
2 Recommence
3 Eastern lands
4 Flaw
5 Convenient
6 Pair
7 Aim
8 Polluted
9 Resist
10 Slender

17 LEVEL 3

CLUES

1 Arm muscles
2 Type of energy
3 World's largest desert
4 Japanese robe
5 Portugal's currency
6 Frozen subarctic region
7 Copper alloy
8 Blood vessel
9 The bay tree
10 Set of prayers

18 Definitely maybe...

An oxymoron is a phrase that has two contradictory parts. An example is 'constant change', because 'constant' and 'change' are opposite notions. The following ransom note, obviously written by a man with a grudge, has been delivered to the authorities. Unfortunately, 40 of the words in the note have come unstuck. As it happens, these words can be paired together to form 20 oxymorons. How does the completed note read and how quickly can you do it?

LEVEL 1: 20 minutes
LEVEL 2: 15 minutes
LEVEL 3: 10 minutes

ACCURATE
ACT
ALIEN
ALMOST
ALONE
ANARCHY
APPROPRIATE
BEER
CIVIL
CLEARLY
CROWD
ESTIMATE
EXACT
EXACTLY
FIRE
FLIGHT
FORCE
FOUND
FRIENDLY
GLASSES
INTELLIGENCE
MANDATORY
MILITARY
MISSING
MISUNDERSTOOD
NATURALLY
NON-ALCOHOLIC
NON-STOP
ODDLY
OPTION
PEACE
PLASTIC
PRETTY
RESIDENT
RULES
SMALL
STEREOTYPE
TOGETHER
UGLY
WAR

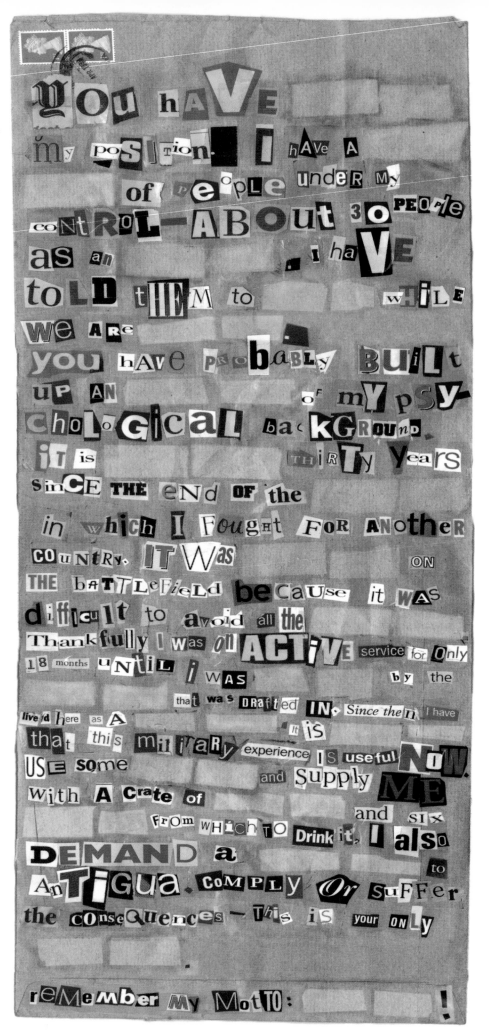

19 A to Z of synonyms

Synonyms are words that mean the same thing, such as 'eager' and 'keen'. In this puzzle you have to find a synonym for each of the words in the left-hand column. The synonym for each word contains at least one mention of a particular letter of the alphabet, as you can see from the letters we've already supplied. How many words can you identify? Some are easier than others.

LEVEL 1:   10 words
LEVEL 2:   18 words
LEVEL 3:   24 words

MERGE   A _ A _ _ A _ A _ _

FAT   B _ _ B B _ _

LUST   C _ _ C _ _ _ _ C _ _ C

CHEATED   D _ D D _ _ D

FIZZ   E _ _ E _ _ E _ _ E _ E

FEATHERY   F _ _ F F _

CHUCKLING   G _ G G _ _ _ G

TOURIST   H _ _ _ H-H _ _ _ _

PRIME   I _ _ I _ I _ I _ _ _

SPELL   J _ J _

ORNAMENT   K _ _ _ K-K _ _ _ K

DEFAMATORY   L _ _ _ L L _ _ _

LEAST   M _ _ _ M _ M

VACUUM   N _ _ _ _ N _ N _ _ _

BIRDWATCHER   O _ _ _ _ _ O _ O _ _ _ _

SPRINKLED   P _ P P _ _ _ _

EMBODIMENT   Q _ _ _ _ _ _ _ _ _

COOLER   R _ R _ _ _ R _ _ _ R

STUPIDITY   S _ _ S _ _ _ S S _ _ S S

GOSSIP   T _ T T _ _ -T _ T T _ _

DISHONEST   U _ _ _ _ U _ U _ _ U _

TAP   V _ _ V _

BEATEN   W _ _ _ _ W _ _ _ _

PHOTOCOPYING   X _ _ _ _ _ _ _ _ _

ANNUAL   Y _ _ _ _ Y

NAP   Z _ Z Z

20 Z to A of antonyms

Antonyms are the exact opposite of synonyms – in other words, they are pairs of words that are opposites of each other, such as 'lazy' and 'energetic'. In this puzzle you have to find an antonym for each of the words in the left-hand column. Again, see how many words you can identify – some of these are very tricky.

LEVEL 1:   8 words
LEVEL 2:   15 words
LEVEL 3:   20 words

MODESTY   _ _ Z Z _ _ _ _ Z Z

MONOTONE   _ _ _ Y _ _ _ _ Y

ECCENTRIC   _ _ _ _ _ _ _ X

SNOOTY   _ _ W _ _ _ W

STALL   _ _ V

BEGINNER   _ U _ U

CONSTANT   _ _ T _ _ _ _ T T _ _ T

TRUST   _ _ S S _ S S _ _ _ _ _ S S

SELLER   _ R _ _ _ R _ R

TRANSPARENT   _ _ _ Q _ _

INTELLECTUAL   _ _ _ _ _ _ P _ _ P

NOVICE   _ _ _ _ _ O _ _ _ O

SEPARATION   _ N _ _ _ _ _ _ N N _ _ _ _ _ N

LEAST   M _ _ _ M _ M

COHERENT   _ L L _ _ _ _ _ L

ELECTRONIC   _ _ _ _ K _ _ _ K

UMRA   _ _ J J

CIAO   _ _ _ I _ _ _ _ _ _ I

OVERT   H _ _ H-H _ _ H

DIRECT   _ _ G _ _ G G _ _ G

ELITE   _ _ F F-_ _ F F

QUIT   _ E _ _ E _ E _ E

NEAT   _ _ D D _ _ D

TYPICAL   _ _ C _ _ _ _ C _ _ _ _ _ _ C

ARCHANGEL   B _ _ _ _ _ _ _ B

PRELUDE   _ A _ _ _ _ A

21 Match this LEVEL 2

Listed below in random order are 20 pairs of matching words. Work out which words go with which. Can you also identify the three 'unwanted' pairs?

anchor	fish
red	bee
queen	Achilles
bow	white
elephant	frog
cocktail	mountain
court	triangle
writer	man
chain	goose
whistle	tears
Roman	money
berry	herring
wolf	rubber
leap	fruit
gold	nose
rain	spinner
stamp	ghost
heel	kangaroo
Bermuda	saw
goat	crocodile

Doing a cryptic crossword

There is real satisfaction to be had from a cryptic crossword, once you know the ground rules. In this crossword an explanation has been provided for every clue. If you can master these principles, a world of puzzling will open up to you.

1 ACROSS The answer is a synonym for intentional; 'being false' implies an anagram; and 'lie, debater' adds up to the right number of letters. It must be DELIBERATE.

8 ACROSS 'How old someone is' is their age. To state is to aver. aver-age: AVERAGE, meaning mathematical 'mean'.

10 ACROSS The answer going to mean 'criminal activity'. The word 'in' is sometimes a marker for a hidden phrase. Sure enough, in 'bars ongoing': is concealed the word ARSON.

12 ACROSS Method can be 'mode'. British sailors could be RN for Royal Navy. Mode-RN gives MODERN, meaning current, 'up to date'.

13 DOWN It looks like an anagram of 'sure' at the end. 'Little fellow' could me a short man's name – such as Dan. It must be DANSEUR.

17 DOWN Two words, six letters, and it looks like an anagram of 'dosage'. SEA DOG – a 'salt' in the sense of 'old sailor'.

18 DOWN Can only be a word meaning both pole and position. POST fits: long stick, and position in the sense of your job.

18 ACROSS Criticise is 'pan' in crossword speak. A revolutionary could be 'a red', but here it seems to be 'a Che' (Guevara). 'Pan a Che' = PANACHE, flamboyance.

22 ACROSS 'About' implies that there is a word spelt backwards in here. It can only be SLEEP, which is 'peels' (undresses) backwards.

24 ACROSS One thing is for sure: it is not going to be anything to do with football. Match could be 'wedding'. Man of the wedding? That would be the BRIDEGROOM.

ACROSS

1 Intentional lie, debater is false (10)

8 State how old someone is, being mean? (7)

9 Utter nothing when there's wickedness about (5)

10 Evident in bars – ongoing criminal activity (5)

11 Formerly in California in disguise (7)

12 Current method used by sailors (6)

14 Countryman is curt when disturbed (6)

18 Criticise a revolutionary. This is flamboyance (7)

20 Follow mum in principle (5)

22 Undresses, about to nod off (5)

23 Sweetheart left without courage (7)

24 Man of the match! (10)

DOWN

1 Robe contributing to padre's splendour (5)

2 Student, 50, someone in employment (7)

3 River entering sandy area creates severance (6)

4 Bird is cowardly, about to fly away (5)

5 Travel, carrying round explosive missile (7)

6 Salutation upset master, sad to say (6)

7 The sound of genuine dance (4)

13 Little fellow, sure odd as a ballet-dancer (7)

15 Suffer below, then disappear (7)

16 Alter notes? No (6)

17 Salt dosage must be modified (3,3)

18 Pole position (4)

19 Together policeman and journalist got by (5)

21 Writer of fairy stories is harsh male (

1 DOWN An easy hidden word, now that we know the answer begins with D. A robe is a DRESS, embedded in 'padres splendour'.

2 DOWN 50 is L in Roman numerals. Someone in employment is an earner, which with the Roman 50 makes LEARNER a student.

3 DOWN A sandy area is a beach, since it starts with B. Insert R for river, and that gives BREACH, a severance.

4 DOWN Probably the name of a bird. RAVEN springs to mind. Why? Because it's craven (cowardly) minus c. (the abbreviation for circa in dates).

5 DOWN Explosive could be TNT. 'Carry around' could mean a word for travel inside TNT: 'Ride' fits neatly, giving TRIDENT, the nuclear missile.

6 DOWN 'Upset' implies an anagram or a backwards word. Master is often 'MA' (Master of Arts). 'Alas' could stand in for 'sad to say'. The reversal of 'MA alas' gives SALAAM, the Arabic greeting.

7 DOWN 'Sound' is a strong clue that the answer is in the pronunciation, not the spelling. Genuine is real, which sounds like the Scottish dance REEL.

9 ACROSS Nothing often means the letter O. Wickedness is evil or 'vice'. Vice with 'O' gives VOICE which means 'utter'.

15 DOWN 'Below' could be 'under', leaving just two letters for 'disappear', which can then only be 'go': To UNDERGO an ordeal is to suffer it.

16 DOWN Could be another word for 'alter'. The opposite of (or complement to) notes when you are talking about money is CHANGE.

11 ACROSS Formerly can mean 'ex' or 'once'. California can be cut to CA or Cal. 'Once' and 'cal': juggled up give you CONCEAL, meaning disguise.

14 ACROSS An anagram of 'is curt' flagged by 'when disturbed' Citrus? No, RUSTIC – a country person.

19 DOWN Policeman could be PC, CID, cop. Journalist could be hack, or editor or ed for short. Cop-ed: if you COPED, you 'got by'.

20 ACROSS Mum is often 'ma'. To dog someone is to follow them so that gives 'madog'? – no DOGMA, a moral principle.

21 DOWN Writer often means 'pen', but that does not feel right here. Writer of fairy tales in 5 letters can only be GRIMM – 'grim' for 'harsh', plus 'M' for male.

23 ACROSS 'Left without courage' could be a 6 letter word for courage around letter L. That's it: 'daring' with an L dropped in the middle gives DARLING: sweetheart.

Hints and tips

Look for the word that denotes the answer: it will often be the first or last word in the clue.

The apparent context is nearly always misleading. If a clue says 'Scot able to get drunk in bar', the answer will not be a word meaning 'pub'. (In fact it is OBSTACLE.)

The word 'flower' often means the name of a river (because it flows), and the word 'river' often means just the letter R.

A question or exclamation mark at the end of the clue means the whole thing is a pun or joke where you must guess the punchline. So, for example, 'Agent removing shades?' is not a spy in glasses, it is PAINT STRIPPER.

Many words indicate particular letters: hot and cold are H and C; love and ring are O; point or quarter can be N, S, E or W; loud is F; soft is P; five is V; junction is T. But never make the mistake of trusting this cryptic shorthand: it may be intended to fool you.

Other words imply clusters of letters: 'soldier' can be GI, TA or RE; 'sailor' can be AB or TAR; 'doctor' can be DR, MO or MD.

The word 'say' or 'sounds' usually implies that the clue involves a homophone, two words that are spelt differently but are pronounced the same: 'Sounds like a powerful little coin' is MITE (which sounds like 'might').

Some crosswords expect you to know a few foreign words. If a clue begins 'The French…' (or 'The Parisian…') the answer might contain the letters LE, LA or LES; 'The German…,' DER or DAS; 'The Spanish…', EL'.

Look for the short synonyms of long words, because the short forms may make up part of the answer: celebration is DO; fashionable is IN or U; deception is CON.

Don't fall into the trap of treating the puzzle as a code. Good crosswords break conventions and flout your expectations. It is meant to be a challenging exercise.

Sometimes the interests and the hobbies of the setter – even his sense of humour – show through in the clues. Turn this to your advantage: if you can work out how the setter's brain works, you will leave the crossword feeling as if you have just had a satisfying conversation with a like mind.

22 Letter logic 1 LEVEL 1

There are no clues to this puzzle other than the letters in the grid and the length of the word.

ACROSS	DOWN
ACE	GOA
GEM	MEE
ANONYM	ALBINO
ARIOSO	CEREAL
GOTHIC	ENJOIN
KARATE	INTONE
OFFSET	OVERDO
TANIST	STUDIO
ALLEGRO	CORNCOB
ESSENCE	INCENSE
ABANDONED	BACKSTAGE
ACCORDION	CLARINETS
ACROBATIC	COGNISANT
GARDENING	COMMITTEE
GREENBACK	EGOTISTIC
IRONSTONE	TRANSFUSE

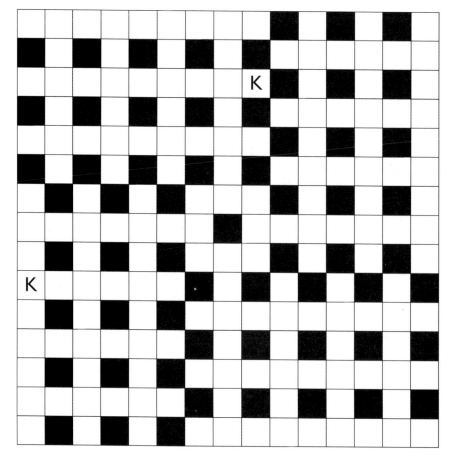

23 Letter logic 2 LEVEL 1

Once again, there are no clues to this puzzle other than the sole letter in the grid and the length of the word.

ACROSS	DOWN
AQUA	OHM
DEER	ADAM
HEEL	AHOY
KOHL	ALUM
EDGES	BILL
SCOUT	EONS
BABIES	VOTE
BOLERO	AHEAD
ORIENT	BEGAN
PERSIA	CHEERS
ATLANTIC	FERRET
OBSOLETE	SHIVER
RATTLING	TEEPEE
VIRGINIA	AUCTION
TARAMASALATA	TABLEAU
GOOD-HUMOURED	BLOCKAGE
	BRIGHTON
	MARQUESS
	CASANOVA

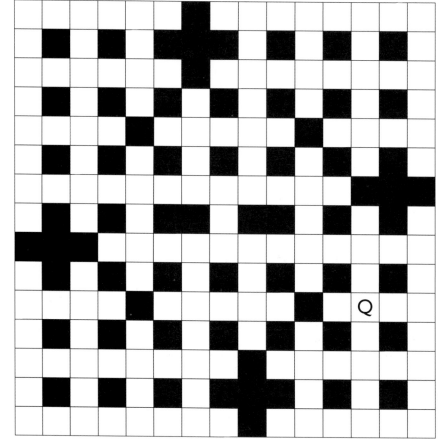

24 Time for tea   LEVEL 1

Two quick and easy teatime crosswords.

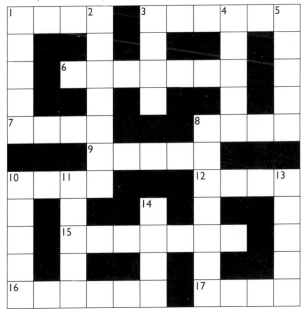

25

ACROSS

1 Simple (4)
3 Root vegetable (6)
6 Budapest's country (7)
7 Suspend (4)
8 Colour (4)
9 Go in (5)
10 Ale (4)
12 Vow (4)
15 Idea (7)
16 Motive (6)
17 Corrosion (4)

DOWN

1 Soil (5)
2 Not as old (7)
3 Animal pen (4)
4 Regal (5)
5 Number (5)
8 Family member (7)
10 Bread maker (5)
11 Additional (5)
13 Body organ (5)
14 Scorch (4)

ACROSS

1 Dissolve (4)
3 Notion (4)
5 Quick (5)
6 Stringed instrument (4)
8 Israel's currency (6)
10 Thrilling tale (9)
13 Travelling show (6)
15 Leg joint (4)
16 Big (5)
17 Inform (4)
18 Small horse (4)

DOWN

1 Strength (5)
2 Stumble (4)
3 Lazy (4)
4 Fully grown (5)
7 Horseman (5)
8 Nasal duct (5)
9 Holy book of Islam (5)
11 Fragrance (5)
12 Answer (5)
14 Summon (4)
15 Retain (4)

26 Zoo clue   LEVEL 2

Test your knowledge of the animal kingdom. The answers to all the clues are creatures of some kind, including fish, birds – and one cartoon character.

How quickly can you find them all?

10 minutes: tortoise
7 minutes: bloodhound
5 minutes: cheetah

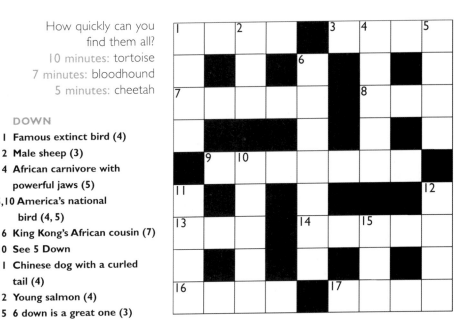

ACROSS

1 John ——, a golden sea fish (4)
3 Small, fat fish of the carp family (4)
7 Disney's flying elephant (5)
8 Fish shaped like a snake (3)
9 Bird with a huge pouched beak (7)
13 Greedy pig (3)
14 South American beast of burden (5)
16 Little songbird (4)
17 Animal with antlers (4)

DOWN

1 Famous extinct bird (4)
2 Male sheep (3)
4 African carnivore with powerful jaws (5)
5,10 America's national bird (4, 5)
6 King Kong's African cousin (7)
10 See 5 Down
11 Chinese dog with a curled tail (4)
12 Young salmon (4)
15 6 down is a great one (3)

27 Gridlock LEVEL 2

This is an American-style crossword: very few blanks are used in this kind of grid. This should help you to solve the longer and more difficult clues – though we don't tell you how many letters or words are in each answer. The best way to start a crossword like this is to pick a small region of the grid and try to complete it before moving on. If you get stuck, move to a different area and try again. Before long the areas you solve should start joining up.

ACROSS

1 Long narrative poem
5 Type of lock, perhaps
9 Sit for a painting
13 Charts
17 State of unconsciousness
18 Single amount
19 Responsibility
20 Let out
21 Member of Native American people in Arizona
22 Greek covered walkway
23 Not in a rush
25 Computer program that runs applications
28 Digit
29 The Jewish Pentateuch
30 They come before the final
31 You spend them in Thailand
33 Large African antelope
35 Before (poetic)
36 Married
37 Skilful in craft
38 Watch
40 Ran through before the final performance
46 Normal
48 Choose
49 Daughters of the American Revolution (abbrev.)
50 _____ium, metal occurring in uranium ore
51 Units of magnetic flux
53 _____s, part of the roof
56 Fix
58 Speak
59 Outdoor area containing rides, stalls and attractions
63 Pear-shaped fruit
66 A high mountain
67 Look very carefully
68 Horse-drawn carriage with four wheels
72 Greek god of love
74 Key on a keyboard
76 A short publication?

78 Abscesses
79 Early photographs
84 Festive season (abbrev.)
85 Like a long, thin fish
86 Status _____, the current situation
87 Genus of grass
89 To be inaccurate
90 Type of shallow glass dish
92 Brave
94 Ignore the alarm clock
96 Practical skill
97 Used for close-ups
102 Bit by bit
104 Will
105 Girl's name
106 Unbleached linen
107 Prefix meaning 'after'
108 Layer
109 Lower part of the back
110 Grating sound
111 Grey
112 _____ d'oeuvre, appetizers
113 Extremities

DOWN

1 Recurring sound
2 Deck on a ship
3 Unreasoned
4 Capital city of Egypt
5 Sauce made with eggs, sugar, milk and cornflour
6 Accidental main character in a story

7 Elementary particle
8 Male deer
9 Compound containing large chains of molecules
10 Biased
11 Hearts, clubs, diamonds, spades
12 Actual existence
13 French for 'sea'
14 Pieces of quartz
15 Test programme
16 Swellings on the eyelid
24 Shadow
26 Plural of the present indicative of 'to be'
27 Joins together by thread
32 Psychi_____, study of mental illness
33 Sudden oversupply
34 Bouquet of wine
37 Antenna
39 _____-azar, tropical fever contracted via sandfly bites
41 Fencing sword
42 Trample
43 String instrument
44 Estimated time of arrival (abbrev.)
45 Out of water
47 Dalai _____, spiritual leader of Tibetan Buddhism
52 Sweltering
54 The 22nd letter
55 Foe

57 Grasp suddenly
60 Train to box
61 Capture
62 Fort _____, site of US gold depository
63 Given food
64 Woman's name, meaning 'watchful' in Hebrew
65 Ambitious, energetic people
69 Aspect
70 Pertaining to a wing
71 Union of Soviet Socialist Republics (abbrev.)
73 Claimant
75 Leave personal property to another
77 One who studies the Earth's crust
80 Chosen few
81 Defeat at sport
82 Nonsense
83 Seaworthy boats
88 Support for a golf ball
90 An essay or other literary contribution
91 Woman's name
92 Part-songs
93 Early life
95 Fireplace
98 Girl's name
99 Threesome
100 Woman's name
101 Without
103 Drinking vessel

Not all crosswords are square. On this page you are invited to fit the words into an altogether more complex geometry.

28 Honeycomb crossword
LEVEL 3

TRAVEL EAST

1 **Reverie (8)**
3 **Cell specialized to transmit impulses in the body (6)**
5 **Form of silicate mineral used in industry for insulation (4)**
8 **Fine, stiff dress material (7)**
11 **Small, dried seedless grape (7)**
13 **To make designs on metal or glass using acid to eat out the lines (4)**
15 **Confection containing chopped nuts and cherries (6)**
17 **Frantic movements to prospect the Klondike, for example, in the 1890s (8)**

TRAVEL NORTH-EAST

7 **Champagne or wine bottle holding 1.5 litres (6)**
8 **A Feudal ruler (8)**
9 **The raised arm on a sundial (6)**
10 **A standard or typical way of behaving (4)**
14 **German equivalent of mister (4)**
16 **Treeless regions of the Northern Hemisphere lying just south of the polar ice cap (6)**
17 **River that flows into the Bay of Bengal and is sacred to the Indian people (6)**
18 **One whose lifestyle is devoted to the seeking of pleasure (8)**

TRAVEL SOUTH-EAST

1 **An electric generator (6)**
2 **First name of the author of *Gone With the Wind* (8)**
4 **American state, capital Carson City (6)**
6 **Tree, also known as Maple (4)**
8 **Extroverted and friendly (8)**
9 **Unit of capacity equal to 8 pints (6)**
10 **Number of planets in our Solar System (4)**
12 **Roof covering of straw or reeds (6)**

29 Crystal crossword   LEVEL 3

Here, every pentagonal blank is numbered. Answers begin in the space with the ringed number, and progress to the adjacent space of the same number. The letters in the coloured pentagons will spell out the name of a planet. One more thing: the clues are just a little bit cryptic.

CLUES

1 They're into guacamole! (8)
2 Modernizing tall dinner companion? (8)
3 Lures, like a magnet (8)
4 Something with real star quality (4)
5 Unfamiliar, and unusual (7)
6 Eat fish? This one eats you! (7)
7 An eight-sided knot? (8)
8 Ocean on top of the world (6)

This is a crossword puzzle with something for all the family. Clues are coded to indicate the type and level of difficulty:

RED These are cryptic clues: they are all about wordplay and convoluted logic.

ORANGE These are difficult general knowledge clues: you may have to do a little bookwork for some of the answers.

BLUE The answers to these trivia clues will mostly be at your fingertips.

GREEN These are for young crossword solvers, who may need help with some of the clues.

ACROSS

1 Scandinavian baked treat, sugared and sometimes filled with apple or raisins. (6,6)

6 Someone who is incapable of serious thought or concentrating on a topic (12)

13 Mythical horse-like creature with a single horn on its forehead (7)

14 Having a membrane of skin between the toes to facilitate swimming (3-6)

16 Person who inflicts punishment and causes misery and death (7)

17 Tenants who have a legal right to possession of a property for a fixed length of time (12)

18 Author who described a nightmarish world in his book *Nineteen Eighty-Four* (6,6)

20 Walt Disney's baby cartoon deer (5)

21 Name for a young deer under the age of one year (4)

22 Insect that makes honey (3)

23 Optical device found in cameras and spectacles (4)

25 City in West Maharashtra, India, which, under British rule, was capital of the Bombay presidency (5)

28 Economize to construct new drainage (8)

29 Caesar crossed it to clean a church painting (7)

30 Brightly coloured beetle (8)

33 For instance, nothing is needed for self-esteem (3)

34 ___ City; home of the comic-book heroes Batman and Robin (6)

35 Chart that represents places in the world indicating relative position and distance (3)

36 Farm animal and oddly one that flies (6)

38 To and ___ : another way of saying 'back and forth' (3)

41 Cheerful and carefree (5-7)

42 Fail to understand the precise meaning of something spoken or written (12)

44 Lever used to thump a computer device (8)

45 Shack (3)

46 Note to get one hooked on music? (8)

50 Mountainous area of south-west Italy (8)

51 Greek hero, oddly sly in habits (7)

52 TV chat-show host who made her name in a sitcom about a working-class US family (8)

56 Shut oneself away from society (7)

57 An aircraft, like the Space Shuttle, that gets aerodynamic lift from its shape rather than its wings (7,4)

58 Small river (6)

61 A spicy Spanish vegetable soup, served cold (8)

62 Reasonable (7)

63 A friend or adviser who attends a sovereign (8)

67 Language of the Scandinavian peoples prior to about 1350 (3,5)

68 Under here monsters lurk (3)

69 A terpsichore where the toes and heels of the foot make an audible, rhythmic noise (3,5)

73 Forming the Richmond borough of New York City, this heavy industrial area is in New York Harbor (6,6)

75 Hydraulic platform, usually mounted on a truck, that allows a person to work high above ground (6,6)

78 Lyricist and brother of George Gershwin (3)

79 Tourist attractions overlooked by gunmen (6)

80 Australian flightless bird (3)

81 Sportsperson who uses a sword (6)

82 Rocks constituting a hazard to shipping (3)

85 They open out for a novice (8)

87 Members of the Arachnida class (7)

88 Pretentious or vulgar art or literature that still has popular appeal (6)

92 Affirmative answer (3)

93 US divorce city (4)

94 Young lion (3)

95 Term for a series of movies made by Bob Hope and Bing Crosby in the 1940s and 1950s (4)

96 In Chinese philosophy, the course of life (3)

99 Journalist to be followed? (6-6)

101 Leading band leader and clarinet player of the jazz 'swing era' (5,7)

104 Listing dispensing advice to horse race-goers (7)

105 Decides not to compete due to minor injuries (9)

106 Pamphlet with two pages to rent (7)

107 Rock singer and movie star who died at the age of 42 in his 'Graceland' mansion, Memphis (5,7)

108 Toy pony mounted on curved supports allowing a mounted child to see-saw (7,5)

DOWN

1 Like Lee-Enfield in name, but not by design? (6-9)

2 American astronaut who was the first man to step on to the Moon on July 20, 1969 (4,9)

3 The edge of a large body of water (9)

4 ___ bean; type of mottled kidney bean grown in the USA as fodder (5)

5 ___ the Bruce, king of Scotland 1306–29 (6)

7 Large towns (6)

8 Result in directions being put to wrong use (5)

9 Life story (9)

10 Eat for greed if mad, but don't argue (5,2,6)

11 This combination might well have you in stitches (6,3,6)

12 Hound (3)

14 Bereaved wives (6)

15 Change a shade by removing lightness (6)

19 Pouched-billed waterfowl (7)

21 Take punishment before the orchestra (4,3,5)

24 A joint project of NASA and many other international organizations (5,7)

26 Move quickly using your legs (3)

27 Homer Simpson's habitual exclamation on realizing his own stupidity (3)

31 Saint of Ireland (7)

32 Nice environment, by the sea (7)

34 Abraham Lincoln's speech made at the dedication of the national cemetery following the Civil War (10,7)

37 Northernmost province of Pakistan, bordering with Kashmir, Afghanistan and Jammu (5-4,8)

39 Simply ___ ; pop group led by vocalist Mick Hucknall (3)

40 Tree that has its flowers inside a pear-shaped receptacle that later develops into its fleshy fruit (3)

43 New York City waterway that is linked to the Great Lakes (6,5)

44 'I've got a gal in ___' ; so goes the song made famous by Glenn Miller (9)

47 Small orange (9)

48 Title of an Oliver Stone film about the Vietnam war (7)

49 South Slavonic language, almost identical to Croatian, but written in Cyrillic script (7)

50 Maintain grasp (5)

53 ___ Fudd ; Bugs Bunny's adversary who may be found 'hunting wabbits' (5)

54 Artificial hair (3)

55 Count up (3)

59 Filming celebrity associated with meteoric career (8,4)

60 According to the old rhyme would be 'fair of face' (7,5)

64 To cut off is nothing new (7)

65 Nursery-tale spirits (7)

66 Game in Moscow casino could be fatally dangerous (7,8)

70 Queen consort of King Louis XVI of France: she was guillotined in 1793 (5,10)

71 Writing fluid (3)

72 Bashful (3)

74 Chess Grand Master (7,6)

76 Member of a military religious order founded by Crusaders in 1118 to defend the Holy Sepulchre (6,7)

77 Film about Mozart that took the 1984 Academy Award for best movie (7)

83 Primate, especially of the anthropoid type (3)

84 Endeavour (3)

86 Frenzied emotional state or simply a bout of uncontrolled laughter (9)

89 Vegetable dish consisting of cooked sweet corn and lima beans (9)

90 Slow-moving creatures that have shells and leave a slimy trail (6)

91 Hunting dogs (6)

97 University honour (6)

98 Old Testament priest, father-in-law of Moses (6)

100 To make a bet (5)

102 Second-century Greek physician (5)

103 Seventh letter of the Greek alphabet (3)

31 Mind the gaps 1 LEVEL 1

Complete the crossword in under
10 minutes by filling in the dashes in each
clue to complete the phrase or sentence.

ACROSS

1 The trees were laden with
   spring ___ (7)
5 A Midsummer Night's
   ___ (5)
8 Oriental secrets of the
   Kama ___ (5)
9 Arrogant young ___ ! (7)
10 Few prisoners ___
   from Colditz (7)
11 Neither right nor left, but
   straight___ (5)
12 'Rockabye your baby with
   a Dixie ___' (6)
14 You can't enter the club
   unless you're a ___ (6)
17 The ___ Pavarotti sings
   'Nessun Dorma' (5)
19 There are 26 ___ in
   the English alphabet (7)
22 The groom adjusts the
   horse's ___ (7)
23 From his shifty expression,
   she knew he was ___ (5)
24 As white as a ___ (5)
25 ___ and brothers (7)

DOWN

1 Count ___ and his
   Orchestra (5)
2 A mirage is an ___
   illusion (7)
3 Rub hair restorer into
   your ___ (5)
4 Left too long, the bread
   had gone ___ (6)
5 Measles is an infectious
   ___ (7)
6 Running and hiding to ___
   capture (5)
7 The ___ taunts the bull
   with his cape (7)
12 He used a whole box of
   ___ lighting his pipe (7)
13 It's always ___ just before
   the dawn (7)
15 The queen and her
   workers live in the
   ___ (7)
16 ___ and minuses (6)
18 He panicked and lost his
   ___ (5)
20 Chaucer wrote *The
   Canterbury ___* (5)
21 The Bridge of ___ is
   in Venice (5)

32 Mind the gaps 2 LEVEL 1

Again, finish this crossword by filling in the gaps in
each clue to complete the phrase or sentence, but
this time try to do it in 7 minutes.

ACROSS

1 **He keeps exotic birds
   in an ___ (6)**
4 **Her husband suspected
   she was having an ___ (6)**
9 **A full-grown buffalo
   weighs nearly a ___ (3)**
10 **French policemen are
   called ___ (9)**
11 **Giuseppe ___ wrote the
   opera Aida (5)**
12 **A stoic ___ hardship
   without complaining (7)**
14 **Hobday's wild scheme
   to farm penguins
   was ___ (11)**
18 **The planet Venus is
   sometimes called the
   ___ star (7)**
20 **Marry in ___, repent at
   leisure (5)**
21 **An eight-sided shape is
   ___ (9)**
23 **___ or even? (3)**
24 **Spaniards take a ___ in
   the middle of the day (6)**
25 **Her photograph was ___
   in silver (6)**

DOWN

1 **Though over 70, she is
   still very ___ (6)**
2 **___ is bliss (9)**
3 **Scott Joplin, the 'King
   of ___' (7)**
5 **The con-man was found
   guilty of ___ (5)**
6 **To chance your ___ is
   to take a risk (3)**
7 **A temptation that's hard
   to ___ (6)**
8 **Not stupid – in fact, very
   ___ (11)**
13 **She was drenched by a
   sudden ___ (9)**
15 **He is a diligent ___,
   always studying (7)**
16 **___ are long-legged
   water birds (6)**
17 **Least said, soonest ___ (6)**
19 **Straight from the
   mould, an ___ of pure
   platinum (5)**
22 **Dipping his ___ in the
   water (3)**

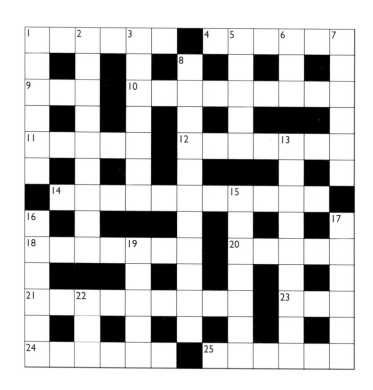

33 Flying colours 1 LEVEL 2

The clues are standard, but the letters in the coloured squares are an anagram of a famous 34 down.

ACROSS

1 Crept quietly (5)
6 Common practice (5)
9 34 Down who hasn't taken vows (3-6)
10 Confidential comment (5)
11 Rendezvous (5)
12 Short beginning (5)
13 Primp (5)
16 Slow mollusc (5)
19 Stir (7)
22 Sticks out (4)
23 South African prairie (5)
24 Overshadow (7)
28 Stringed instrument (5)
30 Press together (5)
32 More spacious (5)
33 Goddess of the moon (5)
35 German city in the Ruhr (5)
37 Substitute (9)
38 Correct (5)
39 Legends (5)

DOWN

2 Yellow-green colour (5)
3 Young man (3)
4 Glancing at (6)
5 Order or decree (6)
6 Greatest (6)
7 View (3)
8 Concert venue (5)
14 Awaken (5)
15 Artist's stand (5)
17 At no time (5)
18 Relation by marriage (2-3)
20 Not well (3)
21 Electrical unit (3)
25 Noel ___, British song-writer (6)
26 Situated within a building (6)
27 Piercing cry (6)
29 Rental contract (5)
31 Beginning (5)
34 Member of religious order (3)
36 Filthy place (3)

34 Flying colours 2 LEVEL 3

The clues are standard, but the letters in the coloured squares are an anagram of a creature that might be attracted to a 24 across.

ACROSS

1 Stood up to (5)
4 Book room (7)
8 Coming up (7)
9 Examination (5)
10 Advantage (4)
11 Famous Apache (8)
13 Peculiarly (5)
14 Hold up (5)
19 Retaliatory action (8)
21 Mix with spoon (4)
23 Last letter of Greek alphabet (5)
24 Flourish (7)
25 Over the top (7)
26 Foundation (5)

DOWN

1 Hesitate (6)
2 Blocked (7)
3 Platform (4)
4 Recorded (6)
5 Fastened (8)
6 Excuse (5)
7 Cowardly (6)
12 Final (8)
15 Witnesses (7)
16 Furrow (6)
17 Mob (6)
18 Perfumes (6)
20 Fold (5)
22 Sarcophagus (4)

35 Arrow route 1   LEVEL 2

Solve the straight clues in the grid and follow the arrows to fill in the answers.

Arrowword puzzles

The clues to arrowword crosswords are to be found within the arrowword grid itself. The arrows in the squares indicate where your answers should go.

Bitterness / Jazz dance		Clairvoyant / Outspoken		US university		Fools			Collapse / Fish eggs	
				Worry / Allege						
Supportive						Dandy / Japanese wrestling				
			Boat							
Dry	Ogre		Genetic material		Unpleasant		Therefore / Roman god of sun			
									Dimension	
Dumps, depression		Study again		Web-footed bird / From Wales						
						Removable cover / Third planet				
Scribble	Repeat		Observe / Gambling stakes					Close		Funeral meal
					Once more					
Wild / Criticism									French 'the'	
Archaic form of 'have'					Speech					
Keatsian poem			Number of Musketeers							

36 Four square 1   LEVEL 1

Word squares

Word squares have been known since Roman times. To solve these, write the missing words in the grid so that they read the same across as down.

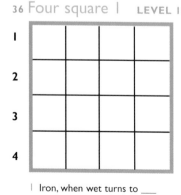

1
2
3
4

1 Iron, when wet turns to ___

2 Cinderella had ___ sisters

3 ___stick – a form of comedy

4 A good secretary can ___ 60 words a minute

37 Four square 2   LEVEL 1

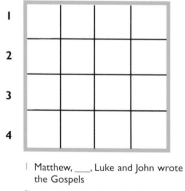

1
2
3
4

1 Matthew, ___, Luke and John wrote the Gospels

2 ___ vera is used in skin lotions

3 A chestnut horse is a ___

4 Clark ___ is the real name of Superman

38 Arrow route 2 LEVEL 3

Luxury		Lordly / Gangster's girl	Remark / Young horse		Estimated time of arrival		Part of a nail		Each		Open-mouthed		Portents
							Pasta dish		Omelette ingredient / Australian bird				Harbour
Explosion				Change							Monkey / Raises		
Peruvian pack animal					Goal				On top of / Golf average				
				Bird of prey	Wrecks								
Southern beauty	Jimmy Carter's crop	Cancel	Himalayan country					Like / Burnt remnants			Laudable		Honey-mooners
Italian food					Cogwheel						Border		Festival
		Cultivated	Firearm / Concentrate				Warble		Poems				
Write / Heavenly being					Reflected sound						Gaping jaws		
Hospital worker					Hence	Tilts		Carpentry tool					
				Exclusive							Beam / Ache		
Asses		Person clothed / Before						Health resort / Bashful				Allow	
			US TV hospital drama	Spaces / Knockout						Competent			
Snake / Dual sound	Tally						Exalted						
				Observe secretly					Catches				

39 All square 1 LEVEL 2

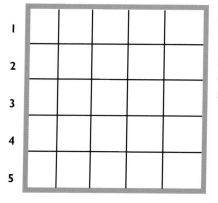

1 Pierces
2 People and language of Southern India and Sri Lanka
3 More than enough
4 Lowest part of a ship
5 Snowy rain

40 All square 2 LEVEL 2

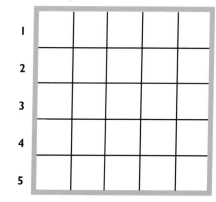

1 To delay evasively
2 The shinbone
3 Building occupied by a group of monks or nuns
4 One bound to give feudal homage or service to a superior
5 Hen, for example

Cryptic crosswords call for a roundabout way of thinking, but they are addictive once you have the knack. See page 20 for some beginner's tips – and good luck!

41 Warm up

Here are some cryptic clues to prepare you for the road ahead. You do not need to know all the conventions of cryptic crossword clues to have a stab at these – just use your wits, imagination and a little lateral thinking.

LEVEL 1

1 Good at tennis or flying a plane (3)
2 Warp U or S? (4)
3 Pack STUVW (4)
4 In charge after underground church like this clue (6)

LEVEL 2

1 A wicked thing (6)
2 Water spanner (6)
3 Incensed, angered exploded (7)
4 Powered flight takes you higher (9)

LEVEL 3

1 Cccooorrrsssiiicccaaa! A place in the USA? (4, 6)
2 0014 – a professional deceiver (6, 5)
3 Airs here are stratospheric, possibly (9, 4)

42 Dual clues I   LEVEL 2

In this crossword, the across clues are cryptic, but the down clues are straightforward definitions. This is a blocked-out grid, which means there is little interlocking between words, making the puzzle more difficult. If you find it too much, try Dual clues 2 (opposite) first: it's a bit easier.

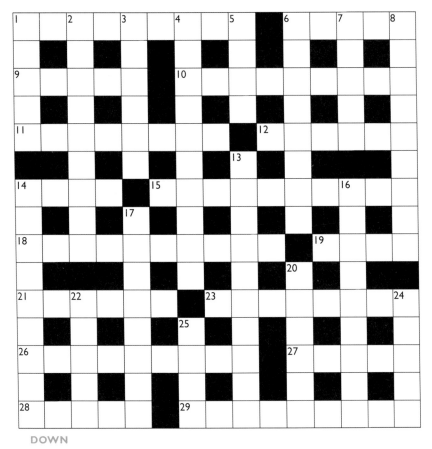

ACROSS

1 Crazy genius had tormented (9)
6 The Sun is going back. It is blocked during the cold (5)
9 Earthenware centre where learner is halfway through being experienced (5)
10 Crazy mod graced fairground attraction (6,3)
11 Confused adolescent with bent fork is a thing that holds tightly (4,4)
12 Maintenance raise then look back (6)
14 Our father, a mad gadabout (4)
15 Creepy scab engineered web (10)
18 Excited medallist gains right to obtain training equipment (10)
19 Security devices found in Florida (4)
21 Sturdy doorway missing an article. Yes. (6)
23 Inexperienced, sounding like an over-worked librarian? (4-4)
26 Maybe hours? Halt! This journey doesn't last very long! (5-4)
27 Clumsy writer goes back in it (5)
28 Animal with too much hesitation (5)
29 Centre: drill out halfway (9)

DOWN

1 Variety of deciduous tree (5)
2 Period of great artistic achievement (6,3)
3 Number of people admitted into an organization (6)
4 A chemical reaction where a compound reacts with water causing decomposition (10)
5 US slang for a fashionable boy or man (4)
6 Quietly embarrassed (8)
7 Specialized market (5)
8 Without support from the shoulders (9)
13 Having a large income (4-6)
14 It starts an Italian meal (9)
16 When mixed with oxygen, this gas is used in welding (9)
17 A devoted admirer (8)
20 One who uses a keyboard (6)
22 Where a bird sleeps (5)
24 Singular of data (5)
25 Friendly, cosy (4)

43 Dual clues 2 LEVEL 2

As before, the across clues are cryptic, the down clues are definitions. The large amount of interlocking should make your task easier. If you are new to cryptics, try to be sure you have figured out how each Across clue works.

ACROSS

1 Drunk misses pit. He's not happy (9)
7 Degrade a foundation (5)
11 Payment in Saharan sombreros (6)
12 Air been heard before (3)
13 Turn in doctor for dirt (3)
14 Village play (6)
15 Part of nudist affected by mother's side of the family (7)
18 Acid in vinegar induced champion spasm (6)
21 Pouch that redundant French workers get? (3)
22 Temperature zero? Great! It's a measure of thermal efficiency (3)
23 Clue: an arrangement to take off shoes (6)
24 This dance can go all over the place! (5)
25 Rioting tows us the way of 225 degrees (9)

DOWN

1 **Spread through (8)**
2 **Californian city (3, 5)**
3 **Strip of cloth (4)**
4 **Child's word for mother (5)**
5 **Dry, withered (4)**
6 **In computing, rate of communication (4)**
8 **Water-bound activity (7)**
9 **Identical (8)**
10 **Reluctant to speak (8)**
16 **Dangerous feat (5)**
17 **Side of a mountain (4)**
19 **Popular name for a clown (4)**
20 **Pincer (4)**

44 Quick cryptic LEVEL 3

How quickly can you solve this purely cryptic crossword?

40 minutes: steady
30 minutes: impressive
20 minutes: genius

ACROSS

1 Drew a weird water bird (5)
4 Puck initially tried beer? An unlikely story! (5-4)
9 Layabout British king in the endless maze (9)
10 Direction followed by healthy sea creature (5)
11 Unseen danger – mine comes before autumn (7)
12 Unable to see, bend lid out of shape (7)
13 Leisure wear comes from his pool, right? (4,5)
16 Sounds like denims are inherited (5)
18 Upset saver goes wild (5)
20 Communist workman and Edward caught in the act (3-6)
22 Slaughter horse in trouble (7)
23 Murder a broken membrane (7)
25 Odd rock contains nothing for criminal (5)
26 Tin I aim to turn into counterfeit (9)
27 False report is about Hawaiians, for instance (9)
28 Girl gets round terrible start and continues (5)

DOWN

1 Stick-on decoration might make lapel warp (9)
2 I enter obligation to charge (5)
3 Again studies funny red ears (7)
4 Some proof in a letter is decisive (5)
5 Enid is confused about nun's costume that's occupied (9)
6 After a year, canopy is showing signs of tiredness (7)
7 One died after a group gave up (9)
8 Correct me climbing over limit (5)
14 City dweller put into common fund (9)
15 I see trail leads to Old Testament character (9)
17 Rising southern tides engulf men and grounds (9)
19 Can elks possibly relax? (7)
21 Ventilate armour for overseas posting (3,4)
22 Though bill is under a hundred, it's returned by prickly customers (5)
23 Sends forth second time around (5)
24 Checks rules, by the sound of it (5)

These two crosswords have dual sets of clues, but only one set of answers. If you are stuck on a cryptic clue, you can sneak a peek at the standard set. If, on the other hand, you prefer solving the standard set, you might at least find it interesting to look at how the cryptic set of clues approaches the same word.

LEVEL 3/LEVEL 2   Double trouble I 45

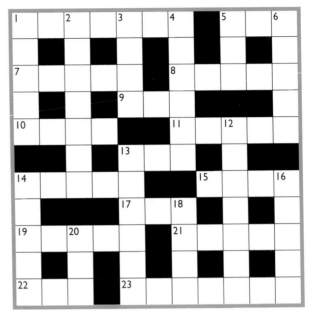

Cryptic clues

ACROSS

1 A floral wreath for Judy the actress (7)
5 Sailor taking back a rodent (3)
7 Celia changes her name (5)
8 Missile that may be found on the beach (5)
9 Wriggly fish comes back to the sheltered side (3)
10 Group of three involved in riot (4)
11 It can detect aircraft going backwards and forward (5)
13 Do something with a piece of legislation (3)
14 What fire does, according to a Scottish poet (5)
15 Flightless birds seen in the museum (4)
17 Share of profits called for by movie director (3)
19 Covering for the hand – of some doting lover? (5)
21 Not left? That's correct! (5)
22 Be agreeably sleepy? (3)
23 Serious crime that upset senator (7)

DOWN

1 Huge American soldier meets small insect (5)
2 More wet weather for the prince of Monaco? (7)
3 Cain's brother is competent, so we hear (4)
4 Abandon an arid region (6)
5 Bond to make the score equal (3)
6 Measuring device for a monarch (5)
12 Gas made to explode causes harm (7)
13 Going up – for a small coin? (6)
14 Start being slightly confused (5)
16 Glossy material didn't stand out? (5)
18 Ash, for example, kept in the family by genealogists (4)
20 This is not even strange (3)

Standard clues

ACROSS

1 Wreath of flowers (7)
5 Sailor (3)
7 Wonderland girl (5)
8 Hard outer covering (5)
9 The side away from the wind (3)
10 Musical composition for three performers (4)
11 Navigation aid using radio waves (5)
13 Take part in a play (3)
14 Scotland's national poet (5)
15 Large flightless birds (4)
17 Incision (3)
19 Covering for the hand (5)
21 Proper (5)
22 Lower and raise the head (3)
23 Traitor's crime (7)

DOWN

1 Very large person (5)
2 Prince of Monaco (7)
3 Victim of his brother Cain (4)
4 The Sahara, for example (6)
5 Bind, fasten (3)
6 Implement used for drawing straight lines (5)
12 Compensation awarded in court (7)
13 Movement upward (6)
14 Commence (5)
16 Smooth glossy material (5)
18 Tall woody plant (4)
20 Peculiar (3)

46 Double trouble 2 LEVEL 3/LEVEL 2

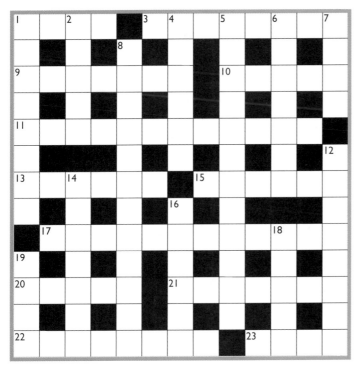

Standard clues

ACROSS

1 Whirlpool (4)
3 Display cabinet (4-4)
9 Have a disagreement (4,3)
10 Become liable for (5)
11 Elderly relatives (12)
13 Final part (of story) (6)
15 Writing implement (6)
17 Main part of the Internet (5,4,3)
20 A subject for discussion (5)
21 From part of Asia (7)
22 Composition for orchestra
   plus solo instrument (8)
23 _____ Xiaoping, Chinese leader (4)

DOWN

1 Dolls showing crude likenesses (8)
2 End of, for example, the River Nile (5)
4 Paid killer (3-3)
5 Marriage ceremony in church (5,7)
6 One forgoing earthly pleasures (7)
7 Wyatt _____, US Marshal (4)
8 It was stolen by Jason (6,6)
12 Going out dancing; beating with a cudgel (8)
14 Pays a visit (5,2)
16 Petty, insignificant (3-3)
18 Large marine mammal (5)
19 Circular shape (4)

Cryptic clues

ACROSS

1 He's in a whirl (4)
3 It exhibits what Latin
   word-endings may do (4-4)
9 Quarrel that's in the air
   after Big Bang (4,3)
10 Get yourself landed with a
   fashionable scoundrel (5)
11 £1,000 a year hires up to four
   family members (12)
13 What Doug and Morag do could
   be happy or sad (6)
15 This writer's in the lead? Exactly
   the opposite! (6)
17 Vast network commonly makes
   the same point three times (5,4,3)
20 Magazine for children (5)
21 Asian of Belgian extraction (7)
22 It's performed by company and
   cornet, possibly (8)
23 Chinese leader's written some
   good English (4)

DOWN

1 Models that may suffer attacks of
   pins and needles? (8)
2 Classical character describing
   river's end (5)
4 Number one piece for Assassin? (3-3)
5 Spooner's to marry fish – traditional
   nuptials (5,7)
6 A sceptic gives away money to
   become a holy man (7)
7 Lawman from a city near Phoenix (4)
8 It was stolen in Greece's first
   ancient swindle (6,6)
12 Out on the town – using an
   offensive weapon? (8)
14 Calls to renounce evil? (5,2)
16 For a quarter, it's pretty
   contemptible (3-3)
18 Sea creature said to sound like
   a Siren (5)
19 CD is shaped like this (4)

A s a bit of light relief, a do-it-yourself crossword that you can put together without having to solve any clues.

47 Tile teaser LEVEL 3

Place the pieces in the grid so that a crossword is formed. It will be useful to know that the answer to the word occupying the 'one down' position is GATEAU.

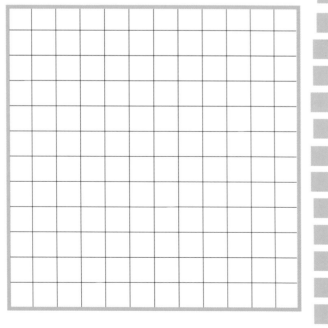

48 Eureka! LEVEL 3

In this themed cryptic crossword, all the coloured clues refer to a discovery of some sort – for example, a location, a pioneer or an invention. When the grid is complete, the middle row will spell out a word relating to the theme.

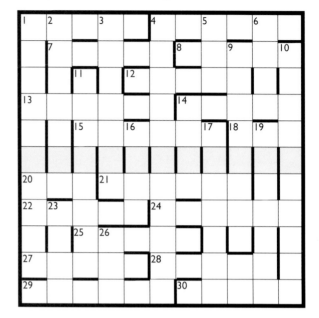

ACROSS

1 **Partly my fault? (5)**
4 **Hanging decoration that gets around (6)**
7 **Amino stirred for a girl (5)**
8 Tear out of apartheid for greenfly (5)
12 For 102 is text written by computer (5)
13 Sounds quite a task – you and me making a baby-to-be (6)
14 **A long time with gas outside that keeps you in (5)**
15 **A thing in earth orbit, I'm a woman (6)**
18 Electricity production with assistance without novice (3)
20 And looking at it another way, it's a double-helix (3)
21 **One of the Borgias has an awkward crease (6)**
22 **No Alun, cancel (5)**
24 **I climb pole for flowers (6)**
25 **Catches broken strap (5)**
27 **Mexican plant contained in cassis alcohol (5)**
28 A quiet instrument (5)
29 **Old boys and you in Milan quake (6)**
30 **Was he the first American satellite? (5)**

DOWN

1 Strong chest blocks dehydrating barrages (10)
2 **One French woman with cooker becomes disentangled (7)**
3 **Michigan city's muddled caption (7)**
4 River lady is going both ways – very quiet, I conclude (11)
5 Bits per inch. Billion plus 3.14159... (3)
6 Insects make Wonderland character lose her head (4)
9 **Royal altitude (8)**
10 **Mixing up, mixing up. So inspired (10)**
11 **Adornments – do without and arrange what's left over (8)**
14 **Spanish house while in a West coast state (4)**
16 **Lire used in Cambodia? (4)**
17 **Slight warlike disruption pertains to weddings (7)**
19 **Level part of speech the Spanish lead on (7)**
23 **Type of fixture, of which you have 20? (4)**
26 Mess up the computer memory (3)

49 The hard stuff I   LEVEL 3+

On this page you'll find two extremely difficult cryptic crosswords containing some pretty obscure words. If you can finish these, consider yourself a cryptic champion.

ACROSS

1 Not at all a routine car repair (2,9)
7 Heads of school are playing the fool (3)
8 Boz character's blunders (7)
9 Prompt and somewhat detailed (5)
10 Satellite found by university, unknown by South Dakota (5)
12 Grass scare (5)
14 A measure raising a little capital (5)
16 Vain court star in America (7)
18 Peter's face (3)
19 Flower god set with sun god (11)

DOWN

1 A rebel heading north for Norse gods (5)
2 Turner outdoes Brown (7)
3 Aristocrat valued more than the crown (5)
4 Uncle turning up in ancient civilization (5)
5 Consecutive numbers written badly (3)
6 Devereux County (5)
11 Head part: copy one quietly inside out (7)
12 Sound choice sound (5)
13 The best emollient (5)
14 A Midwest and Central European story-teller (5)
15 Paean about cessation of respiration (5)
17 A letter from the taxman (3)

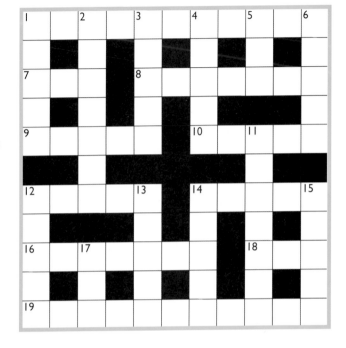

50 The hard stuff 2   LEVEL 3+

ACROSS

1 Note about ingredients needed for pie, perhaps (6)
4 Boat from South heading for Jersey or Guernsey (4)
8 Novel story of March issue (6,5)
9 Immediate response in letter I posted (7)
11 Result of fire in wood (3)
12 Coach bringing replacement player back (3)
13 Boy suffering as champion (7)
15 Not an unlucky number for the breadmaker (6,5)
17 Scored slowly, nonetheless advanced (4)
18 Plant brought back inside biology notebook (6)

DOWN

1 Drawing instrument found among the dividers? (5)
2 Queen, perhaps, allowed to see King (3)
3 Vehemently opposed to Europeans getting a share (5,5)
5 General has to move on out and issue orders (7)
6 Device for moving weight over a distance (5)
7 One of Lewis Carroll's brothers – not the ultimately dumb-sounding one (10)
10 Russian poet with offensive relatives (7)
12 Ruth left scene of total confusion (5)
14 Female who looks after kids (5)
16 Where zebra or ostrich initially may be seen (3)

Simply acrostics LEVEL I

In these puzzles the trick is to discover the answers to the down clues (all of an astronomical nature) by first solving the clues across. The first and the last letters are what matter, and to make it more difficult we've omitted the number of letters in each word.

51 ACROSS

1 SAINT ASSOCIATED WITH LOVE ☐————☐

2 MATERIAL EXCITING AMOROUS PROPENSITIES ☐————☐

3 THE DRINK OF THE GODS ☐————☐

4 SINGLE THING OR PERSON ☐————☐

5 AUDIBLE BREATH ☐————☐

52 ACROSS

1 STANDARD ☐————☐

2 ANIMAL THAT SOUNDS LIKE YOU ☐————☐

3 MODERN VERSION OF PAPYRUS ☐————☐

4 MAGNESIUM SILICATE POWDER ☐————☐

5 INDIC LANGUAGE ☐————☐

6 AND NOT ☐————☐

7 NOT DIFFICULT ☐————☐

Double acrostic puzzles such as those on the next few pages need twice the puzzling ability. Once you've completed the grid you'll find a famous quote or saying. First answer the clues at the top, then fill in the grid beneath by transferring the individual letters of the answers to the appropriate squares, indicated by the numbers below each letter.

A Not classical painting (6,3)
28 57 51 14 10 44   49 34 3

B It's risky, but could be profitable (7)
13 25 50 38 30 55 5

C Hefner's cuddly pets (7)
24 7 18 2 43 12 48

D World soccer bosses (4)
37 21 26 54

E Appallingly, dreadfully (8)
53 17 47 32 9 58 23 52

F Cause of kids' lockjaw? (6)
46 29 6 35 11 40

G Presidential dwelling (5,5)
20 56 1 8 39   4 33 45 31 19

H First name of Hollywood legend (7)
42 27 15 36 22 16 41

---

53 Crystal ball

LEVEL I

In this puzzle, there's a prediction in the squares. In the green squares, you'll find the name of the person who made the prediction (the identity of whom is suggested by the answers to clues A and H).

1 G	2 C	■	3 A	4 G	5 B	■	6 F	7 C	8 G	9 E	10 A	11 F	■
12 C	13 B	14 A	15 H	16 H	17 E	18 C	19 G	■	20 G	21 D	22 C	23 E	■
24 C	25 B	■	26 D	27 H	28 A	29 F	30 B	31 G	■	32 E	33 G	34 A	
35 F	36 H	37 D	38 B	39 G	40 F	41 H	■	42 H	43 C	44 A	45 G	46 F	47 E
48 C		49 A	50 B	51 A	52 E		53 E	54 D	55 B	56 G	57 A	58 E	

54 Expert advice LEVEL 2

The quotation here comes from a world-class puzzle-solver, whose identity is hinted at in the answers to clues A and B. So if you want some expert advice, solve the cryptic clues and fill in the squares in the grid.

A   Confound alert enemy? That's simple! (10)
50 59 12 41 92 8 23 15 69 31

B   Doctor was assistant to solver of note, originally (6)
78 25 18 95 87 43

C   Out of date, like one reading a broadsheet newspaper? (6,3,5)
88 29 100 13 74 17   105 24 79   6 57 93 38 55

D   Spot some terrible mishap (7)
58 39 67 52 73 14 34

E   Speaking of presents, I couldn't agree more! (4,4)
9 98 89 68   62 46 72 103

F   Toiletry relaunched as Oomph! (7)
75 28 10 84 53 77 19

G   Survey showing deliveries to rival West (8)
2 66 37 86 11 51 7 27

H   Music collection that's nice to listen to (5)
56 22 83 102 70

I   Eric's first into bed, all changed like a good boy (8)
54 97 81 47 16 101 30 64

J   FBI in trouble? It's not true (3)
5 40 90

K   In addition, your old grin might be (6)
48 4 32 26 76 20

L   What's at the back of the throat? We're told you view French article! (5)
104 36 33 91 63

M   Where to fade away, say? (7)
61 1 42 99 106 60 82

N   Purple type of light seen in West (5)
71 44 94 80 65

O   What top organization provides a track for horses? (7)
96 21 3 85 35 45 49

1 M	2 G	3 O		4 K	5 J	6 C	7 G	8 A		9 E	10 F	11 G	12 A		13 C		14 D	15 A
16 I	17 C		18 B	19 F		20 K	21 O	22 H		23 A	24 C	25 B	26 K		27 G	28 F	29 C	30 I
	31 A	32 K	33 L		34 D	35 O	36 L	37 G		38 C	39 D	40 J	41 A	42 M	43 B	44 N	45 O	46 E
47 I		48 K	49 O	50 A		51 G	52 D	53 F	54 I	55 C	56 H	57 C	58 D	59 A	60 M		61 M	62 E
63 L	64 I	65 N	66 G	67 D	68 E		69 A	70 H	71 N	72 E	73 D	74 C	75 F		76 K	77 F	78 B	79 C
80 N	81 I	82 M	83 H	84 F	85 O	86 G	87 B	88 C	89 E	90 J	91 L	92 A		93 C	94 N	95 B	96 O
		97 I	98 E		99 M	100 C	101 I		102 H	103 E	104 L	105 C	106 M			

55 Lost in space LEVEL 2

A To the Greeks, a wanderer (6) — — — — — —
17 33 3 7 27 32

B The first on clue C (9) — — — — — — — — —
41 39 10 9 1 20 6 31 2

C Earth's close companion (4) — — — —
40 19 25 26

D Imitate or leave (4,3) — — — — — — —
4 35 43 8 38 18 37

E The opposite of clue D (4) — — — —
13 30 24 46

F The sort of *king* that makes us superior to clue I? (4) — — — —
15 2 29 42

G Clue B's Uncle? (3) — — —
14 11 22

H He could be illegal or from further afield (5) — — — — —
23 12 44 34 45

I Imitates relatives of clue B more distant than clue G (4) — — — —
21 36 16 5

Puzzles 56 and 57 are cryptic acrostics. Solve the clues then find the quotation.

56 Stage secret LEVEL 3

A Pink bird represented by a burning letter (8) — — — — — — — —
49 31 18 9 4 59 36 51

B What a fisherman does could be instrumental (8) — — — — — — — —
2 32 8 15 30 28 25 20

C Penguin and concerto (7) — — — — — — —
35 52 40 12 19 45 11

D In a drinking place it makes one who seeks alms (3) — — —
48 6 34

E According to some, a way of ruining a walk in the country (4) — — — —
60 38 13 22

F Lofty greeting? (4) — — — —
57 7 29 16

G Big creature poses the end of the whelk (3) — — —
10 47 23

H Oddly crony is shy (3) — — —
53 54 14

I French for *flow* (4) — — — —
43 21 55 37

J Number found at the heart of my cash (3) — — —
41 5 17

K My whole is a big example and my first half a small example of my second half (10) — — — — — — — — — —
56 50 1 46 24 42 33 39 58 3

L Three-fifths of piece is the whole of it (3) — — —
26 27 44

57 Lover's plea LEVEL 3

A Sauciest of containers (8)
— — — — — — — —
82 4 30 10 37 47 40 53

B Number with a point (7)
— — — — — — —
84 69 75 56 70 25 19

C Ice house (5)
— — — — —
54 58 24 14 83

D Finger list (5)
— — — — —
6 80 81 12 36

E Quiet: as two peas (10)
— — — — — — — — — —
63 1 79 78 43 49 5 67 33 41

F Tangled knot is noted symbol (5)
— — — — —
55 15 76 9 57

G Writer brought back by osteopath (4)
— — — —
64 17 22 59

H Initially, for instance, several halibut (4)
— — — —
18 74 39 11

I Nourished friend, oddly enough (3)
— — —
42 32 16

J To act thus is to exist and to possess (6)
— — — — — —
8 65 46 71 31 61

K Semi-divine maiden speeds after New York (5)
— — — — —
28 26 3 23 60

L Half the quadruped's quota, though it sounds like all (8)
— — — — — — — —
13 20 51 34 2 35 38 68

M Though green, she's a bit of a climber (3)
— — —
85 21 72

N Written law (7)
— — — — — — —
73 66 62 44 50 48 77

O Continuation indicated at heart sketchy (3)
— — —
86 45 7

P Horn, bank or light (3)
— — —
52 27 29

1 E	2 L		3 K	4 A	5 E	6 D	7 O		8 J	9 F		10 A	11 H	12 D
13 L	14 C	15 F	16 I			17 G	18 H			19 B	20 L	21 M	22 G	
23 K	24 C	25 B	26 K		27 P	28 K		29 P	30 A	31 J	32 I		33 E	34 L
		35 L	36 D	37 A	38 L	39 H	40 A		41 E	42 I		43 E	44 N	
45 O	46 J	47 A	48 N		49 E	50 N	51 L	52 P	53 A	54 C	55 F	56 B	57 F	58 C
	59 G	60 K	61 J			62 N	63 E	64 G	65 J	66 N	67 E	68 L	69 B	
70 B	71 J	72 M		73 N	74 H	75 B	76 F	77 N	78 E			79 E	80 D	81 D
82 A	83 C		84 B	85 M	86 O								

lexiCONfusion

58 WHAT DOES THAT WORD MEAN?

Test your vocabulary with these verbal teasers. We've provided explanations of 75 words – but each word has only one correct definition, with three more designed to confuse you. Without resorting to a dictionary, how many correct definitions can you spot? You should have little difficulty with the first 15 words. However, the next 20 are rather more testing, and the 20 after that even more so. The final 20 words should challenge the largest vocabularies.

EASY

1 BAZOOKA
A Greek instrument
B Russian taxi
C simple person
D anti-tank gun

2 DEBRIS
A rubbish
B debate
C demolish
D uncover

3 ESPERANTO
A Spanish fizzy drink
B Italian seaside resort
C international language
D fairground entertainment

4 GNU
A large antelope
B type of glue
C type of gun
D small dog

5 GOBLIN
A young turkey
B mischievous spirit
C precious stone
D drinking vessel

6 HARICOT
A worried
B athletic
C spiky hat
D French bean

7 MINESTRONE
A very small
B vegetable soup
C naval ship
D opera singer

8 POPPY
A young dog
B sea creature
C type of flower
D favourite sweet

9 PORTAL
A ship's gangplank
B gate or doorway
C drink from Portugal
D cartoon character

10 RABBLE
A damage
B scratch around
C noisy mob
D fragments

11 SPRIG
A pompous person
B freshwater fish
C mineshaft
D small shoot

12 SYCAMORE
A type of tree
B breed of horse
C long road or avenue
D shipwreck

13 VAULT
A boast
B leap
C press
D damage

14 VESTIBULE
A small umbrella
B undergarment
C wasps' nest
D entrance hall

15 WAN
A shrink
B waste
C pale
D tall

HARDER

16 ABATE
A priest
B annoyed
C become less widespread
D encourage

17 CAROUSE
A opera singer
B excite
C reindeer
D drink

18 CORPOREAL
A physical
B military
C friendly
D mythical

19 DIFFUSE
A unplug
B spread widely
C perplex
D convex

20 DILATE
A angry
B mix with water
C expand
D discuss

21 DISMEMBER
A insincere
B forget
C tear limb from limb
D disease of dogs

22 EXHUME
A put down
B dig up
C use up
D breathe out

23 GOULASH
A prison camp
B deep drain
C large explosion
D rich stew

24 HEMLOCK
A protective headgear
B poisonous plant
C zip fastener
D half-open

25 INERT
A rare gas
B import
C not moving
D compose

26 JEMMY
A female donkey
B burglar's crowbar
C close-fitting jacket
D bad joke

27 NIMBUS
A cloud
B golf club
C poisonous gas
D large explosion

28 ONEROUS
A solitary
B burdensome
C amusing
D made of marble

29 PARLEY
A type of herb
B discussion
C contradict
D swimming stroke

30 RIBALD
A gambling game
B hairless
C type of pony
D lewdly humorous

31 SALVE
A to soothe
B to greet
C to drown
D to extract

32 SOUCHONG
A Japanese noodle dish
B Chinese tea
C German beer
D Korean film star

33 TONSURE
A sandal
B swelling in the throat
C bald patch
D guaranteed weight

34 WISTFUL
A angry
B gaseous
C smelly
D sad

35 ZITHER
A hesitate
B walking frame
C stringed instrument
D more lively

TRICKY

36 ALTERCATION
A fierce argument
B changing around
C taking turns
D part of a church

37 CHUNTER
A railway engine
B to mutter
C to vomit
D small fraction

38 CONY
A rabbit
B ice cream
C comfortable
D hilltop

39 CORSAIR
A rude song
B powerful drug
C pirate ship
D dead body

40 CREEL
A lentil soup
B Scottish dance
C narrow coastal inlet
D fisherman's wicker basket

41 INSENSATE
A lacking feeling
B lacking intelligence
C lacking food
D overfed

42 JELLABA
A hooded cloak
B sugary sweet
C Arab tent
D desert rat

43 JONGLEUR
A French game
B fortune teller
C jealous person
D medieval minstrel

44 KELP
A small barrel
B seaweed
C Scotsman's skirt
D anger

45 KRAKEN
A alarm call
B legendary sea monster
C broken into pieces
D unit of electricity

46 KUMMEL
A desert animal
B meteorite
C Jewish holiday
D liqueur

47 LAPWING
A type of car
B type of bird
C type of dance
D eating greedily

48 OCCIDENTAL
A by chance
B pointed
C cloudy
D western

49 ODONTOLOGY
A study of teeth
B study of hymns
C study of bats
D study of ears

50 QUINCE
A set of five
B church choir
C defeat
D fruit

51 SCHISM
A spot
B spit
C split
D sprint

52 SERE
A approach
B dried up
C prophet
D slave

53 SPINET
A carpenter's tool
B musical instrument
C part of the body
D spider's web

54 TOCCATA
A ancient map
B Roman cloak
C reddish colour
D musical composition

55 WINSOME
A grapevine
B imaginary
C charming
D attack

DEVILISH

56 BACILLUS
A tobacco pouch
B microscopic organism
C Roman emperor
D board game

57 CONTUMACY
A wilful disobedience
B reckless overeating
C mindless rage
D heat exhaustion

58 CYCAD
A young swan
B plant resembling a fern
C curdled milk
D one-eyed giant

59 DECALOGUE
A animated conversation
B jury of ten people
C unit of measurement
D the ten commandments

60 FLOCCULENT
A flecked
B flighty
C fluffy
D fluky

61 HORNBEAM
A exotic bird
B powerful light
C cow's width
D hardwood tree

62 HYSSOP
A speech defect
B aromatic mint
C small lake
D rabbit's burrow

63 ICHOR
A blood of the gods
B yak's milk
C distant galaxy
D wooden chair

64 LANGUR
A long-tailed monkey
B weariness
C region of Switzerland
D bright light

65 MARABOU
A Islamic hermit
B African stork
C Indian buffalo
D Navajo canoe

66 METACARPUS
A transformation
B type of cactus
C horse's back
D palm of the hand

67 MINIVER
A small stream
B cartoon mouse
C white fur
D fragrant herb

68 OMOPHAGOUS
A deep purple
B shallow breathing
C vegetarian
D eating raw flesh

69 PALLIUM
A horse race
B papal cloak
C lack of colour
D surrounding fence

70 RAJPUT
A turban
B elephant trainer
C aristocratic Hindu
D teapot

71 RETICULE
A shy
B laughable
C wake-up call
D small handbag

72 SAPONIFY
A dry up
B sweeten
C take apart
D turn into soap

73 TESSELLATION
A impact
B mosaic
C turning green
D retaliation

74 TRIOLET
A horse-drawn carriage
B eight-line poem
C three-cornered hat
D surgical instrument

75 ZYMOLOGY
A study of fermentation
B study of reptiles
C study of religious relics
D study of cyclones

Clock that

How many words of three letters or more can you make from these letters without using the same letter twice? The added difficulty with three of the puzzles is that you must include the letter in the middle of the clockface in each word. The puzzles get progressively harder as you move clockwise, so you may find it becomes harder to reach your target score. In the answers section you'll find a list of the most common answers.

25 words = average
45 words = well done
50+ words = genius

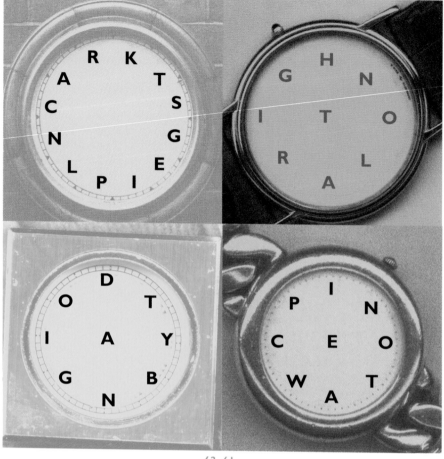

59 60

62 61

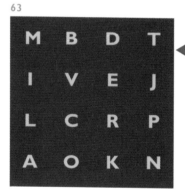

63

20+ words = average
35+ words = well done
50+ words = genius

Letter linking

Link the letters horizontally, vertically, forward or backwards, up or down and diagonally to make as many words of three letters or more as you can. You can't use a letter more than once per word or have plurals of other words. In puzzles 65 and 66 (below) you can only travel along the lines.

15+ words = average
25+ words = well done
35+ words = genius

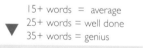

64

10+ words = average   20+ words = well done   30+ words = genius

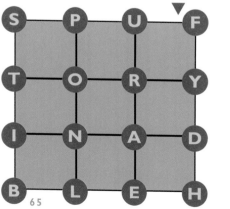

65

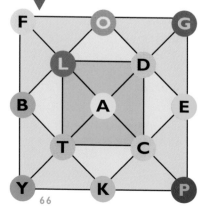

66

67 Hidden cities LEVEL 2

Each one-liner below is a cryptic clue to the name of a city somewhere in the world. For example, if the clue was 'Happy Granite', the answer would be 'Glad Stone' = Gladstone (an Australian city).

1 Crazy cast-away
2 Blow up old agreement
3 Villain of Watergate
4 Equality exists!
5 Conflict perceived
6 Shoot a nuisance
7 Make music a study
8 Fashionable in the past
9 Telephoned with nothing on
10 Small boulder

68 On with his head! LEVEL 2

Below are ten clues. Solve the first part and then add a new letter to the front of the answer to solve the second part.

(Hint: Suppose the clue is 'Possess city'. 'Possess' = OWN. Add 'T' to the front of 'own' to make TOWN. TOWN is another word for city.)

1 Hair-piece, time-piece
2 Trivial insult
3 Fish hook
4 Summit address
5 Ancient wrinkle
6 Sick note
7 Hasty accident
8 Money concern
and a bit trickier...
9 Single single
10 Choose choose

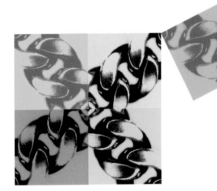

69 Missing links LEVEL 2

Find the word that links each of the pair of words below. Which of the missing words might be a penny bun?

1 pine .... turnover
2 sword .... finger
3 spring .... run
4 short .... basket
5 runner .... stalk
6 pan .... hole
7 oyster .... cloud
8 sweet .... flake
9 cottage .... bald
10 swiss .... mop

70 From A to B... LEVEL 1

The green letters in each of the world cities below can be arranged to spell the name of another international city. The destination country of the new location is given as a clue. Give yourself 10 minutes to complete the puzzle – to make it a bit more difficult we have left the key letters in the last three clues unshaded.

LOS ANGELES TO NIGERIA ....
SAINT PETERSBURG TO FRANCE ....
ROTTERDAM TO ITALY ....
INDIANAPOLIS TO ITALY ....
JOHANNESBURG TO GERMANY ....
BUENOS ARIES TO BRAZIL ....
DUSSELDORF TO SOUTH KOREA ....
REYKJAVIK TO THE UKRAINE ....
VLADIVOSTOK TO NORWAY ....
SAN FRANCISCO TO EGYPT ....

The aim of wordsearches is to find the words listed. They may run up, down, forward, backwards, diagonally in any direction – and may overlap. Beware, though: some of these wordsearches have an extra twist.

72 Wood for the trees LEVEL 1

Can you spot the listed trees in the grid?

FIG	MAPLE	LIME	PEAR
CEDAR	ELM	WILLOW	CYPRESS
BIRCH	PINE	YEW	GINKGO
ASH	POPLAR	PALM	BAY
BEECH	OAK	REDWOOD	WALNUT

```
B E E C H A R G L E B E
E L E P H A O G K N I G
T P I N E S T B E A R S
U A A B L U R A D E C K
N M P L I N S E C T H E
L R E A M H A T C H E D
A O R S E W A B R U S O
W A M D O R E A L E A O
E A G L E B A Y X K E W
F I L L E O P E R D I D
K I T T S S E R P Y C E
W I G H I P P O P L A R
```

73 Cry havoc! LEVEL 2

Fifteen minutes should be more than enough time to complete this battler of a puzzle.

AGINCOURT	IWO-JIMA	SLUYS
ALAMEIN	MARATHON	SOMME
ANZIO	MARNE	STALINGRAD
BALACLAVA	METZ	THERMOPYLAE
BUNKER HILL	MIDWAY	TRAFALGAR
GETTYSBURG	NILE	VIENNA
GUADALCANAL	OKINAWA	WATERLOO
HASTINGS	PLASSEY	ZAMA

71 Cool shades LEVEL 1

All these colours can be found in our wordsearch grid. Give yourself 10 minutes to complete the puzzle.

AQUA
AZURE
BLUE
BRONZE
GOLD
GREEN
GREY
INDIGO
LILAC
MAROON
OCHRE
RUSSET
RUST
SAND
SIENNA
SILVER
TURQUOISE
UMBER
VIOLET
WHITE
YELLOW

```
D Y B Y U O C H R E
L G E M O C A D E E
O R B L F G L S S R
G E E G L N I M I E
R E Z H I O L D E V
U N N A U O W D N L
S J O Q K R H N N I
S E R U Z A I A A S
E U B A L M T S U R
T E L O I V E U L B
```

```
W E A L Y P O M R E H T U G T S
R I Z N H A S T I N G S M R M I
S V A W A N I K O N E O U A A S
O L I N G N F T I A E O H L R T
M L E E I E Y A T N C R L N A A
M T N L N R T K V N M A M E T L
E N E R N N O T I A N E Y C H I
T E N R A M A G Y A L E T L O N
R S Y U L S A Y C S S C L Z N G
A Y A W D I M L E S B I A W M R
F A G M Z A A A A A A H U A L M A
A L W A A D A L M R L T R U A D
L A M S A N P A E I E A O G H B
G A B U Z E T K S R J C M N O J
A E G I A G N P L A Z O L E M T
R D O M L U E O N A I X W R I O
R M D I B V O L Y S E O S I P N
```

74 Stripes and stars LEVEL 1

Here are 15 states of the USA. You'll find most of them in the square – but one state has been left out. You have 15 minutes to find the other 14, and name the missing state.

CALIFORNIA
DELAWARE
FLORIDA
GEORGIA
IDAHO
IOWA
MAINE
MARYLAND
NEW JERSEY
OREGON
TENNESSEE
TEXAS
UTAH
VERMONT
WASHINGTON

```
A W G U N L E F T P O D
S N E W J E R S E Y M E
I O W A I D O R X N A E
R T C F E V I G A K U S
O G P O L R E G S D A S
S N E R H O M R N Y L E
Z I F E R E R A M T O N
A H U G B P L I N O R N
H S I O S Y P U D H N E
T A I N R O F I L A C T
S W T A M E W R O D L U
R I M U D R Y E N I A M
```

75 A place out of place LEVEL 3

The square contains the names of 15 well-known places. However, one of the places does not belong with the others. In addition to solving the puzzle in 10 minutes, can you find it?

```
E F Y O D A G R L P O W S T O
W A C R E B H U M I S D E R N
O Y J E R U S A L E M X I C O
C E T S U E H G N O R A F E P
S L G A C N I B R A C D O M I
O R E V N O T G N I L L E W S
M B L A B S P E S G I J Q U A
S N E H T A D E W Y L P A L T
A D I R J I T O N K D U I T E
M I N A I R O B I H O N P O G
Y O N W R E H A M I A T E K H
S K R O C S U V E M I G L Y A
U L L T N D O N T A R H E O R
G A R T E I L P B E R L I N C
W I N O D N O L I P O W T H A
```

76 Word wild web LEVEL 2

Believe it or not, the word INTERNET is concealed in this grid only once. Can you locate it?

```
I T I N T I R N E I I I
N E T T E N R E T N N I
T R E N E T E N E T T N
E N R E T N N N E U E T
R I N T E R R R R I E
N T E R N E N E E N R R
T R T R E I T R T E E N
E N E I T I E E T T T T
R T I I N T R T E N N E
N E N T E N R T E T N I
E N T T E T E N T N I N
T E N T E R N I N I R N
```

77 Busy canvas LEVEL 2

All the highlighted words in our mini-biography of a famous mystery person can be located in the wordsearch grid. When all the words have been crossed off, the remaining unused letters in the grid will spell out the name of our mystery person. Give yourself 15 minutes to complete the puzzle.

This diminutive artist was born in Albi, France, in 1864. He started painting in childhood and proved good enough to study for several years under some of the most respected French academic painters, but he was no dusty scholar. He preferred to spend his time in the company of actors, dancers and ladies of the night in the shady districts of Paris. His portraits of the Moulin Rouge and other cabarets of Montmartre are some of the most vivacious ever committed to canvas. Despite standing a little under five feet tall and always being frail of health, this celebrated and talented soul lived his short life to the full, and produced a body of work that few others have equalled.

```
L T D A N C E R S T O U
A L B I A S O U L E L P
D O U N R R O U G E E A
I E V O S I E Y R F V I
E A T L C A E T H G I N
S C C A B A R E T S T T
A N V F R A N C E S U E
E I U S M B T F I F N R
V L I T T L E T R R I S
I U N D E R R L E A M L
F O E Q U A L L E D I C
M M A C A D E M I C D L
```

78 Pop picker LEVEL 1

All of the words listed can be found in the puzzle. They are always in a straight line but can be written in any direction. You'll need a keen eye to finish in less than 15 minutes.

BARRY WHITE

BILLY IDOL

BILLY JOEL

BOB DYLAN

BONO

BRYAN ADAMS

BRYAN FERRY

CELINE DION

CHER

CHRIS REA

DAVID BOWIE

DIANA ROSS

ELTON JOHN

ELVIS PRESLEY

JOAN BAEZ

MADONNA

MEATLOAF

PAUL SIMON

PHIL COLLINS

SHERYL CROW

STING

TINA TURNER

TOM JONES

TOM PETTY

```
W O R C L Y R E H S A E I D I N
O N S P R O S S O R A N A I D E
O N O B E N S T M Y A G N I T S
U N B O H A O A O L M B N I Y L
P Y T R C P D I O M R R H R O N
E O E E Y O A D D Y P W R Y W I
L C L L N A I U A E Y E E I L W
T I H N S Y N N L R N D T E B Z
O O A R L E F A R S A I O T E F
N B M L I E R A D V I J L A Y A
J O I J R S B P I A Y M B E O O
O B S R O H R D S L M N O M C L
H D Y E B N B E L I A S A N L T
N Y V S O O E I A O V N J O D A
O L O B W T B S J Y L L F N T E
R A R I T I N A T U R N E R V M
A N E J L S N I L L O C L I H P
```

79 From A... LEVEL 3

All the words and compounds in this grid use the letter A at least three times. Even the grid is a letter A. How quickly can you crack this speed challenge?

ABERRATIONAL
ABLATIVAL
ABLE SEAMAN
ABRACADABRA
ABRAHAM
ACADIA
ACCLAMATION
ACCUSATORIAL
ACQUAINTANCE
ACROBATICALLY
ADAMANT
ADAPTABLE
AEOLIAN HARP
AERONAUTICAL
AFGHANISTAN
AGAMA
AGAPAE
AGORAPHOBIA
AGRARIAN
ALAMEDA
ALASKA
ALGEBRAICALLY
ALLAMERICAN
ALPACA

ALPHABETICAL
AMBILATERAL
AMERICANA
ANABAPTIST
ANAEMIA
ANAESTHESIA
ANAPHORA
ANAPLASMOSIS
ANTAGONISTICALLY
ANTIAIRCRAFT
ANTICAPITALIST
ANTIQUARIAN
ANTIRATIONAL
APANAGE
APATHETICALLY
APOCALYPTICAL
APPALOOSAS
ARCANA
ARCHAEOLOGICAL
AREAWAYS
ARMADA
ARRAYAL
AVAILABILITY
AZALEA

```
              A I S E H T S E A N A C R A
            A N T I Q U A R I A N A N A E M I A
          E G A N A P A T H E T I C A L L Y Q
        R A A E X A L P H A B E T I C A L Y J A
        A N A P L A S M O S I S A B R A H A M F
        N A I R A R G A C C U S A T O R I A L G
        T C J W C G A G O R A P H O B I A P A H
        I I I K I A A B W     O X P A B D O C A
        A R Y Y G C H D       P T T V E C I N
        I E T L O Q Z         F I K M A T I
        R M I A L U           C I A L U S
        C A L N O A L G E B R A I C A L L Y A T
        R L I O E I C M L A V I T A L B A P N A
        A L B I A N T I C A P I T A L I S T O N
        F A A T H T F E T Q R A P H Y L K I R O
        T R L A C A D I A S E B A G A M A C E I
        S E I R R N L A N O I T A R R E B A A T
        I T A I A C A P L A E N L D E M Z L D A
        T A V T N E P I S A S O O L A P P A A M
        P L A N A M A E S E L B A G W C G Y P A
        A I D A P N                A D A A T L
        B B A M H Y                Y T J R A C
        A M M A O Q                S R N R B C
        N A R D R U                N H R A L A
        A P A A A O                A Z A L E A
```

80 ...to Z LEVEL 3

The letter Z is often neglected in wordsearches, so we've sprinkled a fistful of zeds on this puzzle to make up the difference! Again, see how quickly you can complete the puzzle. Then you can have a short rest.

```
N S I X A Z O O P H I L E S B E R G A Z
I D A I B O H P O O Z Y M O G E N I C J
L Z E A L O T T E H C C U Z A C H A R Y
E Z Y M O L Y S I S O V T S M E Z E B U
P Z I R C O N I U M S I H P R O M O O Z
P E E N D G B C I T S A L P O M Y Z I N
E T Z D G I             W G W M O Z Z
Z A I R E S             O G M T O D D
Z E S T Y T         X L Y E K O E S
                Z X O Z R N G T F Y
              R A A H E F A E A R Z A
            X E N I T B R L N N A Z
          C I T I S A R A P O O Z
        I Z N S E A P A M O U Z
R R Z O A R R O C E O S
A Z E O S E O R E Z
B Z R L O Z O Z         V G E U N Z
I O T O G S             D Z L S A I
Z O Z G S E             O U U C M L
N M S I N A I R T S A O R O Z O H X R L
A S N C S G A Z N R E D N A L A E Z E I
Z G Z A B A I O N E M S S A R B E Z M O
S N E L M O O Z E I T G E I S T E E M N
E P O C S O M Y Z I G Z A G G E D U I T
J Z O O G E O G R A P H I C A L R S Z H
```

ZACHARIAH
ZACHARY
ZAGGED
ZAGREB
ZAGS
ZAIRE
ZANIER
ZANY
ZANZIBAR
ZARFS
ZAXIS
ZEALANDER
ZEALOT
ZEALOUS
ZEBRA CROSSING
ZEBU
ZED
ZEITGEIST
ZEMSTVOS
ZEPPELIN
ZEROES
ZESTY
ZETA
ZEUS
ZIEGLER
ZIGZAGGED
ZILLION
ZILLIONTH
ZIMMER FRAME

ZIMMERMAN
ZINGS
ZIRCONIUM
ZOE
ZONATED
ZOOERASIA
ZOOGENOUS
ZOOGEOGRAPHICAL
ZOOLOGICAL
ZOOLOGIST
ZOOM LENS
ZOOMORPHISM
ZOOMS
ZOONS
ZOOPARASITIC
ZOOPATHOLOGY
ZOOPHILES
ZOOPHOBIA
ZOOPLANKTON
ZOOS
ZORN
ZOROASTER
ZOROASTRIANISM
ZUCCHETTO
ZULU
ZYMOGENIC
ZYMOLYSIS
ZYMOPLASTIC
ZYMOSCOPE

P U O G S E E D L D O M
E R A D I S H A E A M U
S D U E N G E T M L A S
R G B R A D R M O O R H
O R E G A I S A N D W E
H A R A S S A R G L I M
E P G N N H E R C E C I
E N I O T A A P P L H M
M O T U O R M A R J O U
A G R A C P B G L I R S
T A P R I S A U D R A T
O R R A T T N A N A M E

81 Square meal LEVEL 2

All the words in this grid are to be found in an 'L' shape – that is, there is a 90-degree turn somewhere along their length. There are no diagonal words. The remaining letters spell out the name of another food – what is it?

ANISEED	LIME
APPLE	MARJORAM
APRICOT	MUSHROOM
AUBERGINE	MUSTARD
BANANA	OREGANO
CARP	RADISH
DATE	SALAD
GOURD	SANDWICH
GRAPE	SPROUT
HORSERADISH	TARRAGON
ICE CREAM	TOMATO
LEMON GRASS	UGLI

J U C N E D I C O B F N T R U M P E T B
Q O E B R R P N I L O I V S L E L A A E
I H L G J E K L I K L M P E A T R N N N
N R E O U E T I E L T E U P S R J I B O
A C S R C I W T X R O A C I N O M R A H
P G T H O C T S I K E D H P N F D A S P
M R E A E L I A H G W W N G F O N C S O
I A N N E L N P R A N O Z A U N H O D X
T T I D A G D E N I R U O B M A T P R A
R D R B L G D D T B P P L D Z I Y H U S
O U A E W U R L I T Z E R F B P O X M E
M X L L R M O O O F B E P O I L L A C W
B Y C L Z A H B L A N I G R I V O Z U H
O L Z E A R C A S T A N E T S K Z C A I
N O I B M A I S I A L G N A R O C Y K S
E P T W R C V S D R U M S S N M I M B T
H H H O E A A O V R E C O R D E R B A L
R O E C T S L O N O I D R O C C A A S E
Z N R O H H C N E R F B E T P H Q L E S
Z E P I P N A P F F L U T E N I P S B P

82 Everything must go LEVEL 3

All the words in this wordsearch are synonyms of the word 'disappear'. Unfortunately, some of the squares in the wordsearch itself have disappeared – but don't let that put you off completing the puzzle.

abscond
decline
decrease
depart
diminish
disappear
disband
disperse
dissolve
dwindle
ebb

escape
evacuate
evaporate
exit
expel
expire
extract
fade
flee
leave
lessen
liquefy
melt

migrate
pass
perish
proceed
quit
recede
relinquish
remove
retreat
soften
suspend
vanish
wane
wilt
withdraw
wither

```
Q U I T ■ E C E D E J Q P J ■
B ■ R Z T G S M I N W ■ E E E
Q E E ■ A C U A ■ E A S R L T
L X T C A ■ I T H E R B I D F
Q T ■ P R O C ■ E D D K ■ N O
I R E S R E P S I ■ H A H I S
Y A A R V K ■ U I D T ■ F W D
F C T ■ I W H S I N I M I ■ E
■ T A R O P A V E E ■ D T V C
U X ■ Z A P X ■ T P V N L W L
Q Q P X ■ P S E A S S O E A ■
I ■ L E E E ■ S R U S ■ M N N
L X A N L N S D ■ S B S Y E E
O R E L I ■ Q U I S ■ B I V R
H S ■ N A V C D M E V A ■ L I
```

83 Carthorse LEVEL 3

In the wordsearch on the left you are given the letters you are looking for, but not necessarily in the right order. All the clues are anagrams of musical instruments. Once you have solved them, look for the correctly spelled instruments in the wordsearch. If you can't solve any of the anagrams, you can still use the wordsearch to complete the puzzle. Carthorse, incidentally, is an anagram of ORCHESTRA.

anoiodrcc	oblelwc	rdmteultek	ittewnlsih
egsppbia	sbclamy	dnniolam	riletgna
ojnab	usasbbelod	acsmraa	ernotbmo
bamusrds	dsrum	anoairc	tmruetp
sonbosa	ephmouuin	ranog	oniliv
icrsraerdb	fldied	neppaip	liivangr
policlea	fetul	opfnoetrai	eihwlts
ssatteanc	rrnohhncef	lpocioc	wbcoodkol
tseelec	irettng	errdocre	lzretwuir
elloc	artiug	noeapxhos	expylhono
ltncerai	lhldenba	spteni	ierzht
clodrhivac	ohaamcinr	aoieutnrbm	
nriacslgao	jswprahe	itapinm	

The tricks of the tongue

Language is not just a tool, it is also a toy. Wordplay is an ancient human instinct, and we cannot stop ourselves making puns, coining new expressions, or just admiring the verbal trick shots of others.

Twisted words

Tongue twisters are games played with the spoken word. Some of the hardest are also the shortest. Try saying 'Mixed biscuits' or 'Red lorry, yellow lorry' over and over again.

It is safe to say that almost as soon as people started using words, they began making puzzles and games out of them. Nobody knows what the first verbal game was, but here is a piece of wordplay, dealing with the very early days of humanity. It is the shortest poem in the world; it's anonymous; and it's entitled 'On the Antiquity of Microbes':

> *Adam*
> *Had 'em.*

Not just this poem, but all poetry, even the most serious, is no more than a rarefied form of wordplay. One of the oldest forms of poetry is the riddle, in effect a poem with a tease attached. In Greek myth, Oedipus saved Thebes by solving the riddle of the Sphinx: 'What creature moves on four legs, then two legs, then three legs?' Here by way of contrast, is a thoroughly modern riddle:

> *I'm stiff as a biscuit and black as the night*
> *And I will remember the things that you write.*
> *When no one can see me I spin like a top*
> *So why do they say that I'm limp as a mop?*

Speaking of things to do with computers, the Internet was invented (historians now believe) as a means of spreading word games around the world at the speed of light. Some of these games are so new that they do not even have a name yet. Here is an anonymous game that has been causing jams on the cyberhighway. Take a word or expression; add, subtract or substitute one letter; then provide a witty definition of that new word. For example:

Bob Vylan: busker with a criminal lack of musical ability.
Bronto sister: literary dinosaur of either sex, for example, Gore Vidal, Arthur C. Clarke, Germaine Greer.
Bungee lump: contusion on top of head caused by slightly too long elastic.

The game of the name

Naming children is a kind of word game, but few new names catch on. One of the successes is 'Wendy' (from toddler-speak for *friend*), coined by the writer J. M. Barrie; another is 'Imogen', probably a misreading of 'Innogen', invented by Shakespeare to suggest innocence and gentility, for a character in *Cymbeline*.

Answers to riddles on page 319

A novel novel

E is the most common English letter. But in 1939 Ernest Vincent Wright wrote a 50,000 word novel called *Gadsby* without using the letter E once.

Daylight Shaving Time: five minutes you would rather spend in bed
Indensification: the sense of feeling more stupid the more detailed the explanation becomes
Marple syrup: Agatha Christie's more purple passages
George Borwell: tedious bar room socialist

Once you begin to rough up the lexicon in this way, it is only a short step to the mischievous bodily harm of the anagram. One of the best anagram games involves tearing a phrase limb from limb and reconstructing it as a kind of verbal Frankenstein's monster. The only rule is that the new creation has to bear some meaningful resemblance to the original. Here is a simple example:

Clint Eastwood is an anagram of **Old West Action**

But the best ever meaningful anagram – and it is probably unbeatable – is this:

To be or not to be: that is the question, whether tis nobler in the mind to suffer the slings and arrows of outrageous fortune.

is an anagram of

In one of the Bard's best thought of tragedies, our insistent hero Hamlet queries on two fronts about how life turns rotten.

The Victorian word factory

Lewis Carroll was a master of wordplay and an obsessive neologist (inventor of new words). His famous poem 'Jabberwocky' consists almost entirely of new-minted and strangely convincing neologisms, some of which, such as *chortle*, have entered the mainstream lexicon. Lewis Carroll is also responsible for inventing the word game called 'couplets', where the task is to change APE to MAN or HEAD to FOOT by altering one letter at a time.

Alpha beater

The alphabet itself can be used for puzzling challenges. One of the holy grails of the wordbending world is to come up with a sentence that uses all the letters of the alphabet just once. Some of the unsatisfactory and frankly nonsensical solutions so far offered are 'Blowzy night-frumps vex'd Jack Q' and 'J. Q. Schwartz flung V. D. Pike my box'. For now, when trying out a new pen or an old typewriter, we will have to make do with the less economical 'The quick brown fox jumps over the lazy dog' with 35 characters, or 'Pack my box with five dozen liquor jugs' at 32. A solution to the 26 letter-phrase problem will probably have to wait for new words to enter the language. English already has more words than any other language – at least a quarter of a million at the latest count. As the lexical universe expands, word explorers will no doubt find new answers to old problems, and will encounter new verbal life forms to marvel at.

Long stretch

There is a word game where you are given three letters and you have to come up with the longest word possible using those letters in the given order. So if you are given C, D and S you can offer ConDenSation, but not DisCuSsions. If you ever play the game, here is a word to bear in mind:

pneumonoultramicroscopicsilicovolcanoconiosis

This is the longest word in the Oxford English Dictionary and means a lung disease caused by inhaling dust.

Scrabble is one of the most popular word games of all time, enjoyed by millions around the world. On these pages you will find a variety of puzzles that test your **SQ**: your Scrabble quotient. Each puzzle is a separate challenge with its own rules – so read the introductions carefully – and some are more difficult than others. The only thing they have in common is that you have to use the letters shown in the rack.

These are the values of the boxes on the board. The letters' values are shown on the opposite page.

| DOUBLE LETTER SCORE | TRIPLE LETTER SCORE |
| DOUBLE WORD SCORE | TRIPLE WORD SCORE |

84 Fourwise LEVEL 1

Four common seven-letter words can be made from the letters in the rack below the board. Find all four, then work out which one can be played on the board, using all the letters.

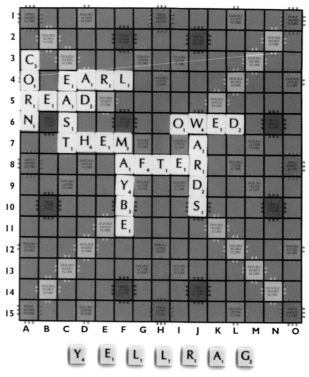

85 Target teaser 1 LEVEL 1

Using the rack provided can you find a play that scores exactly 51 points? Can you also find a play that scores a little more than 51 points? And what is the highest score you can get for playing just two letters?

86 Re-creation 1 LEVEL 2

Imagine that the letters shown below have fallen off the board. Your challenge is to place all of them back on the board to form a valid game situation so that the words are connected. The scores are irrelevant for this exercise.

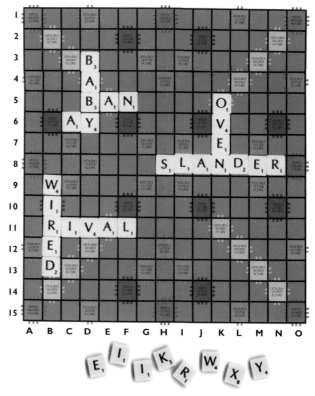

87 Triple tester LEVEL 2

Using the rack of letters, how many different plays can you find that reach triple-word squares by extending existing words? Words may be extended in front and at the end. There may be more than one way of extending some words. Some words cannot be extended to reach triple word squares. You're doing well if you get more than five.

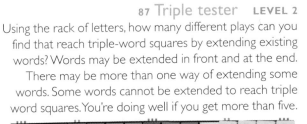

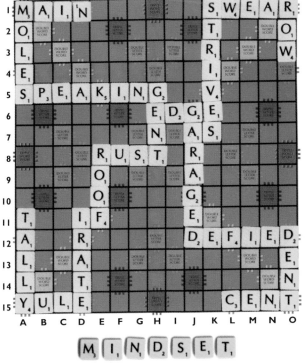

A 1
B 3
C 3
D 2
E 1
F 4
G 2
H 4
I 1
J 8
K 5
L 1
M 3
N 1
O 1
P 3
Q 10
R 1
S 1
T 1
U 1
V 4
W 4
X 8
Y 4
Z 10

88 Target teaser 2 LEVEL 2

Using the rack of letters supplied in each case, can you find two different plays that each score exactly 45 points? There is also one play you can make that scores more than 45 points. See if you can find it.

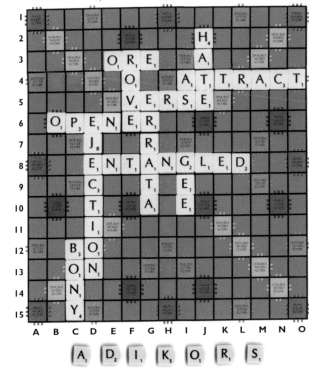

89 Target teaser 3 LEVEL 3

You may be surprised to learn that the two highest scores involving the letter Q on this board are 30 and 31 points. What are they? And for your biggest challenge, can you find the elusive 32-point play without using the Q?

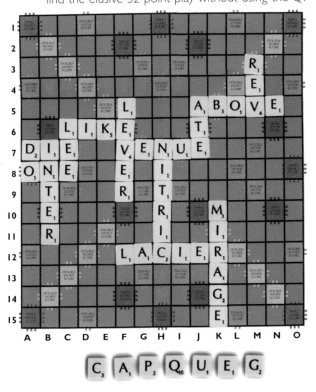

90 Re-creation 2 LEVEL 3

Imagine that all the letters shown below have fallen off the board. Your challenge is to use them all to join up the existing words on the board to form a valid board position. The scores are irrelevant for this exercise.

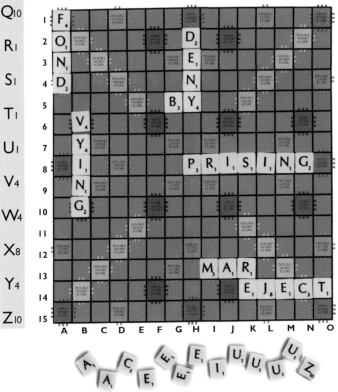

91 Spell wrecker? LEVEL 2

If you do any writing with the aid of a computer, then you will almost certainly have made use of a spell checker. This is a very useful tool that will automatically correct any spelling mistakes you might make. But spell checkers are not infallible, particularly when they fail to recognize a proper noun, such as the name of a person, and replace it with a known word.

Here, just for fun, are the names of some famous figures that have been 'corrected' by a spell checker. Can you guess the original names?

	PAINTERS	COMPOSERS	NOVELISTS	ACTORS AND ACTRESSES
1	Ingress	Grief	Denial Defog	Ale Guineas
2	Raffle	Delis	Gorge Elite	Jams Steward
3	Money	Stares	Jams Joys	Client Eastward
4	Magnet	Holiest	Kingly Amiss	Merrily Strap
5	Grotto	Chopping	Author Canon Dole	Bores Kraals
6	Rosette	Smitten	Smile Bronze	Dine Client
7	Tissue	Bracken	Lens Eighteen	Laurel Bacilli
8	Margate	Vividly	Tibias Smote	Barber Stressed
9	Lancer	Partook	Mogul Servants	Alien Stretch
10	Kerosene	Opulence	Edit Whatnot	Brute Rends

92 Confusibles LEVEL 1

Some pairs of words are so similar in spelling that although they mean different things it is very easy to confuse them and use one word when you mean the other. In each of the sentences below you have to fill in the blank with one of a pair of frequently confused words.

1 This building project is not _____ for a grant.
(ILLEGIBLE, ELIGIBLE)

2 He escaped detection for many years but finally got his just _____.
(DESERTS, DESSERTS)

3 This book is an excellent introduction to the basic _____ of science.
(PRINCIPLES, PRINCIPALS)

4 If you want to be a magician, you must be good at _____ of hand.
(SLIGHT, SLEIGHT)

5 The lawyer asked many questions in an attempt to _____ the truth.
(ELICIT, ILLICIT)

6 In the Andes _____ are used as beasts of burden.
(LAMAS, LLAMAS)

7 We may not be swayed by flattery but we do like to receive _____.
(COMPLEMENTS, COMPLIMENTS)

8 An experienced painter always mixes pigments on the _____.
(PALATE, PALETTE)

9 The way we do business has been transformed by the _____ chip.
(SILICON, SILICONE)

10 Whatever action you take will not _____ my decision one way or the other.
(AFFECT, EFFECT)

93 Give me a brake LEVEL 1

Jill has taken a holiday in the USA with her husband Jack. Unfortunately, Jill left her dictionary at home and the postcard she sent contains a number of mistakes. Can you find them all? And do you know how to put them right without consulting your own dictionary?

Post Card

DEAR FREINDS

WHAT A WONDERFUL EXPERIENCE! JACK AND I THOROGHLY RECOMMEND A VISIT TO THE STATES. PEOPLE HAVE WELLCOMED US WITH THERE ARMS WIDE OPEN. YOUV'E GOT TO SEE IT TO BELEIVE IT — THE ONLY DISAPOINTMENT HAS BEEN THE WEATHER. BECAUSE WE COULD'NT GUAGE WHAT TO EXPECT WE PACKED LIGHT CLOTHING BUT NEW YORK IS COLD. LUCKILY JACKS' ANT LEANT ME A BEAUTIFULL SHAUL. AND THE FOOD! ITS TRULY IRRESISTABLE — ESPECIALLY THE SPAGHETTI. IN OTHER WORDS, AN IDYLIC HOLIDAY IN AN EXCITING AND COSMOPOLITAN CITY.

WISH YOU WERE HEAR Jill

94 Writing wrongs LEVEL 1

Martin has had enough! After putting up for weeks with noisy neighbours he's finally decided to put pen to paper and complain. Unfortunately, he's feeling so stressed about it all that he's not thinking straight and the resultant letter is a spelling disaster. Can you correct Martin's mistakes and help him to get the sleep he so badly needs?

MHG

Dear Sir of Madam,

I am writing regarding the incesant noise coming from you're premises. What is going on in their? Every night I am woken up arround midnight – it sounds like a heard of elephants. What is wurse, it sounds as if the elephants are drunk – but I bet your not even licenced! Whatever is going in in there, if the practise isnt stopped soon I will be forsed to take legall adivce!

Yours in anger,

Martin Griffin

95 Spell well LEVEL 3

Very few of us can truthfully claim that we never make spelling mistakes. If anyone you know makes that claim, put it to the test with the list of words below. They are all reasonably common words, but it's our guess that not one person in a hundred will be able to spell every one correctly.

abysmal
ancillary
apartheid
apparent
aqueduct
bachelor
bureaucracy
catarrh
ceiling
consensus
copyright
curriculum
decaffeinated
desiccated
diarrhoea
exaggerate
fuchsia
gauge
gazetteer
harassment
honorary
hygiene
idiosyncrasy
indictment
innocuous
inoculate
iridescent
meringue
minuscule
miscellaneous
necessarily
occasion
paraffin
parallelogram
physiognomy
posthumous
questionnaire
receipt
reminisce
resuscitate
stupefied
vicious

The aim here is to beat the clock. See if you can do these two pages of assorted word puzzles in less than an hour. Time starts .... NOW!

T	C	E	I	B	S	O	U	S	A
H	H	T	O	S	R	P	N	E	L
G	I	A	R	T	A	O	B	A	M
I	A	N	L	C	L	D	N	I	C
R	N	H	I	L	U	N	G	Z	T
W	T	F	O	K	O	R	M	D	E
L	I	P	U	D	A	W	P	I	N
C	A	V	A	I	E	K	E	J	C
O	R	M	N	D	R	A	K	E	O
T	S	E	R	E	V	E	M	U	N

96 Square of knowledge LEVEL 2

The general knowledge clues should lead you to ten words that are hidden in the square, reading forward, backwards, up, down or diagonally.

1 Greek sun god – and a Moon mission (6)
2 Alloy of copper and tin (6)
3 Italian red wine (7)
4 Highest mountain on Earth (7)
5 31 October (9)
6 She sang 'Like a Virgin' (7)
7 Serious headache (8)
8 The largest ocean (7)
9 John Philip ____, the 'March King' (5)
10 Brothers who built the first aeroplane (6)

97 Try and try again

LEVEL 2

The quotation in this double acrostic is from Benjamin Franklin, a man who knew a thing or two about tackling puzzles. Solve the clues and fill in the squares, number for number, in the diagram below.

A Shakespeare made much of it concerning very little (3)
  ‾3‾ ‾21‾ ‾42‾

B Nylon was named after London and this city . . . (3,4)
  ‾31‾ ‾23‾ ‾33‾   ‾35‾ ‾27‾ ‾47‾ ‾48‾

C . . . where liberty is celebrated in this form (6)
  ‾29‾ ‾44‾ ‾9‾ ‾22‾ ‾19‾ ‾16‾

D Lacquer not right – so disappear (6)
  ‾15‾ ‾34‾ ‾24‾ ‾10‾ ‾36‾ ‾38‾

E To insult is not on at the beginning (6)
  ‾18‾ ‾8‾ ‾17‾ ‾5‾ ‾43‾ ‾13‾

F The last commandment, fractionally (5)
  ‾7‾ ‾12‾ ‾20‾ ‾37‾ ‾26‾

G The Sundance Kid is not one of the in-laws (6)
  ‾46‾ ‾28‾ ‾40‾ ‾11‾ ‾39‾ ‾45‾

H Confused hint for a slight (4)
  ‾25‾ ‾2‾ ‾14‾ ‾6‾

I Didn't have much time for philistines (5)
  ‾32‾ ‾30‾ ‾4‾ ‾1‾ ‾41‾

1 I	■	2 H	3 A	4 I	5 E	6 H	7 F	■	8 E	9 C	10 D	11 G	12 F	13 E
■	14 H	15 D	16 C	■	17 E	18 E	19 C	20 F	21 A	■	22 C	23 B	24 D	■
25 H	26 F	27 B	28 G	29 C	30 I	31 B	32 I	■	33 B	34 D	35 B	36 D	■	
37 F	38 D	39 G	40 G	■	41 I	42 A	43 E	44 C	■	45 G	46 G	47 B	48 B	

98 Tiles LEVEL I

Place the pieces in the grid so that a crossword is formed. To help out, we've placed the first tile in the grid.

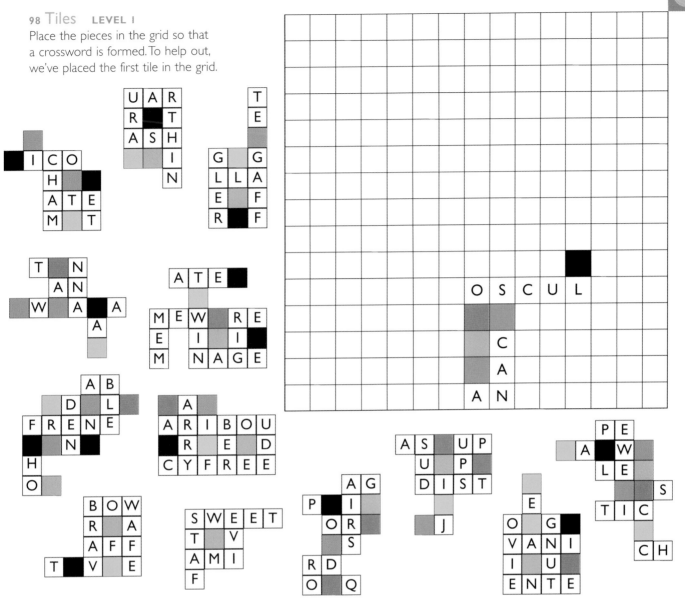

99 Quick crossword LEVEL I

A straightforward crossword with not a cryptic clue in sight.

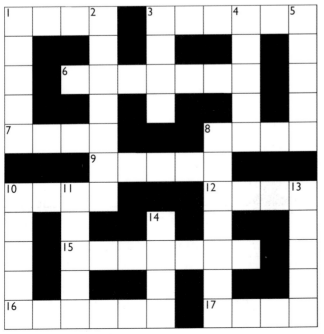

ACROSS

1 **Writing** (4)

3 **Unoccupied** (6)

6 **Quickest** (7)

7 **Waistband** (4)

8 **Ship's company** (4)

9 **Rub out** (5)

10 **Expensive** (4)

12 **Midday** (4)

15 **Apparent** (7)

16 **Rebellion** (6)

17 **Shout** (4)

DOWN

1 **Stories** (5)

2 **Educator** (7)

3 **Ballot** (4)

4 **Change** (5)

5 **Toss** (5)

8 **Hundred years** (7)

10 **Jeans fabric** (5)

11 **Concerning** (5)

13 **Nautical** (5)

14 **Neat** (4)

100 Word pyramids LEVELS 1 & 2

For each puzzle you are given a number of clues. The first answer has two letters, the second three letters, the third four – and so on. Each answer consists of the same letters as the previous one with the addition of one letter. The puzzles get progressively more difficult.

1

_ _   Concerning
_ _ _   Rage
_ _ _ _   Father
_ _ _ _ _   Steeple
_ _ _ _ _ _   Desire eagerly

2

_ _   Account (abbr.)
_ _ _   Expert
_ _ _ _   Step
_ _ _ _ _   Position
_ _ _ _ _ _   Splendid house

3

_ _   French article
_ _ _   Falsehood
_ _ _ _   Reside
_ _ _ _ _   Large gland
_ _ _ _ _ _   Splinter

4

_ _   Street (abbr.)
_ _ _   Group
_ _ _ _   Transmitted
_ _ _ _ _   Fragrance
_ _ _ _ _ _   Rise

5

_ _   A pronoun
_ _ _   Pose
_ _ _ _   Locale
_ _ _ _ _   Malevolence
_ _ _ _ _ _   Imp

6

_ _   Symbol of titanium
_ _ _   Money (old slang)
_ _ _ _   Prong
_ _ _ _ _   Tint faintly
_ _ _ _ _ _   Pleasant sensation

7

_ _   Printer's measure
_ _ _   Logarithm base
_ _ _ _   Sea bird
_ _ _ _ _   Lacking leniency
_ _ _ _ _ _   Back at sea

8

_ _   A constant
_ _ _   Mass of metal
_ _ _ _   Goody-goody
_ _ _ _ _   Shoot
_ _ _ _ _ _   Bound
_ _ _ _ _ _ _   Snare
_ _ _ _ _ _ _ _   Breed of dog

101 Letter change LEVEL 2

Change just one letter in the word on either side of the brackets to form a word that fits the definition within the brackets. For example, the answer to **MATCH (month) DAY** would be **MARCH** and **MAY**.

1. BENT (coin) DICE
2. BENCH (tree) LATCH
3. DITCH (language) CREEK
4. FELL (material) SICK
5. FILE (measure) ITCH
6. TOWN (garment) RODE
7. CAMP (fish) BIKE
8. DULL (herb) MIST
9. FIRE (tool) PINK
10. CLAD (African country) TOGA

102 Fore and aft LEVEL 2

Find the two letters that form a new word when placed after the first word or placed before the second word. For example, the answer to **ROB (_ _) GOT** would be **IN**, giving the new words **ROBIN** and **INGOT**.

1. RUM (_ _) SIN
2. BOW (_ _) BOW
3. PIN (_ _) GAS
4. TOR (_ _) LID
5. CUP (_ _) LED
6. COY (_ _) SHY
7. DRY (_ _) APT
8. FOR (_ _) NET
9. STY (_ _) LAC
10. COD (_ _) ACT

103 Word ladders LEVELS 1, 2 & 3

In a word ladder puzzle you have to change one word into another by altering a single letter at each step. Each step on the word ladder must be a valid word. This type of puzzle was invented in 1878 by Lewis Carroll, the author of *Alice in Wonderland*.

In the examples below we've taken out the clues to make it a little more difficult.

MICE

RATS

Word ladder 1
Turn MICE into RATS
1 Small creature
2 Win at chess
3 Floor coverings

OIL

GAS

Word ladder 2
Turn OIL into GAS
1 Nothing
2 Pinch
3 Doze
4 Aperture

FOOL

SAGE

Word ladder 3
Turn FOOL into SAGE
1 Common fund
2 Number of votes cast
3 Become wearisome
4 Wan
5 Attendant

TEARS

SMILE

Word ladder 4
Turn TEARS into SMILE
1 Scorches
2 Heavenly bodies
3 Look fixedly
4 No longer fresh
5 Steps for climbing over a wall

GRASS

GREEN

Word ladder 5
Turn GRASS into GREEN

ARMY

NAVY

Word ladder 6
Turn ARMY into NAVY

BLUE

PINK

Word ladder 7
Turn BLUE into PINK

Some words are rather like worms: chop them in half and you get two new whole ones. These puzzles explore some other strangely wriggly properties of words.

104 Word centres 1 LEVEL 2
Identify the following nine-letter words from their centres:

1 **SHONE** 4 **THROB**
2 **REPRO** 5 **PETIT**
3 **HEIST**

105 Word centres 2 LEVEL 2
Identify the following eight-letter words from their centres:

1 **TACO** 5 **DUST**
2 **LOIS** 6 **DEAR**
3 **AQUA** 7 **CUBA**
4 **MESA** 8 **COLA**

106 Non-rhyming words LEVEL 2
The following words all end in the same three letters but none of the words rhyme with each other. What are the words?

1 B***
2 C***
3 T***

107 Unusual words LEVEL 1
The word PRIMROSE has an odd property: there is a three-letter word that may be tagged on to the end of its first half or second half, i.e. the end of both PRIM and ROSE, in each case making another word. What is the three-letter word?

108 Alphabetical order LEVEL 1
The number ONE has all its letters in inverse alphabetical order. Which whole number has all its letters in correct alphabetical order?

109 Pronunciation puzzle
LEVEL 1
The word POSSESS is unusual in that it contains a double S pronounced as Z. What common household object has a name in which SS is pronounced Z?

110 Alphabet soup 1 LEVEL 3
The letters A, E, I, O and U have been left out of the following words. Can you identify them?

1 HSMD
2 QTN
3 PHR
4 SQ

111 Alphabet soup 2 LEVEL 3
Which:

1 vegetable
2 instrument
3 mineral

contains all five of the vowels A, E, I, O and U?

112 Alphabet soup 3 LEVEL 3
Add the five vowels A, E, I, O and U to the letters CDNT and stir to get three different nine-letter words.

113 Kangaroo words LEVEL 2
Some words can be shortened by striking out letters to produce another word with practically the same meaning. For example, striking out the letters A and T in CLIMATES gives us CLIMES. Now try these:

1 BLOSSOM 6 DEVILISH
2 INDOLENT 7 FALSITIES
3 UNSIGHTLY 8 EXHILARATION
4 FEASTING 9 PROSECUTE
5 INSTRUCTOR 10 ENCOURAGE

114 In a State LEVEL 3
Which State(s) of the USA:
1 read the same when written vertically down the page in block capitals and viewed in a mirror?
2 has underwear at its centre?
3 can be changed into other States by changing North to South?
4 begin with NEW?
5 is monosyllabic?
6 end in O?
7 becomes another State when you add two letters to the front of it?
8 begin and end in the same letter?
9 becomes another when 'West' precedes it?

115 Inflatable words
LEVEL 2
If you insert letters into each of these words they become different words with practically the same meaning. For example, VARIED becomes VARIEGATED by the insertion of G, A, T and E. Now try these:

1 PIES
2 SATED
3 PREVENTIVE
4 AMIABLE
5 ORIENT
6 INSTANTLY
7 CHARM
8 BOUNDS
9 NURSED
10 APT

116 Common property
LEVEL 2
The words below have a property in common:

HERITAGE, PANORAMA, PALISADE, CHANNELS, MOROSELY

From the words in the following list select the one that belongs in this set:

DECISIVELY, PROMENADE, MAMMALIAN, ELEPHANT, KNICKERS, LEMONADE, SAUSAGE

117 Lost cities   LEVEL 3

Can you find the cities concealed in the following?
To make things a little easier we've highlighted one of the answers in the first example. The number of cities to be found in each is indicated in brackets.

1 'Cas**par', I s**ighed, 'one suspects that Prince Bobritsky won't be dining with us tonight but sulking in his mosquito nets with that butterfly he picked up in Bolivia.' (2)

2 'This go slow's really affecting Uncle Eno's hammer-throwing practice!' grunted Cyrus A. Racehorse, sipping shandy from a discarded shoe. (1)

3 I got used to boring old Len in gradually increasing doses of enforced conversation in the House of Commons. (1)

4 Ah! Stockings made of nylon do not feel the same – electrostatically speaking – as silk ones. (1)

5 On Craddock's writing desk were a bottle of ink, a bullwhip and a snowshoe on which he had once hopped blindfold over the Himalayas to prove his masculinity. (1)

6 As you undoubtedly know, the Khyber links Pakistan with Tibet. (1)

7 I'm afraid the vet does not hold out much hope for Elmo's cow. (1)

8 If ever you go to Vladivostok you must visit Uncle Volodya and his giant turkey. (1)

9 Reg in an old-fashioned sense is constant in every way; see how his hand squashes an ant on Iolanthe's skirt, makes a mark and smoothly, almost negligently, moves on. (4)

10 'You see, "My camel has a hump" is not in essence the same as "My camel has the hump"', explains Wittgenstein, oblivious of the fact that Feisal is burying his head in his hands.(3)

11 Round the bend I go, my car a casualty of yet another attempt by the automobile club to ram me, first into a caravan and then into a Cadillac crashed by the side of the road. (4)

12 Ali made my pet rat sandwiches of old ham to induce it to camp in a soggy garden in Pasadena. (4)

13 With his new bolt-on Meccano wings and stabilisers on springs our manic Air Officer could strafe a duckpond from sixty yards, or land on a sixpence. (5)

14 The outbreak of war saw poor Abel fasting while the more self-obsessed Ali made Hindu blinis stuffed with honey or krill as the season allowed. (5)

15 You could rely on Radu blinking as Rambo got a wig out from his mascara case and donned a pair of jodhpurs to do a passable imitation of the Loan Arranger on a horse. (7)

---

118 Algebraical words
LEVEL 2

In each case identify the missing letters represented by the x:

1 hxy
2 poxtate
3 wxy
4 cax
5 nexrk
6 oxnion

119 What links?   LEVEL 1

What do these words have in common:

FLAMING, HELL, LIMB, QUART, SAG

120 Unusual clusters   LEVEL 2

Find a word in each case containing the following unusual clusters of letters:

HUBA   GNT   PTC

121 Palindromes   LEVEL 2

The block of 7 letters represented by asterisks in P*******R is palindromic: it reads the same if the order of the letters is reversed. Can you find the word? Now do the same for M*******US.

Back to fronts

122 LEVEL 1
Complete the accusation contained in this palindrome:

****** *** EDNA SIN***

123 LEVEL 1
Complete this palindrome, uttered long ago in the Garden:

*****, I'M **** !

124 LEVEL 2
This palindrome airs an important matter of parliamentary etiquette:

**** TO ****, SIR!

125 LEVEL 2
This palindrome is about fund-raising in the National Health Service:

WARD NU**** *** ****

126 LEVEL 2
A tourist asked this question after a whirlwind tour of literary homes:

*** ** ELIOT'S ****** * ***?

127 LEVEL 2
This palindrome describes the genesis of a feat of engineering:

* *** * **** * ***** — PANAMA!

smart

Are you a cold reasoner like Sherlock Holmes, or an instinctive thinker who sees the answer without knowing why? Both casts of mind will find a fitting challenge in this chapter.

solutions

HOW TO SOLVE LOGIC PROBLEMS

PROBLEMS WITH GRIDS

In these puzzles the trick is to deduce what is known for sure from the information given. Each type of item correlates with exactly one of every other item (in this example, one boy dates one girl at one location). The grid covers every possible combination once:

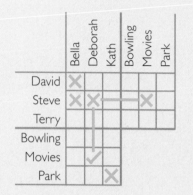

The clues will enable you to fill in the obvious valid and invalid combinations, and from there you can deduce further information. In this example, if Deborah went to the movies (tick) but Steve did not (cross), Steve cannot have dated Deborah (new cross, deduced). As Bella did not date Steve either (cross), he must have dated Kath (new tick, deduced), and so on.

PROBLEMS WITHOUT GRIDS

These problems have an answer box but no logic grid. To tackle these, fill in any certainties, then examine all the clues repeatedly until the answers become apparent. You may find it useful to cross out clues from which no new information can be deduced.

1 Out to lunch LEVEL 1

Three children are having a picnic in the park. Each has a drink of lemonade, but which different sandwiches and cake does each child have? Bear in mind that:

1 Nigel has tuna fish sandwiches but not a slab of fruit cake.

2 Mark isn't the child with both chocolate cake and ham sandwiches for lunch.

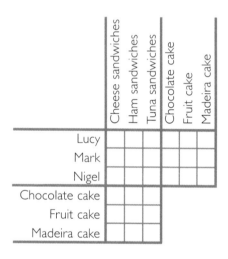

	Cheese sandwiches	Ham sandwiches	Tuna sandwiches	Chocolate cake	Fruit cake	Madeira cake
Lucy						
Mark						
Nigel						
Chocolate cake						
Fruit cake						
Madeira cake						

2 On the shelf LEVEL 1

There are three books on the shelf, as you can see. What is the title of each, who wrote it and what colour is its cover?

1 The red book is farther left than the one by Bob Willis, but farther right than that entitled *Long Days*.

2 The book by Claire Carter is next to and directly to the right of the green book. One of the books has a blue cover.

3 Dave Child's book is next to *Happy Hour*. One of the books is entitled *Magic Moments*.

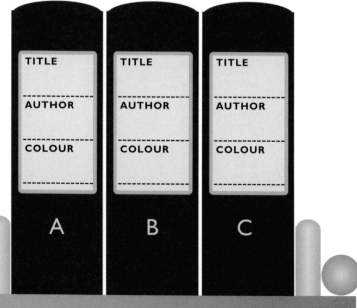

		QUANTITY					COLOUR					DESIGN				
		450	500	600	700	750	Green	Orange	Red	White	Yellow	Bishops	Knights	Queens	Pawns	Rooks
DAY	Monday															
	Tuesday															
	Wednesday															
	Thursday															
	Friday															
DESIGN	Bishops															
	Knights															
	Queens															
	Pawns															
	Rooks															
COLOUR	Green															
	Orange															
	Red															
	White															
	Yellow															

3 Wax works LEVEL 2

Ivor Wick has a small candlemaking shop where he produces and sells candles of different colours and designs. Every day he makes a batch of different colours and different designs: last week his theme was chess pieces. How many candles did he make on each of the listed days and what was the colour and design of each batch?

1 The bishop-shaped candles weren't made on Tuesday, but they were made earlier in the week than the batch of 700 candles.

2 Ivor made 100 more candles in the shape of pawns than the number of yellow candles, which he made on Thursday.

3 The knight-shaped candles were made the day before the green candles and two days before the batch of 500 orange candles.

4 One hundred and fifty more candles in the shape of queens were made than the number of red candles, which he made on Monday.

		RUNNER					SHORTS					T-SHIRT				
		Raymond	Richard	Roderick	Rory	Rupert	Black/purple	Blue/purple	Blue/yellow	Green/pink	Green/yellow	Cream/brown	Cream/orange	Red/brown	Red/orange	White/grey
POSITION	First															
	Second															
	Third															
	Fifth															
	Sixth															
T-SHIRT	Cream/brown															
	Cream/orange															
	Red/brown															
	Red/orange															
	White/grey															
SHORTS	Black/purple															
	Blue/purple															
	Blue/yellow															
	Green/pink															
	Green/yellow															

4 Running commentary

LEVEL 2

Six boys took part in a race. The boy who came fourth wore shorts and a T-shirt that were plain turquoise in colour and he doesn't appear in this puzzle. Of the other five, no two boys wore exactly the same and both their shorts and T-shirts contained two colours apiece (on the grid the colours are shown as main colour/stripe). Can you work out the colour of the shorts and T-shirts worn by the other runners, together with the position in which each boy finished the race?

1 Rupert (whose shorts aren't green with a yellow stripe) didn't win the race, although he came one place ahead of a boy whose T-shirt isn't red.

2 Raymond (who wore shorts of the same main colour as those worn by Richard) came one place ahead of Rory, whose shorts are not green and whose T-shirt hasn't a brown stripe.

3 Richard (whose T-shirt isn't cream and whose shorts haven't got a yellow stripe) came one place ahead of he whose T-shirt is white but whose shorts are not green.

4 Rory did better than the boy whose T-shirt is red with a brown stripe.

5 Driving question   LEVEL 2

Each of the members of the family seen below owns a different-coloured car from any of the others. No 'in-law' relationships are mentioned in the clues, so (for instance) woman B isn't anyone's sister. Who's who in the family tree and what colour is each person's car?

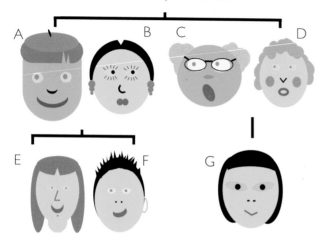

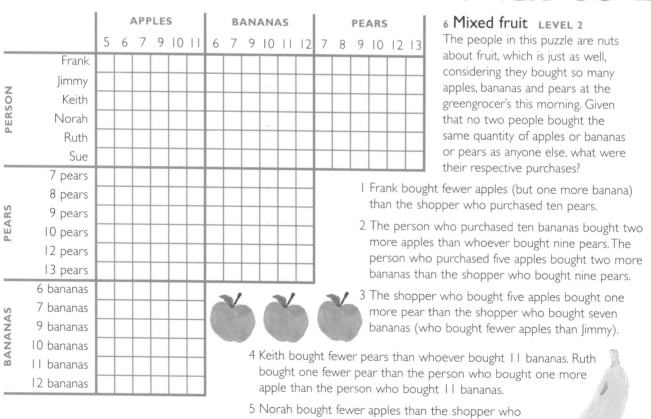

	MOTORIST							CAR COLOUR						
	Adam	Angela	George	Julia	Millie	Ron	Stephanie	Black	Blue	Brown	Green	Grey	Pink	Red
PERSON Person A														
Person B														
Person C														
Person D														
Person E														
Person F														
Person G														
CAR COLOUR Black														
Blue														
Brown														
Green														
Grey														
Pink														
Red														

1 Ron's sister has a blue car.
2 Angela has a grey car and her father has a black car.
3 Millie's daughter has a pink car. Millie's husband (whose car isn't brown) isn't George.
4 Julia sometimes borrows her cousin's car when her own is off the road.
5 Stephanie isn't of the same generation (parent/offspring) as Adam (whose car isn't brown or red).

	APPLES						BANANAS						PEARS					
	5	6	7	9	10	11	6	7	9	10	11	12	7	8	9	10	12	13
PERSON Frank																		
Jimmy																			
Keith																			
Norah																			
Ruth																			
Sue																			
PEARS 7 pears																			
8 pears																			
9 pears																			
10 pears																			
12 pears																			
13 pears																			
BANANAS 6 bananas																			
7 bananas																			
9 bananas																			
10 bananas																			
11 bananas																			
12 bananas																			

6 Mixed fruit   LEVEL 2

The people in this puzzle are nuts about fruit, which is just as well, considering they bought so many apples, bananas and pears at the greengrocer's this morning. Given that no two people bought the same quantity of apples or bananas or pears as anyone else, what were their respective purchases?

1 Frank bought fewer apples (but one more banana) than the shopper who purchased ten pears.

2 The person who purchased ten bananas bought two more apples than whoever bought nine pears. The person who purchased five apples bought two more bananas than the shopper who bought nine pears.

3 The shopper who bought five apples bought one more pear than the shopper who bought seven bananas (who bought fewer apples than Jimmy).

4 Keith bought fewer pears than whoever bought 11 bananas. Ruth bought one fewer pear than the person who bought one more apple than the person who bought 11 bananas.

5 Norah bought fewer apples than the shopper who purchased 12 pears (who bought one fewer banana than whoever bought ten apples).

7 Healthy appetites LEVEL 3

After a strenuous game of football, six lads sought sustenance at the local café. They all sat around a table as shown on the diagram below, although no boy occupied a seat whose identification letter is the same as the initial letter of his forename. Being very hungry, the boys ordered six different cakes, then followed this with a further six cakes so that, overall, each boy ate two cakes. However, no boy finished with the same type of cake as he had started with. Your task is to munch your way through the clues below to discover not only the boys' full names and where they sat, but which type of cake each boy chose first and second.

1 The identification letter of the seat occupied by the boy who started with a pineapple cake occurs one place earlier in the alphabet than that occupied by Master Potter, who chose to start with a blackcurrant cake. Master Veness occupied seat F.

2 Adam (who didn't have a syrup cake second) sat one place clockwise (from your point of view as you look at the diagram) of the boy who started with a syrup cake and rapidly followed this with a pineapple cake. The boy in seat E started with a banana cake. Fred ordered a lemon cake second.

3 Still looking in a clockwise direction at the plan of the table below, David Symes sat one place clockwise of the boy whose second choice was the syrup cake and who, in turn, sat one place clockwise of Brian. The boy who chose the blueberry cake second isn't surnamed Lowe.

4 Ewan occupied seat B. Fred isn't Master Willard. The boy in seat D who started with a strawberry cake isn't surnamed Robertson or Willard.

		Adam	Brian	David	Ewan	Fred	Graham	Lowe	Potter	Roberston	Symes	Veness	Willard	Banana	Blackcurrant	Blueberry	Pineapple	Strawberry	Syrup	Banana	Blueberry	Lemon	Pineapple	Strawberry	Syrup
		FORENAMES						**SURNAME**						**FIRST CAKE**						**SECOND CAKE**					
SEAT	Seat A																								
	Seat B																								
	Seat C																									
	Seat D																									
	Seat E																									
	Seat F																									
SECOND CAKE	Banana second																								
	Blueberry second																			
	Lemon second																			
	Pineapple second																			
	Strawberry second																			
	Syrup second																			
FIRST CAKE	Banana first															
	Blackcurrant first														
	Blueberry first														
	Pineapple first														
	Strawberry first														
	Syrup first														
SURNAME	Lowe							
	Potter							
	Robertson							
	Symes							
	Veness							
	Willard							

The logic puzzles on these pages don't have standard grids, so they are rather more difficult to solve. You will have to apply unbending logic while juggling lots of separate little scraps of information.

8 Card sharp LEVEL 2

In the diagram below left are 12 different playing cards from a standard pack – so no two cards are the same. Moreover, each card is of a different value, with an ace counting as one, a jack as 11 and a king as 13. There are no queens among the 12 cards. In every horizontal row of four cards there are four different suits and in every vertical column of three cards there are three different suits. No card is either horizontally or vertically next to another of the same colour: for instance, the 5 of spades is neither horizontally nor vertically next to a club. Any references in the clues to left, right, above and below are from your point of view as you look at the diagram. Using this information, can you discover the value and suit of the individual cards?

1 The 5 of spades is directly between a 3 to its immediate left and a 6 to its immediate right.

2 The value of card H is two higher than that of card C. Card C (which isn't a diamond) has a value half that of card L (which is a club).

3 Neither the 2 nor the card directly beneath the 2 is a heart.

4 The king is directly next to (and either left or right of) the 7 of hearts, which is directly below an ace. The 10 is directly next to (right of) the jack.

A	B	C	D
E	F	G	H
I	J	K	L

9 Housey housey LEVEL 3

Lottie Betts got lucky at lotto the other evening, matching all 15 numbers to scoop the jackpot in the very first game. Luck isn't part of this puzzle as far as you are concerned – you'll have to rely on the clues below and on your excellent powers of logical deduction to determine the order in which the numbered balls were called. Fill in the letters relating to the balls on the grid below.

1 The ball that was called out sixth is to the right of and touching the one called seventh, which is of the same colour as and has a number either two higher or two lower than the ball that was called eleventh.

2 The ball called second is of the same colour as and has a number either one higher or one lower than the ball called ninth, which is immediately to the right of and touching that called fourth, which has a lower number than the ball called ninth.

3 The ball called third is of the same colour as and has a higher number than the first ball to be called, which is to the left of and touching the ball that was called directly after ball N. Ball L was called directly after ball K.

4 The ball that was called out twelfth is touching and is either directly above or directly below the one called tenth, which is on the same horizontal level as the ball called last, which has a number either two higher or two lower than the ball called eighth.

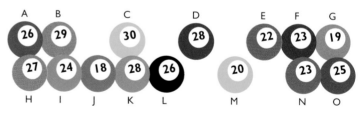

A	B		C		D		E	F	G
26	29		30		28		22	23	19

27	24	18	28	26		20		23	25
H	I	J	K	L		M		N	O

1st	2nd	3rd	4th	5th
6th	7th	8th	9th	10th
11th	12th	13th	14th	15th

10 What the Dickens? LEVEL 3

Charles Dickens was not, as far as we know, a puzzler – but he could have been a good one. The mind that produced a line like 'He felt as much out of his element as a dolphin in a sentry box,' (*Pickwick Papers*) was surely attuned to the creative clash of ideas, which is the key to much puzzle-solving. And Dickens's last book, *The Mystery of Edwin Drood,* was a kind of literary puzzle, made all the more vexing for being unfinished at the time of his death.

But there is no great mystery to this puzzle: just a need for logical thought as you study the series of squares below. In each horizontal row, vertical column and long diagonal line of seven smaller squares, there are seven different letters: D, I, C, K, E, N and S in a certain order. We've filled in some of the squares to give you a start and the clues below will help you to determine the location of the others.

1 **D**	2	3	4	5	6 **I**	7
8	9	10	11	12	13	14
15	16	17	18	19	20	21
22	23 **C**	24	25	26	27	28 **K**
29	30	31	32	33	34	35
36	37	38	39 **E**	40	41 **N**	42
43	44	45	46	47 **S**	48	49

1 Squares 3 and 42 contain the same letter.

2 Squares 4 and 26 contain the same letter, which is different to that in square 43.

3 Squares 5 and 49 contain the same letter.

4 Squares 9 and 36 contain the same letter.

5 Squares 22 and 48 contain the same letter.

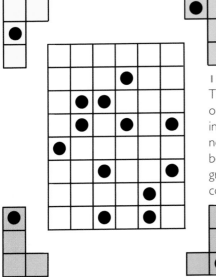

11 Where the L? LEVEL 2

Three pieces of each of the four kinds of L-shapes shown on the left (each with one black dot) have been inserted in the grid. The pieces fit together so well that there are no spaces between them and no overlaps. Any piece can be turned and/or flipped over before being put in the grid, and no two pieces of the same kind touch, even at a corner. Can you tell where the Ls are?

12 Target practice LEVEL 2

Six archers each fire three arrows that hit a target. Alison beats Keith by two points, Keith beats Charles by two points, Charles beats Jill by two points, Jill beats Martin by two points and Martin beats Jonathan by two points. What were the scores of the six players?

6 8 15 21 35

13 Good arrows
LEVEL 2

Robin, Marion and Little John were practising archery in the forest one day. Each fired six shots and each scored 142 points. Robin's first two shots scored 44 points. Marion's first shot scored 6 points. Who scored a bullseye?

The 18 shots are marked on the target.

2 4 6 10 20 40 50 100

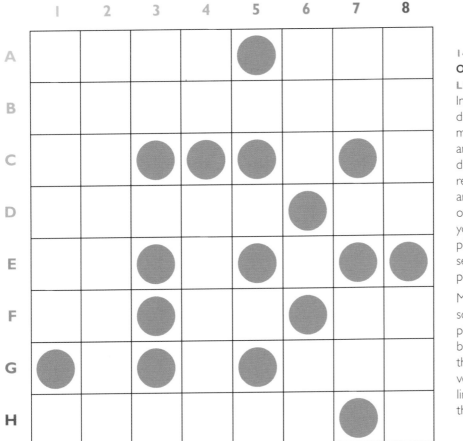

14 Draughtsmen on parade
LEVEL 2

In this game the draughtsmen can move over one another in any direction. A piece is removed when another piece jumps over it. In one move you can make your piece jump over a series of other pieces.

Make just one move so that only eight pieces remain on the board, so arranged that no horizontal, vertical or diagonal line contains more than one piece.

15 Change sides   LEVEL 3

On the board below all the white draughtsmen are on the right-hand side and all the red draughtsmen are on the left-hand side.

Each piece can travel forward only. It can jump over other pieces one at a time, but again only forward. Red pieces can leave the board to the right, white pieces must leave on the left.

How do you make all the pieces pass, using only the two possible forward movements, so that all the red draughtsmen finish to the right of the white draughtsmen?

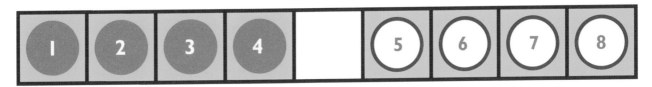

16 One player only LEVEL 2

In this sole-player game, a piece is placed on all the numbered squares except for the central number 8. Pieces can be removed only by jumping backwards or forward along the connecting lines. You can jump over one piece only, and you can jump unoccupied spaces so long as the move conforms to the other rules. So, for example, number 3 can jump over 5 and land in 8, thereby removing piece 5 from the board; and in one move 6 can jump over 7 to land on 8. The object is to remove every piece from the board except for one, which must finish in the central position, 8. What sequence of moves should you follow to achieve this goal?

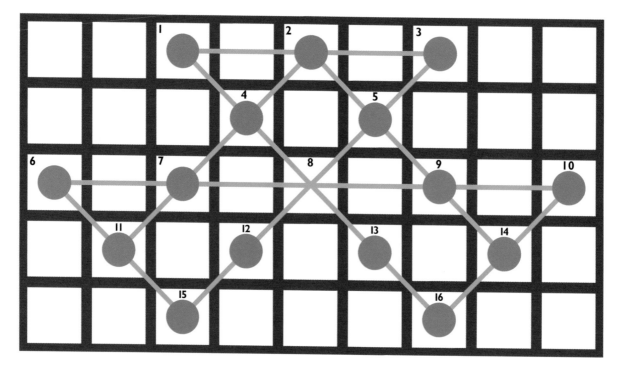

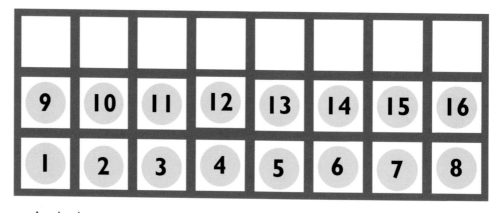

17 At the last count LEVEL 3

The object of this game is to leave just one counter, number 1, on the board.

Counters are removed by moving one over another into an empty space – the one you jump over is removed from the board. Horizontal or vertical – but not diagonal – moves are allowed. For example, counter number 8 can jump over counter number 16 and thus remove it from the board, but it cannot jump over counter 15.

18 Back to black LEVEL 1

In this pool trick, at which exact point on cushion 2 must you hit the black ball so that it hits cushions 3 and 4 and then returns, passing through its original position?

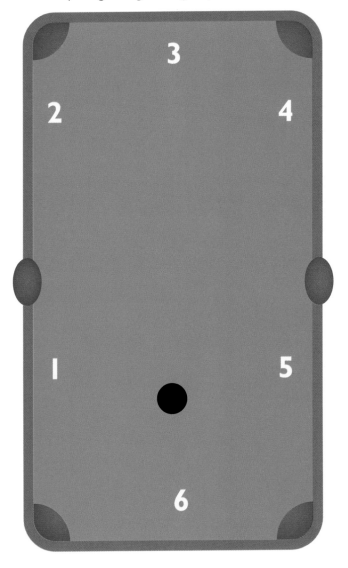

19 Off the cushion LEVEL 2

You are playing the white cue ball. What is the minimum number of cushions you will have to play off in order to sink the black ball – without hitting any of the striped balls first? (Assume that the angle at which the ball strikes the cushion is the same as the angle at which it leaves it)

20 Cipherwords   LEVEL 2

Cipherword puzzles use a basic form of encryption in which each letter of the alphabet is replaced by a number. We could ask you to guess each letter and you could begin to solve it by realizing, for example, that there will be more of the letter 'A' or letter 'N' in the puzzle than of the letter 'X' or 'Q': so if there are plenty of number 9s appearing then the chance of 9 being 'A' are quite high. However, we have given you a start by solving four of the letter substitutions in each of the puzzles.

As an extra clue, two words may be found in these cipherword puzzles that, together would have struck fear into the hearts of the outlaws in the USA's Wild West.

Puzzle 1

4	16	3	7	24	11	■	15	■	24	■	15	■
26	■	24	■	19	■	10	24	15	7	24	6	16
26	15	19	20	4	7	4	19	■	6	■	6	■
14	■	4	■	7	■	19	■	15	2	20	24	23
3	15	17	1	4	■	6	4	17	17	■	6	■
24	■	24	■	■	■	23	■	6	16	15	24	19
16	■	7	■	22	15	7	13	23	■	22	■	2
4	15	26	17	4	■	15	■	■	■	6	■	6
■	7	■	4	15	19	17	■	9	15	16	11	3
3	24	19	15	9	■	24	■	15	■	19	■	3
■	9	■	26	■	6	16	15	11	11	15	16	23
12	15	11	2	17	16	21	■	15	■	11	■	2
■	17	■	4	■	21	■	3	2	7	16	4	19

A	B	C	D	E	F	G	H	I	J	K	L	M
	22			4		26						

N	O	P	Q	R	S	T	U	V	W	X	Y	Z
					6							

Puzzle 2

15	■	17	■	2	■	■	20	■	22	■	20
4	15	4	7	18	20	■	16	18	25	10	8	16
3	■	19	■	12	■	25	■	12	■	10	■	26
3	16	16	12	4	22	16	■	15	4	11	22	16
16	■	20	■	25	■	8	■	16	■	20	■	12
25	4	3	16	■	4	3	2	4	20	■	■	■
6	■	6	■	16	■	1	■	17	■	20	■	20
■	■	4	11	18	2	3	■	20	3	16	3
3	■	4	■	18	■	1	■	15	■	25	■	4
25	16	2	1	7	■	4	1	25	2	1	21	3
1	■	15	■	4	■	12	■	1	■	8	■	18
15	10	18	12	3	6	■	4	11	26	16	12	3
16	■	17	■	16	■	■	16	■	20	■	16

A	B	C	D	E	F	G	H	I	J	K	L	M
											2	17

N	O	P	Q	R	S	T	U	V	W	X	Y	Z
				25							6	

Safe crackers

Can you crack the safe? Your first task (should you decide to accept it) is to decide which of the 14 statements below are false. Then shade out the areas on the combination lock that are true statements (so if you think statement E is true, shade out area E on the front of the safe). The shaded segments should give the digital numbered combination required. There are three games to play – an easy, medium and difficult combination to find. Use the same diagram for each game.

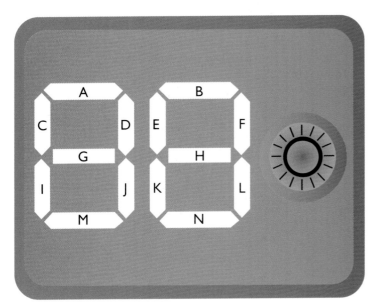

21 LEVEL 1

A The city of Quebec is part of Canada

B A golden anniversary commemorates 40 years

C Nelson commanded the British fleet at Trafalgar

D In the zodiac, Sagittarius is the sign of the water carrier

E Psalms is the book of the Bible with the largest number of chapters

F The chemical symbol for tin is Sn

G Dartmouth lies on the river Dart

H The term *fortissimo* instructs a musician to play very loudly

I Electrical voltage is measured in amperes

J Texas is the 'Lone Star' state

K A hypocaust is a wide-scale nuclear disaster or war

L In bottle sizes, a methuselah is larger than a magnum

M Judas Iscariot was one of the Apostles

N The first letter of the Greek alphabet is beta

22 LEVEL 1

A Buck's Fizz is made from champagne and orange juice

B Rabat is the capital of Morocco

C Mendelssohn wrote the *Eroica* Symphony

D KLM is Holland's national airline

E The German flag is a tricolour of red, orange and brown

F Winston Churchill won the Nobel prize for literature

G A palindrome is a word that reads the same backwards and forwards

H The longest bone in the body is the clavicle

I P. D. James wrote the *Jeeves and Wooster* stories

J Mount McKinley is the highest point in the USA

K Tasmania is a small island country off the coast of Africa

L Edgar Rice Burroughs created the character of Tarzan

M The Beaufort scale goes from 0 (calm) to 17 (hurricane)

N The first colour television broadcasts were made in 1975

23 LEVEL 1

A Bolivia was at one time called Abyssinia

B Emma Thompson won an Oscar in 1993 for her role in *Howards End*

C The Dickens character Miss Havisham appears in *Oliver Twist*

D The song 'A Couple of Swells' comes from the musical *Easter Parade*

E Necrophobia is the fear of death

F Spencer Percival is the only British PM to have been assassinated

G Louis Bleriot flew around the world in July 1909

H There were five Marx Brothers, including Gummo

I The Roman Emperor Nero was so insane he made his horse a consul

J The Suez Canal is roughly twice as long as the Panama Canal

K The Curtis Cup is a coveted trophy in the sport of badminton

L Shirley Bassey performed the title music for the film *Moonraker*

M *Ruddigore* is a play by Tom Stoppard

N Leonardo da Vinci Airport is situated in Rome

24 The Clambake Kid jail-breaks again LEVEL 3

Nothing went right in the Clambake Kid's bank job. The sheriff and his posse rounded up the whole gang as soon as they left the County Bank. The sheriff was sneaky too. He knew that locking the whole gang up together would mean trouble. So he split them up, putting Clambake in his own cell. The Kid was dead set on escaping – but it sure wasn't gonna be easy.

B Running across the room was a wall of metal bars, each 2.5cm (1in) wide and positioned 10cm (4in) apart. Set in the 'wall' was a door of similar construction. The door had a lock on the outside only. Around the lock was a 60cm (2ft) square metal plate, to stop anyone reaching through the bars and unlocking the door from the inside.

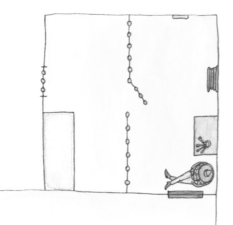

The jail was located through a door at the back of the sheriff's office. The whole room was 5m (16ft) square and 4m (13ft) high. The ceiling, floor and walls were concrete except for a 30cm (12in) square window made of solid iron bars in the centre of the back wall, 2.5m (8ft) from the floor.

The wall of bars created a cell 5m x 2.5m (16ft x 8ft). Inside the cell was a small iron bed bolted to the floor, a wooden bucket without a handle and a blanket. The last prisoner had left behind a table-tennis ball, a silver dollar with a hole through it, a flute, a violin, a rubber band, a tin mug and the score of Handel's *Messiah*. The Kid lost his boots and his belt. The only thing he was allowed to keep was his silver pocket watch.

E Outside the cell was a desk and chair for the guard. On the wall was a fire hose and a broken clock. On the floor was a can of gun-oil.

On the night of the escape, the sheriff was at home with his good lady. His deputy, Wallis, was in the jail, asleep in the chair. His legs were resting against the (unlocked) door through to the office. The cell door keys lay on the desk, a good 2m (6½ft) away from Clambake.

Yet somehow, that son-of-a-gun the Clambake Kid escaped that very night, locking Deputy Wallis in his own cell. How did he do it? We'll be very surprised if you can figure it out.

25 Builder's puzzle LEVEL 2

Twenty matchsticks are arranged in two figures as shown, with one figure having an area three times that of the other. First, move one matchstick from the larger figure to the smaller one so that the smaller figure has seven sticks and the larger one 13. Now, rearrange eight sticks in all so the larger figure is once again three times the area of the smaller one.

Both figures must be completely enclosed and no matchsticks may be placed side by side as though they were one matchstick.

26 Matchstick squares LEVEL 2

Twelve matchsticks have been arranged to make five squares as shown. By moving four matchsticks, make ten squares.

27 Three to five LEVEL 2

Nine matchsticks are arranged to form three triangles as shown. Move three matchsticks to create five triangles.

28 Shaken, not stirred LEVEL 1

Make a 'cocktail glass' as shown with three matchsticks, then place a cherry in the glass. By moving two matchsticks you can engineer it that the cherry is no longer in the glass but the glass is still intact. How?

29 Matchstick maths LEVEL 2

Move just one stick to make the matchstick equation approximately correct.

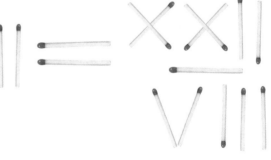

30 'Here, boy!' LEVEL 1

Make the dog face in the opposite direction by moving just two matchsticks.

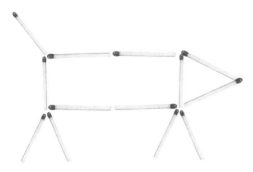

31 Triangles on demand

LEVEL 2

Arrange the six matchsticks shown to construct four triangles.

Cryptography is an unending game of intellectual leapfrog between codemakers and codebreakers. The moment a new code is devised, someone somewhere gets to work trying to crack it. But some of the toughest codes come from the simplest ideas. In the Second World War, for example, the US Army used Navajo Indians as radio operators because their language was so complex and obscure that it functioned as a code: there was no possibility of any enemy being able to speak it. Today's battles are commercial, as global companies fight to find ways of keeping Internet correspondence secret.

Undercover writing

Unlocking the Enigma

At the outbreak of the Second World War Germany possessed the most advanced cipher system in the world. It was called Enigma, and was thought to be utterly unbreakable.

Like Caesar's code, it changed one letter of plain text into one letter of cipher text – but not the same letter every time. So unlike Caesar's code, it had rather more than 26 possible solutions.

Every Enigma machine had three rotating scramblers each containing the 26 letters. This created 17,576 (26 × 26 × 26) possible keys. The scramblers could be positioned in any order, which multiplied the possible keys by 6. A plugboard at the front of the keyboard allowed any six letters in the plain text to be swapped with any six others. This seemingly minor refinement adds 100,391,791,500 more possibilities. So the total number of keys is 26 × 26 × 26 × 6 × 100,391,791,500, giving around 10,000,000,000,000,000 combinations. It would take millions of years for a codebreaker to check all these settings, yet all the operators needed to know was the scrambler and plugboard settings. But Enigma was broken. Before the war Marian Rejewski, a Polish cryptographer, noticed patterns in the ciphertext created by the original settings of the

ALL CODES LEAD TO ROME
Statesmen, generals and spies are the main consumers and connoisseurs of the cryptographer's art. So it is no surprise that many of the great advances have come in times of war or of high political intrigue. Julius Caesar is known to have invented a code that involved substituting each letter in a message for the letter a set number of places on in the alphabet. This kind of code is called a 'Caesar shift' in his honour, though it is doubtful whether the technique would have fooled a determined enemy of Rome for long.

The Enigma machine looked like a rather unwieldy portable typewriter, but it took roo full of machinery at Bletchley Park, the Allie decoding station, to read its hidden messag

How to break a simple code

If a given letter always appears as the same letter (or symbol) in the code, then the codebreaker has a place to start – even if he has no idea of the content of the message. Here are ten tips to get you started:

E is the most common letter in the English language, so the most frequent symbol in the encrypted text is likely to be E.

The next most-often used letters are: A, S, I, N, T, O and R.

A three-letter word ending in E is probably 'THE'. If so, this gives you all the Ts and the Hs in the message.

The most frequently paired letters are TH, HE, AN, IN and ER.

The most frequent short words are, in descending order: THE, OF, AND, TO, IN, THAT and IS.

A single symbol is usually A or I.

Words rarely end in A, C, I, J, O, Q, U or V.

Q is nearly always followed by U.

Almost every word has a vowel.

All of the above rules can lead you astray if you follow them blindly.

Armed with these rules of thumb, try to decode two messages:

CP CRRNG C FCA MGGRU VJG
FQEVQT CYCA
   well-known proverb

  IFHHRZ RH Z IRWWOV
  DIZKKVW RM Z NBHGVIB
  RMHRWV ZM VMRTNZ
famous remark

Answers on page 319

scrambler. He built a machine to seek out those patterns (and called it a 'bombe' after his favourite ice cream). During the war this machine was refined by British cryptographers, who found a way to feed likely settings into the machine, thereby testing their own hunches and saving hours of operating time. In a word, they made the machine programmable. As such, it is recognized as the world's first true computer, the great-grandfather of every mainframe, PC and laptop in the world.

PHARAOHS' TONGUE
For centuries Egyptian hieroglyphics were undecipherable, their meaning lost. The Rosetta Stone (right) provided the key to reading ancient Egyptian texts. It contains one text, but in three scripts: hieroglyphics, and the known languages of demotic and Greek. This let scholars, using codebreaking techniques, unravel the sense of the hieroglyphs.

What is a code? It is a remark wearing a false moustache and some dark glasses. So can you see through the verbal disguise?

32 Hidden intentions LEVEL 3

1 Which death-bed remark was this?

IWXH   XH   CD   IXBT   UDG   BPZXCV   CTL   TCTBXTH

2 If you believe this, then you are not alone.

**V   PHHS   UHHL   ND   COR   URDC   HQ
QENRISD, COR   DVJR   CHSVX   VIS   QHE RARE.**

3 These words were spoken by the leader of a great superpower.

NTIER   EWFRO   EOFAN   HEEDG   AYONT   NDTOD   WESTA

4 Find the clues and you'll find the message.

T C H L I   U S E I C   S L A U S   E E C C L   R U E E T

5 What did the secret agent have to do when he got this set of instructions?

**GOAT   HOOP   HARRISON   APE   LANE
TOMB   EATEN   NOSTRIL   IAN   BUY
THEN   AIM   OFFER   KNEE**

6 Crack the code to discover a saying by German poet Rainer Maria Rilke.

**V XD FK MH JU WD FN PT VQ SK MH JU WD FR TE GN PQ
SD FU WD FQ SS UZ BJ LH JM OF HK MD FZ BU WD F**

7 Can you decode this spy's instruction?

ASSERT GMTNAO EIEEDD NTAMAA THLYRY

8 A French scholar is puzzling over a verse he found scrawled on a nursery wall. Can you help him?

Un petit d'un petit sa tondeur vol, un petit d'un petit a degre ta folle

9 What one-word secret message is contained here?

Most sea lions are vegetarian. Why? Because they like pea soup for tea. And they use their left eye to see it!

33 Who's fooling who? LEVEL 3

1 A choice of two roads lies ahead of you.
To find out how to proceed, read the enigmatic
advice below and break the code.

TRAP	(	)	KNEE
LEEK	(	)	FATE
HEAD	(	)	NUDE
FOOD	(	)	RAKE
INNS	(	)	TOOL
TOOL	(	)	WIND

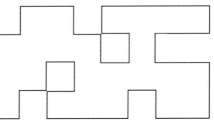

2 They might look like they've
been arranged in random
fashion, but the numbers on
the dartboard to the right
hold the key to a secret
message. Start by counting
how many areas the
board has – this will give
you a clue as to what
each area of the target
represents. Then you have
to think why some sectors
are crowded, and others
completely empty.

3 Can you solve this stencil code? Copy the stencil onto your
acetate and try laying it down in different ways.

O	B	A	N	C	O	N	O
M	E	R	S	E	:	I	S
O	N	N	E	N	O	A	W
O	O	N	M	B	T	E	E

4 You'll find parts of this book easier if you are one of these.

0	3	2	1	1	2	0	2	0	2	0	1
Q	C	I	N	U	H	A	W	P	I	O	Z

Here are some more encryption puzzles. Unravel these tangled word-strings if you can.

34 Rumbled LEVEL 1

An employer was trying to see what the workforce was up to. The mess of letters he found scribbled on the walls of the staff toilets seemed such a strange jumble.

**RGW AREUJW UA RINIEEIQ BUFGR –
VW RGWEW VT BUBW UB RGW NIEBUBF**

He looked down at his computer keyboard while typing a memo and suddenly it become clear. What does the message say?

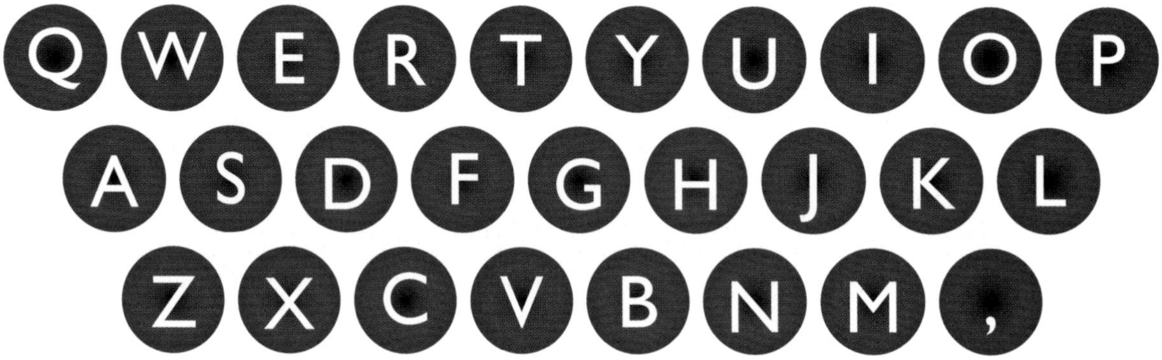

Q W E R T Y U I O P
A S D F G H J K L
Z X C V B N M ,

35 Password problem LEVEL 1

Which four-letter man's name was often used as a password in the early days of computing, until it was discovered that hackers were using this loophole to enter computer systems? (Hint: think about the characteristics that the general public would like in a password)

36 Shhhh! LEVEL 2

1783534 5603248534

corresponds with
QUIETER TYPEWRITER,
what letter is represented by 9?

37 A sense of order LEVEL 2

Put these four numbers in order to obtain a peculiar sentence.
(Hint: you may need an electronic aid.)

378806
4516618
5663
5317738

38 Message received? LEVEL 2

Peter came back from work to find that his no-good flatmate
had left this message by the telephone. It reads:

8447 835374663 47 653 263 3637 668 9675 – 438 2 639 663

What is Peter's
flatmate trying
to tell him?

39 Take a letter LEVEL 3

A boss ran past her secretary on the way to another
meeting. Before she left, she dropped her calculator on
the secretary's desk. 'That's what I would like to drink
when I get back,' she panted. The secretary realized the
calculator was broken, but she then noticed that there
is a hidden message in the display. What drink should
the secretary prepare for her manager's return?

40 Elementary? LEVEL 3

This code is difficult, because the letters in the encryption do not match the letters in the original message. But
the decoding method is surprisingly simple. If you know how to count and use the alphabet, you can solve it.

UJH GKUWY MGWXJX JU BFYESILL CA PPH QQVMYOVV,

UJH TGFSSJ MGWXJX CA UYR QQVMYOVVB, BPG TQ PP...

A ll these codes are filed in a drawer marked 'Odd'. In most of them, the key is hidden in something other than the words.

41 Check this LEVEL 2

The counters on this chequerboard pattern have been moved from their original positions. Each counter has been moved three squares horizontally, vertically, or a mixture of the two (e.g. two up, one right). What appropriate word can be revealed by deducing their original positions? To make things a little harder, two of the counters are red herrings.

42 Spies are us LEVEL 2

Outside an enemy spy base, you notice that six numbers are written in certain shapes (which never change) on a noticeboard every day. You deduce that this tells the enemy agents what the password is for that day.

The diagram above shows the numbers for the day when the password was ANGINA. Previous days' passwords include **643643 = GATEAU** and **174271 = PLAINS**.

Today's numbers read **434341**, in that order. Can you work out today's password and thus infiltrate the enemy HQ?

43 Key code LEVEL 3

What is the key to solving this long sequence of curious numbers?

4 23 51   36 26 33 11   5 25   19 20   22 23 9   32 33 51 46 22 24 14 28

44 Artful arrows LEVEL 2

You've received this message from the enemy. What is it trying to say? Hint: essentially, this is two codes in one.

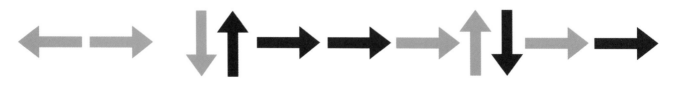

45 Code maze LEVEL 3

This code maze is in four parts. At no time must you travel along the same path twice. Part One requires you to spell out the name of a colour on your route. The letters that spell the colour must be in the right order and you may not pass through any other letters as you go. Part Two requires you to pass through all the squares of the colour revealed in Part One. You may pass through as many other colours as you like. Your route in Part Two will spell out instructions for Part Three. Part Three's route will give a coded clue to Part Four, in which you must spell out, without passing any other letters, the name of a legendary character who would not be fazed by the maze.

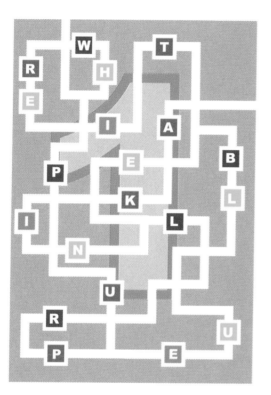

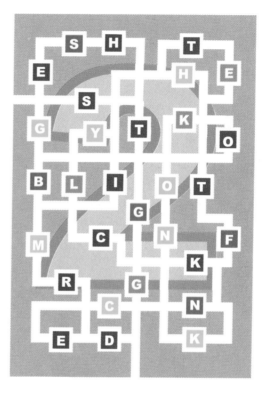

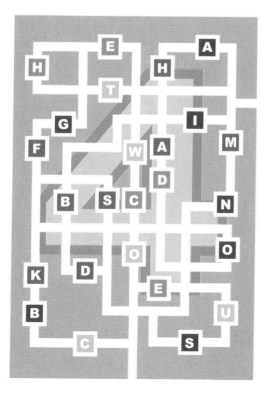

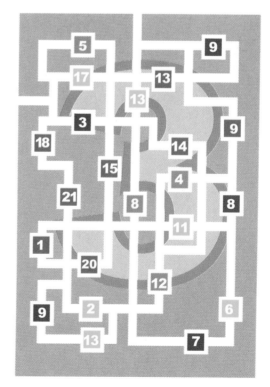

46 Chuck Diamond P. I. LEVEL 3

The following story from the files of Chuck Diamond (Private Investigator) is a logic puzzle and could be solved using a normal logic puzzle grid. Without the grid, you are left to piece together the visual clues to the right with those found in Chuck's story. Like all logic puzzles, the secret is in finding connections between clues by a process of elimination. Gridless, this qualifies as a difficult puzzle, and you should allow yourself 45 minutes to complete it.

To solve the case we need to know which criminal (First Edition Frank, Pages McLeaf or The Bookworm) stole which books (*Corporal Clerk's Kazoo*, *The Beauty of Loneliness* or *Memoirs of an Amnesiac*) by which authors: Tom Fox, Barbara Taylor Broadfoot or Emily Austin, and how they made their escape (via the window, the door or the roof). Good luck!

Now books ain't generally my thing. Last time I read anything longer than the label on a bottle of bourbon I was in short pants (I never did find out who ate that porridge). But a job is a job, so there I was, in the Library of American History in downtown Chicago, surrounded by eggheads. Seems there had been a regular crimewave in the book world. Three of the library's most valuable books had been snaffled in the past week. All those eggheads didn't have a clue between them – sometimes a roomful of mousetraps can catch you nothing, and what you need is a hungry cat. I hadn't eaten since Monday.

Three different thieves stole three different books. One was lifted in broad daylight and taken right out the front door. The other two were break-ins at night, through the window and the roof. One of the books was in a picture frame, one kept in a glass case and one chained to a wooden desk.

I'd heard about The Bookworm: he isn't what you'd call a professional thief, more a guy with an obsession with one writer, Tom Fox. If a Fox book was missing, I knew The Bookworm wasn't far away at the time. He's an unstable character, too, done time in various establishments for the cranially confused. Part of his file says that as well as being the obsessive type, he suffers from vertigo so bad he has to wear extra thin socks, so I guess whoever got into the library through the hole in the roof, it wasn't The Bookworm.

The glass case holding Corporal Clerk's Kazoo was smashed with a hammer. That would have made a racket, too much to have been done while the library was open during the day without somebody noticing and calling the cops.

First Edition Frank is a legendary cat burglar and forger. A class act too – most forgers are blind as bats from all the close-up work they do, but old Frank has 20/20 vision.

I took a couple of photos of the crime scene; there were some pretty useful clues there. The rest was standard detective work. I was able to tell the eggheads which thieves stole which books by which authors, and how they all got into the building. Case closed. All that remained was for me to head over to Sloppy Joe's for a sub sandwich and a good read of Joe's Sports Illustrated (Swimwear Edition).

CRIME SCENE 1.

CRIME SCENE 2.

CORPORAL CLERK'S KAZOO

CRIME SCENE 3.

Memoirs of an Amnesiac
EMILY AUSTIN

CRIME SCENE 4.

THE BEAUTY OF LONELINESS

CRIME SCENE 5.

CRIME SCENE 6.

By now you must feel like a small change, so here are some puzzles that are all about small change. It might help you to visualise the problem if you have some real coins to hand. Any currency will do.

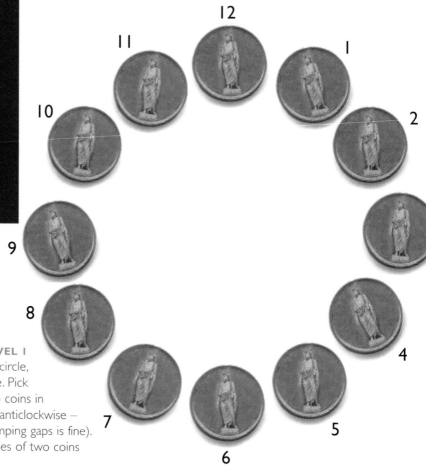

47 What's the dime? LEVEL 1
Twelve coins are arranged in a circle, like the numbers on a clockface. Pick up any coin and jump over two coins in either direction – clockwise or anticlockwise – and place it on a third coin (jumping gaps is fine). Your challenge is to form six piles of two coins each in just six moves.

48 The thin blue line LEVEL 2
Position these three coins so that two heads (the bottom two) are entirely to the right of the line and two tails are entirely to the left.

49 Tricky 19 LEVEL 3
Arrange 19 coins in such a way that they form nine rows of five coins each.

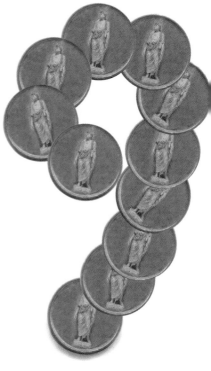

50 Corner challenge
LEVEL 2

Change the position of only one of the coins to the left to produce two straight rows with three coins in each row.

51 Penny dance LEVEL 2

Two coins of exactly the same size and circumference are touching each other as shown. While the bottom coin remains perfectly still, the top coin revolves around it once completely, always remaining touching. In making one complete circuit around the bottom coin, how many times does the top coin rotate through 360°?

52 Mirror image

LEVEL 3

Ten coins are arranged in a triangle as shown. By moving three coins, turn the triangle upside down.

53 Keep the change LEVEL 3

A man pays for his lunch with a £10 note. The lunch costs £7 and the waiter who is bringing him £3 change decides to pocket £2 and hand him only £1. Now the diner has received £1 back from £10 and so has paid £9. The waiter has kept £2, making £11 in all. So where did the extra £1 come from.

figure

it out

Numbers have a satisfying beauty all of their own. A well wrought calculation has all the elegance and precision of a prima ballerina. Try these puzzles, and your mind will soon become attuned to the silent symphony of mathematics.

1 On target

Use some or all of the numbers in the white outer ring together with the four basic arithmetic operations (add, multiply, subtract and divide) to obtain the target numbers in each coloured ring. The six outer-ring numbers can be used only once for any target number.

The numbers in the blue ring **(LEVEL 1)** can be reached in at least ten different ways, the numbers in the red ring **(LEVEL 2)** by at least five different methods and the numbers in the centre yellow **(LEVEL 3)** in fewer than five ways.

We'll do the first one to start you off. The numbers are 2, 3, 6, 9, 10 and 75. The easy target is 341. One of the 17 possible solutions goes: (75 × 3) + ((10 + 9) × 6) + 2 = 341.

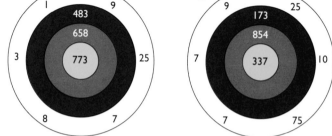

H ere are some number puzzles of a type we like to call 'riddlemarithmetic'. The key here is to be sure that you take the question aright.

2 Testing times   LEVEL 3

1 2 + 2 comes to the same as 2 × 2. Now find a set of three different whole numbers whose sum is equal to their total when multiplied.

2 What is the smallest whole number that is equal to seven times the sum of its digits?

3 Find the smallest whole number that is equal to twice the sum of its digits.

4 My double exceeds my half by 2. What am I?

5 If I had one and a half apples more I'd have one and a half times as many. How many apples do I have?

6 A fish weighs 2 tons plus half its weight. How much does it weigh?

7 In reply to an enquiry about the animals on his farm, the farmer says: 'I only ever keep sheep, goats and horses. In fact, at the moment they are all sheep bar three, all goats bar four and all horses bar five.' How many does he have of each animal?

8 Split 45 into four parts so that if I add two to the first, subtract two from the second, multiply the third by two and divide the fourth by two I get the same number.

9 One brother says of his younger brother: 'two years ago I was three times as old as my brother was. In three years' time I will be twice as old as my brother.' How old are they each now?

10 My twin lives at the reverse of my house number. The difference between our house numbers ends in 2. What are the lowest possible numbers of our houses?

11 Bert scores an average of 73% over his first three exams. What will he need to score on the fourth and final one to bump his average up to 80% overall?

12 A shopkeeper lowered his prices by 20% for a week then raised them by 20%. Are they any different at the end of the price shuffle?

13 A party of people went into a café. They each bought exactly the same meal and the total bill came to £44.11. How many were there in the party?

14 If a hen and a half lays an egg and a half in a day and a half, how many eggs will half a dozen hens lay in half a dozen days?

15 1 + 23 + 4 + 5 + 67 = 100 is one way of inserting plus signs into 1234567 so that the result adds up to 100. Find another way.

16 A house painter was asked to mix 6 litres of grey in the proportions of two parts white to one part black, but by mistake he mixed 4 litres of black with 2 litres of white. What is the smallest amount of paint he needs to pour away to correct his mistake?

17 The trip from Bunstable to Unstable via Dunstable is 8 miles all in. From Dunstable to Unstable via Bunstable is 7 miles. From Bunstable to Dunstable via Unstable is 11 miles. How far is it from Bunstable to Unstable? From Unstable to Dunstable? From Bunstable to Dunstable?

18 Multiplying 54321 by a 5-digit number gives a 10-digit number ending in 12345. That's to say:

$$54321 \times ***** = *****12345$$

Replace each asterisk with the appropriate digit.

19 A farmer grows his cabbages in square grid patterns. This year there'll be 37 more on his patch. How many will there be altogether?

20 What is the smallest number that increases by 12 when it is turned upside down?

21 Fill in this magic square so that the columns, rows and diagonals all add up to 2001 (two numbers have been provided). There is a straightforward way of approaching a magic square with 9 numbers – can you find the principle?

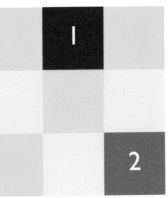

22 A small number of cards has been lost from a complete pack. If I deal among four people, three cards remain. If I deal among three people, two remain and if I deal among five people, two cards remain. How many cards are there?

23 Using each of the digits from 1–6 inclusive once and once only, write down two 3-digit numbers and multiply these together. For example, 654 × 231 = 151,074. But this isn't the biggest number you can produce in this way. What is?

24 What is the largest proper fraction – that is, one less than 1 – that you can make using all the digits from 1–6 inclusive? $^{354}/_{612}$ is more than a half, but can you do better than that?

3
Round the bend

For each wheel, supply the missing number.

1 & 2: **LEVEL 1**

3 & 4: **LEVEL 2**

5 & 6: **LEVEL 3**

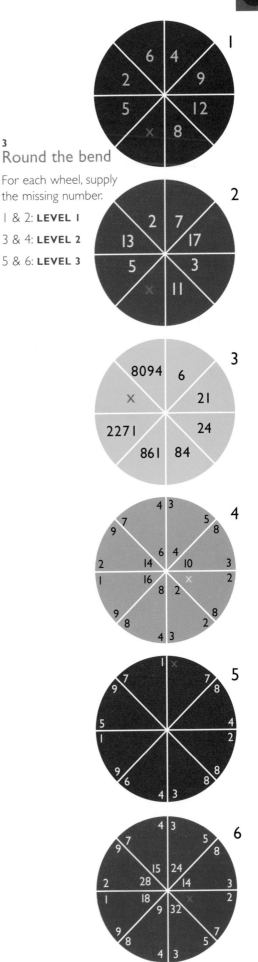

4 Number fun 1 LEVEL 1

Every calculation contains a +, – and x. The number in each blue square is the total of the four numbers at each of its corners. Can you fill in the grid?

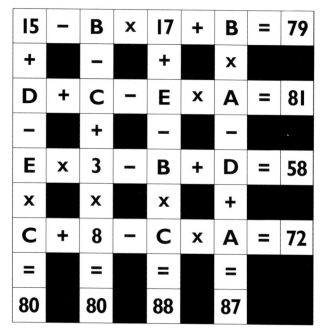

4		1		11		1	=	54
	10		20		30			
3							=	84
	40		50		60			
17							=	198
	70		80		90			
4							=	90
=		=		=		=		
72		23		49		35		

5 Number fun 2 LEVEL 2

Every row and column contains a +, – and x, and ends with a different total number between 20 and 28 inclusive. Can you complete the grid?

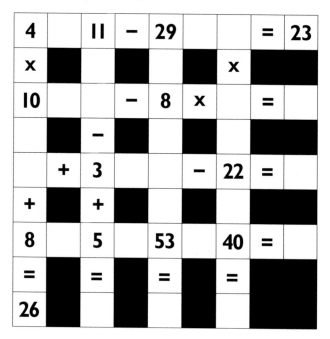

4		11	–	29			=	23
x						x		
10			–	8	x		=	
		–						
	+	3			–	22	=	
+		+						
8		5		53		40	=	
=		=		=		=		
26								

6 Number fun 3 LEVEL 2

Can you replace the letters with the numbers they represent so that all the sums work?

15	–	B	x	17	+	B	=	79
+		–		+		x		
D	+	C	–	E	x	A	=	81
–		+		–		–		
E	x	3	–	B	+	D	=	58
x		x		x		+		
C	+	8	–	C	x	A	=	72
=		=		=		=		
80		80		88		87		

7 Number fun 4 LEVEL 3

In the coloured squares, the numbers 1 to 16 are each used once. Blue squares are odd numbers, green squares are even numbers. Can you complete the grid?

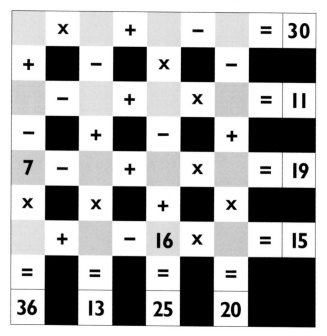

	x		+		–		=	30
+		–		x		–		
	–		+		x		=	11
–		+		–		+		
7	–		+		x		=	19
x		x		+		x		
	+		–	16	x		=	15
=		=		=		=		
36		13		25		20		

8 Number crunch

Fit all the numbers listed into the grid. One number has been inserted in the correct position to get you started.

LEVEL 1 20 minutes
LEVEL 2 15 minutes
LEVEL 3 12 minutes

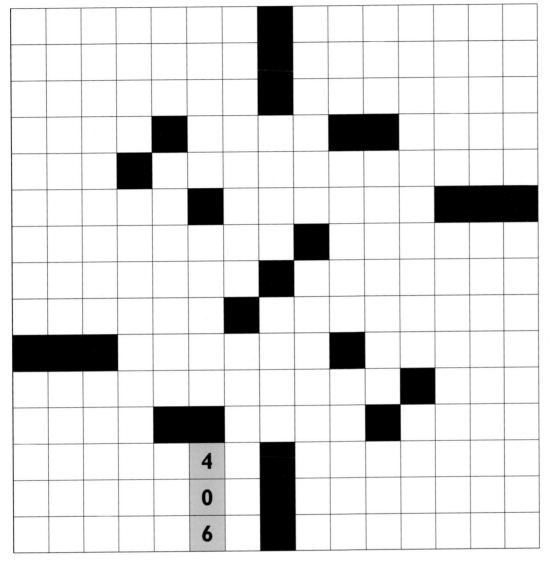

3 digits	4 digits	5 digits	6 digits		8 digits	10 digits
107	1036	13540	123830	5431747	45102846	9019160573
163	2810	25294	239307	5438302	75016014	9199076460
236	3659	27896	526985	5724625	83827248	**11 digits**
247	4475	48260	814065	6255140	85007825	54703110786
~~406~~	7324	55004	939962	6271488	**9 digits**	74965712050
548	9216	57357	956639	6739368	138831523	
601	9404	70253	**7 digits**	6815828	564314872	
633	9529	72694	1027170	8017348	741769179	
	9788	81997	2068157	8474316	811500450	
	9879	84628	2346453	9173528	926928469	
		88237	4003765	9269582	930264313	
		91510		9617006		

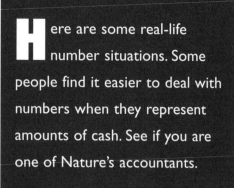

Here are some real-life number situations. Some people find it easier to deal with numbers when they represent amounts of cash. See if you are one of Nature's accountants.

9 Double or nothing LEVEL 2

A gambler, believing in the principle of 'easy come, easy go', doubles his money and gives away £1; he then trebles his money and gives away £2.

'You shouldn't throw your money away,' his mother admonishes him.

'And why ever not?' he retorts, 'after all, I still have four times what I started with.'

And just how much was that?

10 Retail therapy LEVEL 2

A shopper bought a single item at each of three successive stalls in the covered market. Each time she spent ⅔ of what she had and yet at the end she still had 50p left for her bus fare home. How much had she started off with?

11 Heavy load LEVEL 3

A farmer had to weigh four sacks of grain. The weighing machine wasn't very accurate for low weights so he weighed the four sacks in every combination of two, getting readings (in kg):

22   25   31   31   37   40

What are the weights of the individual sacks?

12 Cambio LEVEL 3

In the land of Valuta there are 100 plinks to the plonk. The smallest unit of currency is a plink. The exchange rate is exactly 7 plinks to £3. What sum of money – £ab.cd in pounds and pence – may be converted to plinks and plonks by merely reversing the order of the digits (i.e., dc plonks and ba plinks)?

13 Safe cracker LEVEL 2

A new safe has a 16 digit combination. This number consists of two 8s separated by eight digits, two 7s separated by seven digits, two 6s separated by six digits, two 5s separated by five digits and so on, all the way down to two 1s with one digit between them. The middle two digits are 1 and 6. Can you fill in the rest of the digits?

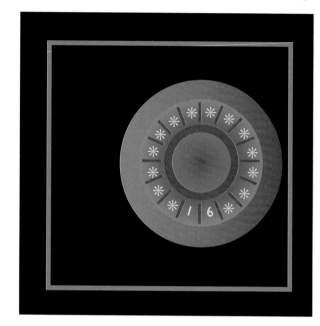

14 I blame this new money LEVEL 2

'Goodness gracious!,' exclaimed Miss Wittering to the counter clerk as she cashed her cheque, 'I must have misread the pence as pounds and the pounds as pence, young man. I never could cope with decimal currency. I have twice as much money as I expected.' 'To be perfectly accurate, Madam,' replied the clerk, 'if you were to spend 2p, you would have exactly double what you expected.'

Incidentally, how much was the cheque for?

15 Three items or less LEVEL 2

Emma bought three items in the supermarket. When she got to the checkout, the operator tapped in the prices. However, he somehow managed to multiply the three numbers together instead of adding them. Fortunately, the result was just the same: £90.09.

How much did each item cost?

16 Digital wizardry LEVEL 3

Add to the number 12345678 a permutation of the same set of eight digits in order to produce the smallest possible result consisting of even digits only.

17 They call it 'math' LEVEL 1

All of these USA-related numbers can be plucked in sequence from the row of ten digits beside each question. The numbers contain either 2, 3, 4 or 5 digits.

1	Year of Marilyn Monroe's birth	1930219265
2	Zip code of TV's famous high school	6039021090
3	Street number of the White House	1616002296
4	Year of American Independence	1767177608
5	Number to dial for a cop in New York	9991111997
6	Number of states in the USA	5251504948
7	No. of TV's *M*A*S*H* unit	7477044077
8	Oscar nominations for *Forrest Gump*	1013911914
9	Number of presidents that preceded Bill Clinton	3441424344
10	Date in 1963 of JFK's assassination (day/month)	2111221111

18 Guesstimations LEVEL 2

We don't expect you to have these figures at your fingertips — the task is to give it your best guess. The answer can be plucked in sequence from the run of ten digits. Some of the answers are three-figure numbers, some four. Only one has five digits, and only one has two.

1	The Moon's diameter in kilometres	8347521698
2	The height of Uluru (formerly Ayers Rock) in feet	2364114399
3	The height of Mount Everest in feet	2902999822
4	The heaviest weighed whale's weight (in tonnes)	2190622223
5	The world's largest diamond, in carats	8064131069
6	The number of albums Bing Crosby made during his lifetime	1256314131
7	The longest ever triple jump by a frog, in feet	1264332929
8	The number of participants in the 1936 Berlin Olympics	1234066543
9	The number of consecutive months that Joe Louis was World Champion	1213215211
10	The number of pages in the largest ever *New York Times*	9981612099

We often suppose that nature is random: that the sea is a formless mass; that volcanoes are as unpredictable as they are violent; that the wind blows where it wills. In fact, the natural world is shot through with patterns. Often these patterns seem to be derived from the realm of pure mathematics, and scientists were astonished when they found that the iron laws of calculus and algebra were minutely reproduced in the arrangement of petals on a daisy or in the slithering of a snake across a sand dune. Now we know that there is order in almost every natural phenomenon. Even the shapes of clouds can be submitted to the analysis of chaos theory – though this is a mathematics undreamt of by the medieval astronomer Johannes Kepler, who noticed that every tiny snowflake is a unique work of art in a hexagonal frame, and wondered why that might be.

Creation by numbers

Fibonacci flowers
The Fibonacci sequence is an arithmetical progression in which each number is the sum of the two preceding numbers: 1,1, 2,3,5,8,13, and so on. The interwoven spirals of seeds on a sunflower follow just this pattern: if a spiral contains 21 seeds, and the next spiral has 34, then the one after that will have 55 seeds, and so on to the flower's outer rim.

Fearful symmetry

Tigers exhibit 'mirror symmetry': their left side reflects their right. But the stripes on a tiger contain a far more complicated regularity. The mechanism which generates biological patterns remains mysterious, but a theoretical basis was put forward in 1952 by the mathematician Alan Turing. Now scientists have invented chemical processes which create 'Turing patterns' in gels. Soon we will know how the tiger got its stripes, and the leopard its spots.

Golden spiral

Each quarter turn of the spiral in a nautilus shell is precisely 1.618 times farther from the centre than the one before. This ratio is called *phi*. It has long been used as the ideal proportion in art and architecture, where it is known as the 'golden section'.

Order out of chaos

Chaos theory established laws which govern random phenomena such as the drip of a tap. These same laws can describe previously inexplicable events – the shapes of clouds, the rise of storms, the spread of epidemics.

The geometry of snow

The intricate lacework of a snowflake is due to the hexagonal shape of the atoms in ice crystals. Every snowflake is indeed a unique and fleeting creation. And the colder the cloud in which a snowflake forms, the sharper its six points.

This is a mathematical speed test. There are 40 puzzles on these two pages, and you have an hour to do as many as you can. You will need some paper, a pencil, a ruler and a cool head. One other thing: no electronic calculators allowed.

19 Number challenge

LEVEL 1: More than 10

LEVEL 2: 21–30

LEVEL 3: 31–40

1 Which are there more of – inches in a mile or seconds in a day?

2 If there are 1.76 pints in 1 litre, how many litres are there in 1 pint to two decimal places?

3 Draw two straight lines across this shape so that every sum or single number equals 13:

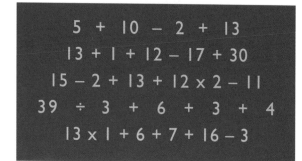

$$5 + 10 - 2 + 13$$
$$13 + 1 + 12 - 17 + 30$$
$$15 - 2 + 13 + 12 \times 2 - 11$$
$$39 \div 3 + 6 + 3 + 4$$
$$13 \times 1 + 6 + 7 + 16 - 3$$

4 Which number gives the same result when divided by -6 as when subtracted from -6?

5 If 1 hectare is 2.47 acres, how many square metres is 1 acre?

6 Which are there more of – Sundays in a millennium or inches in a kilometre?

7 If 30°C = 86°F, how many °F is 15°C?

8 Which two mathematical symbols ($+, -, \times, \div$) must you put into this sum to equal 57?

$$76 \ ? \ 15 \ ? \ 20 = 57$$

9 New South Wales is 801,427 km². South Australia is 380,070 square miles. Which is bigger?

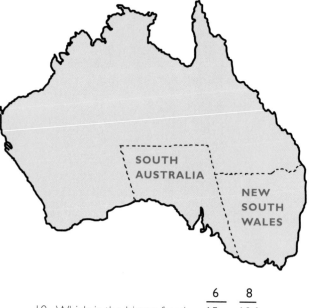

10 Which is the bigger fraction: $\frac{6}{15}$ or $\frac{8}{18}$?

11 Which gives a higher result – adding up all the odd numbers between 1 and 20 inclusive, or all the even numbers?

12 If a man was born on February 29, 1944, and was 55 in 2000, how many birthdays has he had?

13 If π is taken as 3.142 and a wheel has a radius of 30cm, how long is the wheel's circumference?

14 What is the value of a third of three-eighths of two-fifths of a quarter of two-thirds of three-quarters of eight-tenths of 1000?

15 If A must run to each red post and back to the start before crossing the winning line, and the posts are 8 metres apart, how long is his journey?

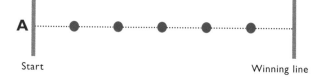

Start   Winning line

16 How many days were there between January 1, 1951, and December 31, 1955, inclusive?

17 Which is higher – the square of 27 or the cube of 9?

18 If I am 21 years older than you, but in 12 years' time I will be twice your age, how old are you now?

19 How many minutes is it past 12, if 74 minutes ago it was half as many minutes past 11?

20 Which number is not divisible by 9?

$$2160 \quad 11,232 \quad 423 \quad 1232$$

21 What percentage of this grid is red and what percentage is yellow?

22 What is 50% of 10% of 25% of 40% of 60% of 2000?

23 Which is the lower figure – the square root of 3 or the cube root of 5?

24 If £3600 is the rate for 45 days' work, how much is 14 days' work worth?

25 The sum of the squares of two consecutive numbers is 1861. What are the two numbers?

26 In a pack of playing cards, what is the total value of the number cards?

27 What is the area of this triangle?

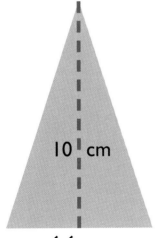

10 cm

6.6 cm

28 1,250,000,000,000,000,000,000 is 1.25 × 10 to the power of what?

29 Which of the following are not prime numbers?

13 29 41 27 17 43 39 11

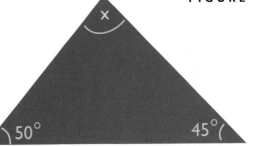

x

50°   45°

30 Fill in the missing angle on the triangle above.

31 Round off the number 138,906 to three, two and one significant figure(s).

32 If a £54 dress now costs 24% more, how much is it (to the nearest whole pound)?

33 Which three consecutive numbers can be multiplied to total 1716?

34 Add two numbers from 4, 5, 6, 7, 8 and 9 to each side of the triangle, so that the numbers on each of the three sides add up to 17.

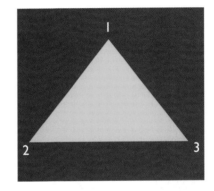

35 Can you express the number 7 using only four 4s?

36 If 1891 becomes 1681, what does 8961 become?

37 If your currency is in coin units of 1, 2, 5, 9, and 50p, what are the fewest coins you need to pay for something costing 85p?

38 How many degrees do the internal angles in this shape add up to?

39 If it takes 12 seconds for a clock to strike 5 o'clock, how long does it take to strike 10 o'clock?

40 How much time is there between 21:47 today and 13:43 tomorrow?

Fingers on buttons, because here is a series of challenges to do with the help of an old-fashioned calculator.

20 Digital conundrum LEVEL 2

In what circumstance would this calculation appear to be correct?

$$8001 = 5 \times (5 + 502)$$

21 Knight moves LEVEL 2

I have a calculator that can display ten digits. How many different ten digit numbers can I type using just the 0–9 keys once each, and moving from one keypress to the next using the knight's move in chess? (In chess, the knight moves in an L-shape – one square up and two across, two squares down and one across, two squares up and one across, and other like combinations – as shown in the diagram on the right.)

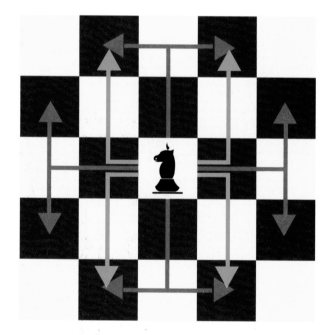

LESS   **EQUAL**   **MORE**

22 More or less? LEVEL 3

The LCD digits above are grouped according to a simple principle. Despite appearances, it has nothing to do with the usual numerical sequence. In which box does the digit 0 belong – the one labelled LESS, EQUAL or MORE?

23 Oddly enough LEVEL 2

Which one of the following is the odd one out, and why?

24 Mobile mystery LEVEL 3

I have a security feature on my mobile phone. I have reprogrammed each key so that the numbers are not in the usual 123 456 789 0 format usually seen on telephones. Furthermore, I have removed the numbers from the keys. So if anyone steals my phone, they will find it difficult to use.

But in case I forget where each number is, the LCD display tells me the product of the digits in each row and column, as shown below. For example, the top three keys when multiplied together give the result 80, and the four keys in the middle column multiplied together give 288. It is also given that the number in row 4 is less than 8. Here are all the known facts:

ROW 1 = 80	**COL 1 = 42**
ROW 2 = 0	**COL 2 = 288**
ROW 3 = 42	**COL 3 = 0**
ROW 4 < 8	

Can you deduce which number is on each key?

These puzzles are based on graphs and charts. Some of the puzzles contain more than one challenge. Make use of the diagrams – they are there to help you.

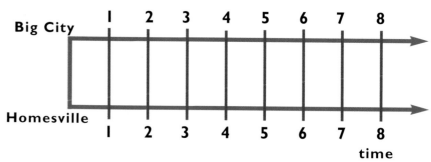

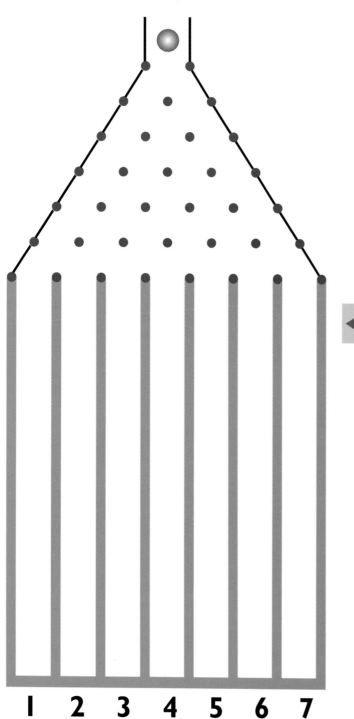

25 Ali's wanderlust LEVEL 2

Ali leaves Homesville at noon and walks towards Big City, where she stays overnight. She takes the scenic route – sometimes stopping along the way for a rest – and arrives in the city in the evening.

The next day Ali oversleeps, not starting her return journey until the afternoon. But although she takes exactly the same route back, she walks at a very brisk pace and returns to Homesville by 7pm.

What is the percentage chance that at one point during the two journeys Ali was at the exact same spot at exactly the same time? The graph shown above will help you.

26 Funnel business

Sixty-four balls are put into an inlet at the top of a funnel and then allowed to tumble between the pins until they land in one of seven bins at the bottom. The balls all have an even chance of going to the left or right at any particular junction.

Work out how many balls will end up in each bin by doing one of the following activities:

LEVEL 1 Trace the paths of a number of balls by repeatedly tossing a coin. If the coin shows a head, move the ball to the left. If the coin shows a tail, move to the right. After six tosses the ball should end up in a bin. Now repeat this as many times as you like.

LEVEL 2 Toss the coin again. The likelihood of a ball landing in a given bin is proportional to the number of different routes there are to each bin. How many routes lead to each bin?

LEVEL 3 Without performing any calculations at all, guess the rough pattern the balls will make.

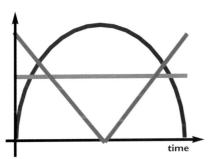

27 Curve ball

A scientist does something to a ball and measures three things while the experiment is running. The measurements have been plotted on the graph above, which measures 'height above ground', 'speed' and 'acceleration towards the ground'.

LEVEL 1 Explain what the scientist probably did to the ball.

LEVEL 2 Match the coloured lines to the labels: 'height above ground', 'speed' and 'acceleration towards the ground'.

LEVEL 3 What name is given to the shape of the 'height above ground' graph?

28 Ages apart LEVEL 2

Peter Out and Gail Force first met 16 years ago. At that time, Peter was twice Gail's age, but now Gail is two-thirds of Peter's age.

How old was Peter when he first met Gail? Use the graph below to help you solve this puzzle.

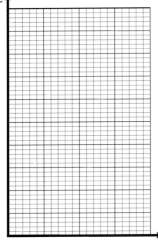

Test your ability at probability by tackling these tricky situational posers.

30 Austrian blonde
LEVEL 2

A survey conducted in the Austrian province of Carinthia produced the following data about the population:

60% were female

70% had blue eyes

80% had blonde hair

From these results can you work out the smallest percentage of the population that is certain to be female with blue eyes and blonde hair?

32 Double the trouble
LEVEL 2

Fred has two children. They are not both girls, although one of them might be. What is the probability that both are boys?

Steve also has two children. The elder is a girl. What is the probability that both are girls?

29 Fishing for numbers   LEVEL 2

Your neighbour has a circular pond in his garden teeming with so many fish they are impossible to count. One day he tells you that he has 1800 of them, give or take a hundred or so.

How might you prove him right or wrong?

31 The three coin fallacy
LEVEL 2

Imagine that you are tossing three coins. The probability that all three coins will come down heads is clearly ½ × ½ × ½ = ⅛. The same applies of course to tails, i.e., ⅛. Hence the probability that all the coins will come down either heads or tails must be ¼. So far, so good. But now consider this:

Of all three coins thrown up, at least two must show either heads or tails. The probability that the third will land in the same way as the other two must be ½ as there are only two possibilities for the third coin, heads or tails. Hence we arrive at the surprising conclusion that the probability of all coins landing alike is ½ – and not ¼ as previously stated.

Can you solve the mystery?

33 It's lovely – what is it? LEVEL 2

Margaret, Joan and Sheila go shopping for Christmas presents. But in the festive rush the parcels get mixed up. There are three boxes; all three of them are the same size and all are wrapped in identical paper. What is the probability that:

A At least one of the women gets the present she bought?

B Only one woman gets a wrong present?

34 Number maze 1 LEVEL 2

Starting at the top left, number 8, complete the sum so that the total
at the end of the equation is 0. You may not pass two numbers in a
row, or two symbols in a row, and you may not travel along the same
path more than once (although your path may cross).

35 Number maze 2 LEVEL 2

Enter the maze at the top and visit all the blue numbers from
1–6 in order. On reaching each blue number the sum of the
numbers you have passed must be exactly ten. Make exactly ten
again to leave the maze after blue number 6.

Here are some puzzles for armchair sports fans everywhere.

36 Game, set and lunch LEVEL 1

Three work colleagues look forward to lunch times, when they are able to play some tennis in the park. The number of sets they manage to play each day varies. Each player has played both of the others once so far this month.

The (currently incomplete) record table reads as follows:

	PLAYED	MATCHES won	MATCHES lost	MATCHES drawn	SETS won	SETS lost
Catherine	2	2			2	
Helen	2			1		
Suzanne	2				3	

Can you complete the table and work out how each match panned out?

37 Duel on the green LEVEL 1

Three men are playing a tournament of 'match play'-style golf, where the greatest number of holes won determines the winner. A player wins a hole by completing it in at least one stroke fewer than his partner, regardless of how many strokes that is. Drawn holes are, effectively, ignored.

You'll notice that someone has rubbed off some of the current standings from the clubhouse blackboard. It currently shows the following:

	PLAYED	MATCHES won	MATCHES lost	MATCHES drawn	HOLES won	HOLES lost
Archie						3
Bernard						6
Chris		1		0	5	0

The three men in question have agreed to play each other once in games consisting of two players. You do not know whether some or all of these matches have been played.

Pick up the chalk and see if you can fill in the missing figures. In addition, can you work out how each two-player match panned out?

38 Football mad LEVEL 3

There are five teams in the Northern Bay Football League. All the teams are scheduled to play each other once. At one point during the season, the incomplete league table looks like this:

	PLAYED	WON	LOST	DRAWN	GOALS for	GOALS against
Brockington		2		0	5	2
Galway	2		1		7	4
Lingmouth			1			5
Shrubville			1	0	1	2
South Keel		1		0	2	2

Which matches have been played so far, and what were the scores?

39 Mr Punch LEVEL 3

Fighters take to the ring in a boxing tournament. Points are awarded on the basis of 50 points for a win and 25 for a draw. A boxer wins a fight if he knocks his opponent down more times than he himself is knocked down. In order to prevent boxers becoming too defensive, a bonus of five points is awarded for every knockdown, regardless of the final outcome of the fight.

	POINTS
Garish Gary	40
Brian Brawny	75
Steve Supreme	110

At the end of one tournament, in which each boxer fought the other two once, the points totals were as shown in the box above, right.

Although Brian Brawny did not win the tournament, he was undefeated in any bout. In every bout, every boxer managed to knock down his opponent at least once. No more than seven knockdowns occurred in total in any single contest.

What was the result of each match, and how many times were the fighters knocked over in each one?

These puzzles are all about missing numbers. Your task is simple, but not always easy: study the numerical patterns and sequences, and fill in the absent figure. You will find that X often marks the spot.

40 What's the time 1? LEVEL 2

The fourth clock is missing its little hand. To which number should it be pointing?

41 Number square 1

LEVEL 2

The number missing from this sequence is represented by x. What should it be?

3	6	2	5
7	10	6	9
4	7	x	6
8	11	7	10

42 Number targets 1 LEVEL 2

The middle panel on the central target has no number. What does x stand for?

12	10	7
21	x	10
30	22	13

43 Mathematical badges LEVEL 2

These lapel badges were issued to delegates of the World Arithmeticians' Congress. But the second badge from the left is missing one of its numbers. What should it be?

44 Pizza poser LEVEL 2

A bored maths student who worked nights in a pizzeria took to numbering the slices of pizza she sold according to a clever sequence. Here one slice of pizza is missing its number. What should it be?

45 Number square 2 LEVEL 2

Once again a number's fallen off our number square. What should x be?

2	3	4	2
7	1	4	5
5	4	6	4
5	1	3	x

46 Umbrella trouble 1 LEVEL 3

A maths teacher bought herself an umbrella which, when folded out, looked like this from above. Can you help her identify the missing number on her brolly?

47 What's the time 2? LEVEL 3

This one's twice as hard as our first clock problem. Work out to which number the little hand should be pointing on the third clock face and also the number to which the big hand should be pointing on the fourth clock face.

48 Stepping stones 1 LEVEL 2

What number is x on the smallest stepping stone?

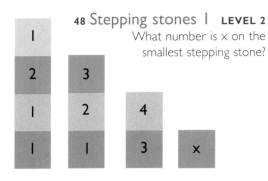

49 Amazing number maze LEVEL 3

Starting at the top left-hand square, move from square to square horizontally and vertically – but not diagonally – to find your way through the maze and uncover a familiar sequence of numbers. The exit is via the top right square.

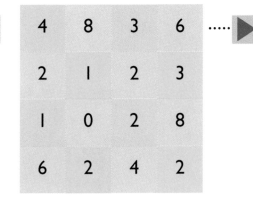

50 Number square 3 LEVEL 3

What number should x be in this number square?

51 Number targets 2 LEVEL 3

What are the missing numbers x and y?

52 Number targets 3 LEVEL 3

What's the number missing from the third target?

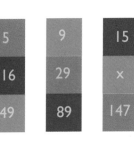

Here is another set of puzzles where the key is to uncover the logic of the sequence. But each one is different: can you fill in the missing numbers?

54 Number in the hole LEVEL 1

Which number's missing from the hole in panel C?

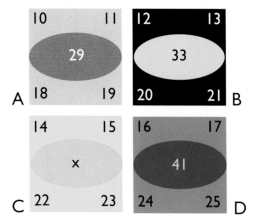

53 Number towers LEVEL 1

The fourth tower (D) is about to topple because a number's missing from its foundations. Can you save the day?

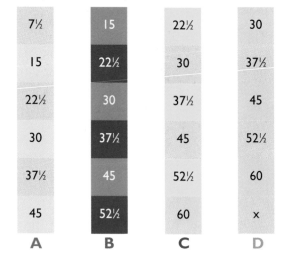

A	B	C	D
7½	15	22½	30
15	22½	30	37½
22½	30	37½	45
30	37½	45	52½
37½	45	52½	60
45	52½	60	x

55 Number roulette LEVEL 2

There's a number, represented by x, missing from the outer rim of this wheel of fortune. Which number is x? (Start at the arrow)

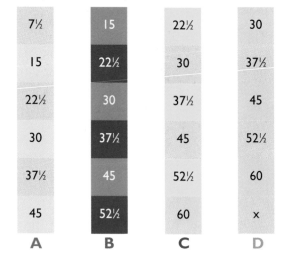

56 Identity parade LEVEL 1

One number's absent without leave from this parade. Can you identify x?

1, 17, 42, 78, x, 191, 272, 372, 493

57 Triangle teaser
LEVEL 1

Which number is missing from triangle B?

58 Umbrella trouble 2
LEVEL 3

What's the missing number, represented by the x, on this umbrella?

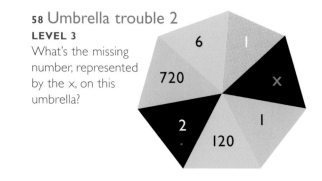

59 Line 'em up! LEVEL 1

Once again a number, represented by x, is not present and correct for this line up. Which number is x?

¼, 1½, 9, 54, x, 1944, 11664

60 Slice of pie LEVEL 3

We don't think this puzzle's easy – but you may decide that it's a piece of cake. Which number should replace the x?

61 Orange segments LEVEL 2

One slice is missing a number. Which number should replace the x?

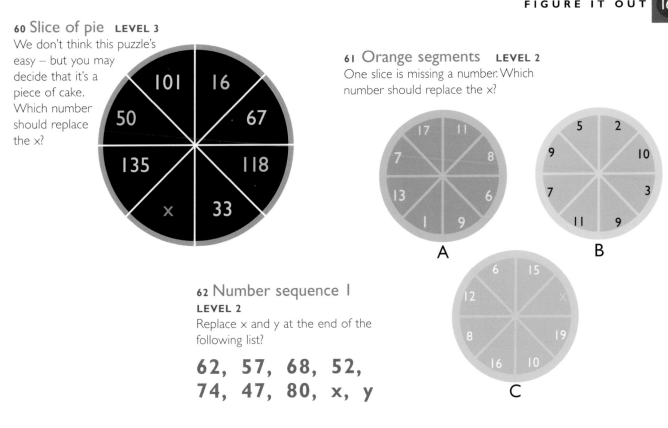

A

B

C

62 Number sequence 1
LEVEL 2

Replace x and y at the end of the following list?

62, 57, 68, 52, 74, 47, 80, x, y

63 Hexagonal place mats LEVEL 1

Dinner is almost ready. Which number should replace the x on the fourth place mat (D)?

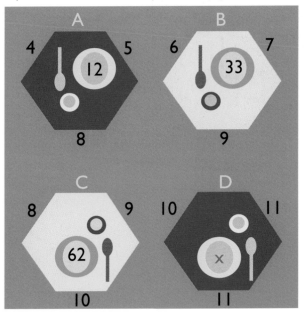

64 Number queue 1 LEVEL 2

This time the number's disappeared from the end of the queue. Uncover x's identity.

17¼, 26½, 23, 32¼, 28¾, 38, x

65 Complete the circle LEVEL 3

The third circle (C) has lost a number. Which number should be where the x is?

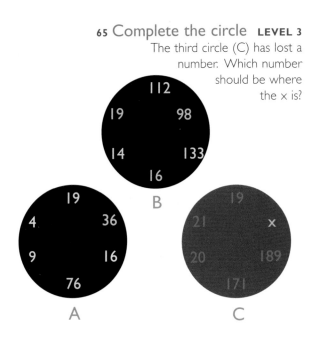

B

A

C

66 Number queue 2 LEVEL 1

A number's gone missing from the middle of this queue. Which number is x standing in for?

16⅛, 28, 39⅞, x, 63⅝, 75½, 87⅜

67 Time watch LEVEL I

Mexico City is 13 hours behind Singapore, which is seven hours ahead of London. If it's ten past four on Tuesday morning in London, what day and time is it in the other two cities?

LONDON

SINGAPORE

MEXICO CITY

68 Round trip LEVEL 2

Helga's a busy woman. On Tuesday she flew directly south from Finland to Egypt, an 8 hour flight. After 3 hours she flew east to Mongolia (10 hours), and an hour later took a connecting flight directly south to Perth in Australia (7 hours). Exactly a week later, she flew home from Perth to Finland, a journey of 16 hours.

If she left Finland at 8am, and if Perth is 6 hours ahead of Finland, what day and time did she get home?

69 Hello L.A.! LEVEL I

You leave Madrid at 3:30pm, and fly to Los Angeles in 16 hours. Spain is 9 hours ahead of California. To what time should you re-set your watch?

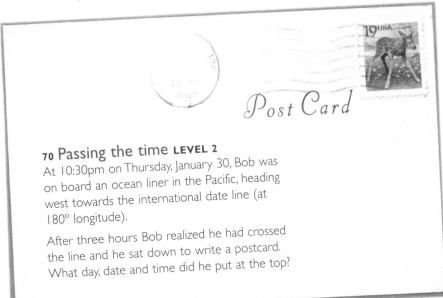

70 Passing the time LEVEL 2

At 10:30pm on Thursday, January 30, Bob was on board an ocean liner in the Pacific, heading west towards the international date line (at 180° longitude).

After three hours Bob realized he had crossed the line and he sat down to write a postcard. What day, date and time did he put at the top?

71 Out of this world LEVEL 1

At the moment, part of planet A is in total solar eclipse because planet B is on the line joining planet A and the Sun. The outer planet takes 24 years to make a complete orbit of the Sun, whereas the inner planet only takes six years. Both planets orbit clockwise and in the same plane.

How many years will it be before planet B again eclipses planet A? If you're stuck, start by working out the number of degrees (out of a full orbit of 360 degrees) that the planets travel in one year.

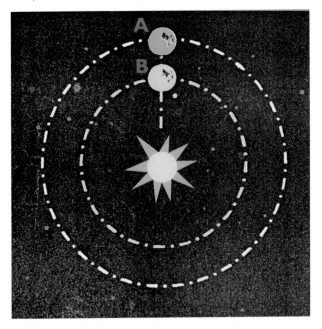

72 LEVEL 2

This is a different solar system: the outer planet takes 24 years to make a complete orbit of the Sun, and the inner planet takes 20 years. Both planets orbit the Sun in a clockwise motion and in the same plane, but planet A is presently 45 degrees behind planet B.

How long will it be before planet A, planet B and the Sun are in a straight line?

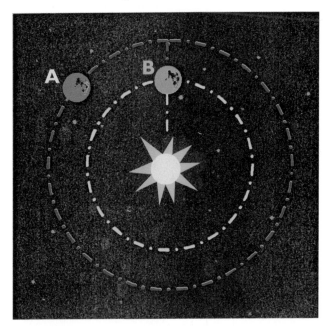

73 LEVEL 3

In this solar system, the outer planet takes 24 years to make a complete orbit of the Sun, and the inner planet takes 14 years. Although both planets orbit the Sun in a clockwise motion, their orbits are inclined to one another — they are not in the same plane. At the moment, planet A, planet B and the Sun are in a straight line.

How long will it be before planet A, planet B and the Sun are once again in a straight line?

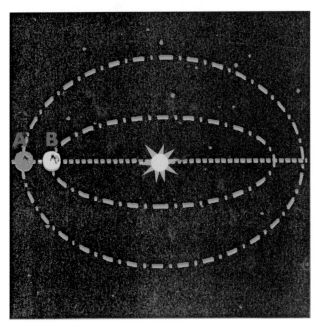

74 LEVEL 3

In this system, the orbits of planet A and planet B are 7 and 24 years respectively. Planet B is in a completely different orbit (around a black hole) that intersects with planet A's orbit at one point.

If planet B is 330 degrees into its new orbit (i.e., 30 degrees away from the intersection point), how long will it be before the two planets collide in a spectacular cosmic pile-up?

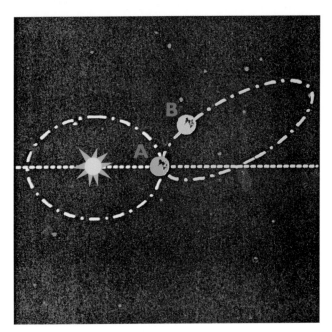

75 Magic 34 square LEVEL 3

Insert the remaining numbers from 1 to 16 so that (firstly) each horizontal, vertical and corner-to-corner line adds up to 34, and so that (secondly) each square block of four numbers – including the central block – adds up to exactly 34.

76 Magic prime square LEVEL 3

Using the prime numbers listed below once only, construct a magic prime square in which each horizontal, vertical and corner-to-corner line totals 219.

Prime numbers: 7, 37, 43, 67, 73, 79, 103, 109, 139

77 Anti-magic square LEVEL 3

In this square none of the horizontal, vertical or corner-to-corner lines total 34, but it is possible by moving just four numbers to convert the square into one in which each horizontal, vertical and corner-to-corner line does add up to 34. Can you make the necessary corrections?

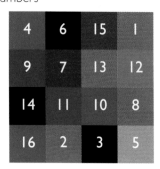

78 Magic 264 square LEVEL 3

In this magic square all horizontal, vertical and corner-to-corner lines total 264. But what other unusual features does it have? Can you find its two secret qualities?

18	99	86	61
66	81	98	19
91	16	69	88
89	68	11	96

79 Magic 65 square LEVEL 3

Insert the odd numbers from 1–25 into the empty squares so that each horizontal, vertical and corner-to-corner line totals 65.

14	20		2	8
10				4
22				16
18	24		6	12

80 DIY magic 111 square LEVEL 3

Make your own magic square by inserting the pieces into the 6 × 6 grid in such a way that every horizontal, vertical and corner-to-corner line totals 111.

These problem pyramids share a curious property — all the bricks are numbered with the sum of the two bricks on which they rest. From the figures given, can you give the blank bricks their numbers?

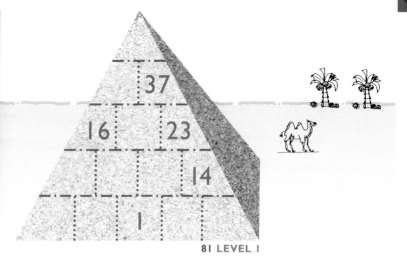

37

16   23

14

1

81 LEVEL 1

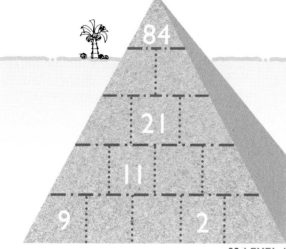

84

21

11

9   2

82 LEVEL 1

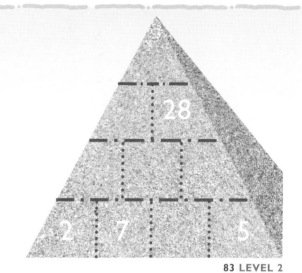

28

2   7   5

83 LEVEL 2

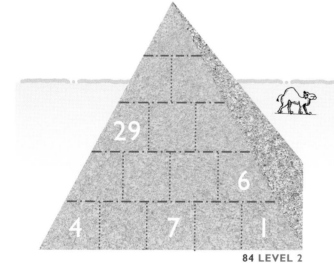

29

6

4   7   1

84 LEVEL 2

37

19   16

3   2

85 LEVEL 3

86 Spell it out   LEVEL 2

The answers to the following questions are all numbers between one and a hundred. They can all be found, spelt out, in the wordsearch grid.

1 Elizabeth Taylor won an Oscar for *Butterfield* ____

2 The number of holes on a standard golf course

3 The number of Fonda's Angry Men

4 The Apollo mission that made it to the Moon

5 An unlucky number

6 The number of days September 'hath'

7 The varieties Heinz still like to advertize

8 The Route taken by Chuck Berry

9 Colt's famous pistol

10 The number of times a German says no.

11 A silver anniversary

12 The number of coins in a fountain

13 A deck without jokers

14 The number of presidents on Mount Rushmore

15 Games required to win a set of tennis

16 Number of gold rings from a true love.

```
Q X I S Y T X I S N
T A B S H F I V E T
N Y T R I H T V Z H
I C E U D X E E Q I
N E K O J S E L T R
E V I F Y T N E W T
F O R T Y F I V E E
Z Q F T H G I E L E
E I G H T E E N V N
F I F T Y T W O E Q
```

87 Total confusion   LEVEL 2

The totals of the following equations can all be found in our wordsearch-style grid reading up, down, backwards, forwards or diagonally. Be bold: don't use a calculator.

1 $9009 \div 9$

2 111×11

3 77^2

4 $\frac{1}{8} \times 1{,}000{,}000$

5 50^3

6 3×7433

7 2^{10}

8 $161616 \div 4$

9 $3 \times 4 \times 5 \times 6 \times 7$

```
1 2 2 1 1 0
8 4 0 4 0 4
1 2 5 0 0 0
4 7 0 9 1 7
8 0 2 5 2 0
6 2 2 2 9 9
```

88 When... and where?   LEVEL 3

Use your eagle eye to spot the following dates (year only) in the grid. A slight aid: the remaining unused digits in the finished grid should all be the same, so if yours aren't you may have made an error somewhere.

1 Construction of the Eiffel Tower begins

2 The Russian Revolution begins

3 The Battle of Hastings takes place

4 The Olympic Games are held in Moscow

5 The Berlin Wall comes down

6 Custer loses at Little Big Horn

7 The Wright Brothers take flight

8 Napoleon meets his Waterloo

9 Yuri Gagarin sees stars

10 The United States is born

11 The Beatles first top the British charts

```
5 1 8 8 7 4
1 9 7 3 4 6
8 8 0 1 1 7
1 9 6 3 9 7
1 9 6 7 8 1
1 4 6 6 0 1
```

89 Tile and tile again 1 LEVEL 2

Place the tiles into the grid, so that:

i The sequence of digits in the first column matches the sequence in the first row, the sequence in the second column matches that in the second row and so on.

ii Each row and column contains one square of each of the six colours.

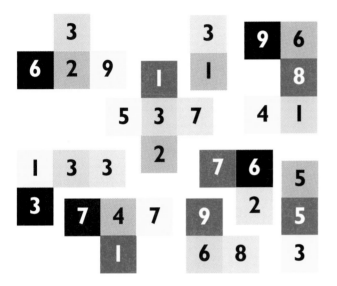

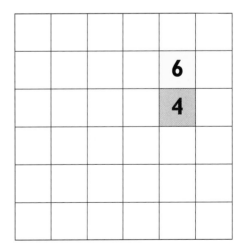

90 Tile and tile again 2 LEVEL 3

Place the tiles into the grid, so that:

i Each column and row contains the digits 1 to 6.

ii Each row and column contains two squares of each of the three colours.

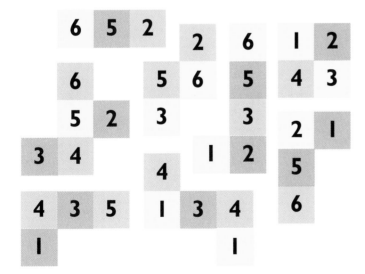

91 A pouring problem **LEVEL 2**

There are many variations of decanting puzzles in which a liquid is poured from one container to another. The one presented for you to pore over here is known to be at least 400 years old.

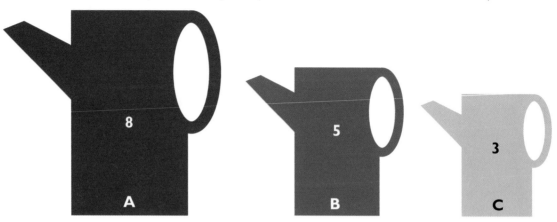

Three jugs (above) have capacity for 8, 5 and 3 litres respectively. The 8 litre jug is filled entirely with water, and the other two jugs are empty. Your task is, by decanting, to divide the water into two equal parts – 4 litres in jug A and 4 litres in jug B, leaving the smallest jug empty. None of the jugs is calibrated, so the only way the task can be successfully performed is to pour water from one jug to another until the first jug is entirely empty and the second jug is entirely full. Assume that the decanting is done with great care so that no water is spilt.

What is the least number of decantings in which the task can be achieved?

92 Heavy duty drink
LEVEL 1

You have a balance scale which is in equilibrium with three bottles of wine on one pan and one bottle of the same wine plus three bars of 24-carat gold weighing 500g each on the other pan. How much does a bottle of wine weigh?

94
A lightweight intruder
LEVEL 1

Paying with a £10 note for a magazine, I received nine £1 coins as change. Subsequently the newsagent telephoned to tell me that one of the coins was a fake, slightly under weight, but otherwise indistinguishable from the real thing.
What is the minimum number of weighings, using a two-pan balance, which will locate the counterfeit coin?

93 Dollar dilemma **LEVEL 1**

The diagram below shows ten stacks of coins, each consisting of ten silver dollars. One entire stack is counterfeit, but you do not know which one. You do know the weight of a genuine silver dollar, and you are also told that each counterfeit coin weighs 1 gram more or less than a genuine coin. You have a pointer scale which you use to weigh the coins.
What is the smallest number of weighings needed to determine which of the stacks is counterfeit?

95 The manuscript **LEVEL 1**

Best-selling author Harry Spicer was given a deadline by his publisher to write the 80,000 words of his latest novel. 'No problem,' Harry thought, 'if I write 4000 words a day I shall be all right.'
However, with one distraction or another, his output for the first half of the manuscript was only 2000 words a day. 'No matter,' Harry said to himself, 'if I write 6000 words daily for the second half of the manuscript my average will still be 4000 words a day.'
Was he right?

96 Piggybank puzzle LEVEL 2

In the currency peculiar to the country of Fennicia, 100 fents (the symbol for which is *f*) are equal to one Fennar (the symbol for which is *F*), so that one fennar + 28 fents is written as *F*1.28. Using the pieces of money scattered around the money-box below, fill the money-box in such a way that each line of five small boxes (down, across and diagonal) contains a sum total of *F*1.63. Some coins have already been placed in their correct boxes – just to give you a start.

97 In the pink LEVEL 3

Using the coins scattered around the money-box, fill it in such a way that each line of six small boxes (down, across and diagonal) contains a total of *F*6.56.

Nonograms are puzzles in which the aim is to reveal a hidden picture. As you work out which squares on the grid should be filled in, you will see an image emerge. The instructions below tell you how to get started.

HOW TO COMPLETE A NONOGRAM

The numbers alongside each row or column tell you how many blocks of black squares are in line. So, for example, 2, 3, 5 tells you that from left to right (or top to bottom) there is a group of two black squares, then a group of three black squares and finally a group of five black squares. Any of the blocks may (or may not) have a number of white squares before or after them, but each block of black squares on the same line has at least one white square between it and the next block of black squares.

Sometimes you will be able to tell which squares are going to be black without reference to other lines or columns: for instance, in the first example below we can deduce that any block of six black squares must incorporate the two central ones. It will also help to put a small dot in squares where you know them to be empty.

Here is a simple example filled in:

98 Novice nonogram   LEVEL 1

Armed with your new nonogram knowledge, can you fill in the grid below to reveal a message?

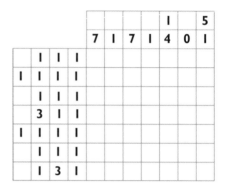

99 Calm your thoughts
LEVEL 2

When completed, this nonogram presents a picture of a place of peaceful reflection.

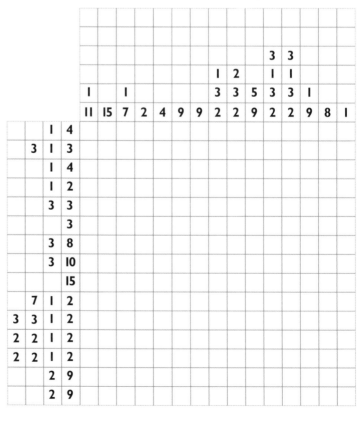

Big test **LEVEL 3**
Complete our giant nonogram to reveal the image of an everyday gadget.

Nonogram grid with the following clues:

Column clues (top):

						2		2										2	
						2		2											
					1	2	2	2	2										
			2	2	6	1	1	2	2	1	1	1	2	2				2	
	2	1	1	5	2	1	2	3	2	2	3	2	6	2	5	1	1	3	1
1	3	4	5	3	1	1	1	1	2	2	1	1	1	1	3	5	4	1	4
2	8	10	11	5	3	2	1	1	1	1	1	1	5	3	5	11	10	8	2

Row clues (left):

- 2 2 3 3 2 2
- 1 1 1 1 1 1
- 1 1
- 14
- 16
- 4 1 1 4
- 4 1 4 1 5
- 4 8 5
- 2 2 1
- 3 1 1 3 1
- 3 4
- 3 1 2 1 3
- 3 4 3
- 3 1 1 1 1 3
- 3 4 3
- 4 1 2 1 4
- 4 1 4
- 5 1 1 6
- 7 7
- 20

101 Saturation point
LEVEL 2
A wet sponge weighs 1kg and is 99% water by weight. Squeeze it so that it is only 98% water by weight. How much does it weigh now?

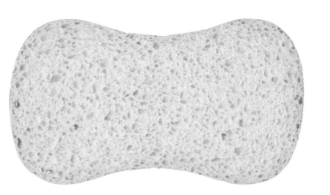

102 Card magic
LEVEL 2

First arrange these cards in a line in which the values range from 1 to 16. The Jack, Queen and King equal 11, 12 and 13 respectively. To make 14, 15 and 16 you must double up cards of the same suit – for example, a Queen and a two would make 14.
(S = spades, H = hearts, C = clubs and D = diamonds).

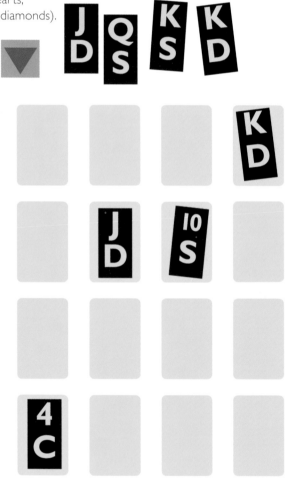

Now put these cards into a 4 x 4 grid in which every row, column and the two diagonals contains 4 different suits and adds up to 34. The first four have been positioned to give you a head start.

103 It's a frame up!
LEVEL 2

In this frame of playing cards, each side adds up to 22. Can you make the constant 23 by taking two new cards of the same suit from the same pack, and laying each one over an existing card?

 +  + 5 + 4
+
 7
+ +
6 6
+ +
 + 9 + + 5

104 Cards at the table
LEVEL 1

In the looking-glass spirit, the following Kings, Queens and Jacks are taking tea.

However, their seating etiquette is very complicated and four rules must be followed:

1 No one of the same suit may sit opposite or next to each other.

2 The Kings must have equal status.

3 Queens without their Kings must sit between a King and his Queen.

4 The Queen of Diamonds has asked to sit on the King of Clubs' left (she's his sister!).

Can you work out who must sit where? To help you, one card is already in place.

105 Mismatched cards **LEVEL 2**

From a conventional pack of cards, the numbers 2, 3, 4 and 5 of each suit have been selected.

Can you lay out the 16 cards in a 4 × 4 grid so that no row, column or (corner to corner) diagonal contains cards of the same number or the same suit? Four cards have been put in place already.

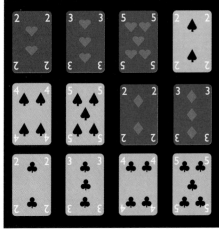

107 Flat out
LEVEL 2
Here is a paper dice in which three faces are showing:

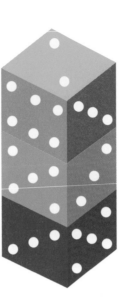

106
Three blind dice
LEVEL 1
Three identical dice are piled on top of each other as follows. Seven faces are visible. What is the total of the other 11 sides?

Alongside are three paper dice that have been unfolded. How many of these dice will fold up into the dice above?

108 Roll over **LEVEL 2**
A sum has been made from the upper faces of three dice – but it doesn't make sense.

To make it work, you must roll each dice over in any direction by a quarter turn. How many solutions are there, and what are they?

109 Seeing spots **LEVEL 2**
Below are three different views of a single dice. It's unusual because the numbers (1–6) are in random positions.

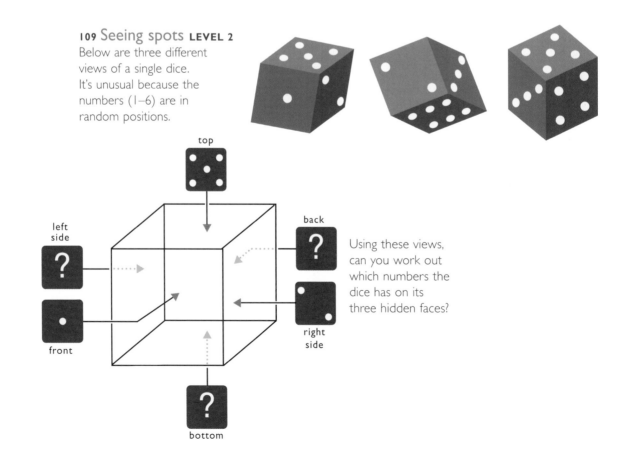

Using these views, can you work out which numbers the dice has on its three hidden faces?

top

left side

back

front

right side

bottom

110 Picture this

LEVEL 2 Dominoes can be arranged into square 'picture frames':

Can you arrange the eight dominoes below into two square frames made of four pieces each, so that all the sides of both frames add up to nine?

111 Domino-henge LEVEL1

Imagine giant dominoes in place of standing stones in the celebrated circle of Stonehenge, southern England.

If the numerical value of each horizontal domino is as shown and equal to the total value of the two dominoes supporting it, can you arrange the nine dominoes (right) in the correct configuration?

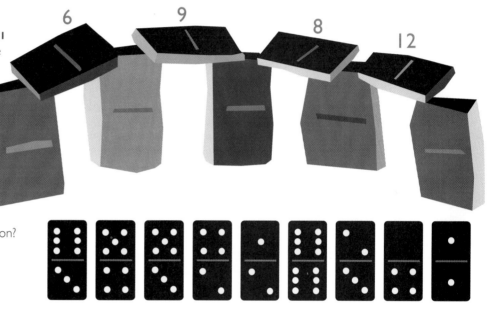

112 Wall of dominoes

LEVEL 3

Twenty-two dominoes have been used to build the wall on the left, but nine of them have been masked out. Can you identify the nine dominoes correctly, bearing in mind that each vertical line of four numbers — as well as the two end vertical lines of two numbers — adds up to ten? Place the dominoes below into the blank spaces.

Lateral thinking means making a mental knight's move. To solve the puzzles in this chapter you must come at them from an unexpected angle. Discard the obvious, leave behind traditional modes of thought, and throw out all preconceptions. The answer will be in your grasp.

Lateral thinking means taking your thought processes one step further. You have to move beyond your initial response to a problem, then come at it again from an unexpected angle. So bend your brain into strange new shapes with this lateral workout.

1 Think about it   LEVEL 1

1 David and Sarah's children are called Peter, George, Robin, Chris, Derek and Sam. If Peter has a sister-in-law called Clare, can you deduce who Clare is married to?

2 A scientist claims to have invented a unique machine that allows him to disappear for an hour, then re-emerge at exactly the same point in space one hour later. He has not tried it out yet, but is keen to do so. Why would he be ill-advised to try the machine out?

3 There is a well-known *aide-memoire* which states that Christmas Day and New Year's Day fall on the same day of the week. However, in the year 2000 Christmas Day falls on a Monday whereas New Year's Day falls on a Saturday. Why doesn't the rule seem to work in this case?

4 A woman married 14 different people during the course of a day. How is that possible?

5 The 60th and 62nd prime ministers of Great Britain had the same mother and father but were not brothers. How come?

6 Some people wish they could have a birthday every day. Technically, there is a place where this is possible. Where is it?

7 A man is in a car pointing north. Without changing the direction of his car, he drives along a straight tarmac road for a mile. He is now one mile south of his original starting position. How did he achieve this?

8 One day, I was walking down the street and happened by chance to meet my uncle. I had never met him before, nor seen a photograph, but recognized him instantly. How was this possible?

9 A woman lives in Texas in the USA. Over the course of a couple of days, she drives to New York and then home to Texas. All the while, she is using the south-bound carriageway. Explain.

10 Which month of the year lasts the longest?

2 Weird words   LEVEL 2

1 A regular six-sided dice has three sides marked with 'YES' and the other three sides marked with 'NO'. What question about the outcome can be answered truthfully no matter what the result happens to be?

2 Name a seven-letter English word that contains eight other different words therein, which can be formed without rearranging any letters.

3 Which everyday five-letter English word sounds the same even if you remove its last four letters?

4 Which plant's name can be made from these letters without using any letter twice?

T O W A R

5 Using each symbol below exactly once, form the name of an eight-letter mammal.

e h a t
d u l e

3 A number of puzzles   LEVEL 3

1 There are 35 identical pairs of red woollen gloves, 33 identical pairs of blue woollen gloves and 31 identical pairs of green woollen gloves all mixed up in Susan's large storage box. During the night, Susan fancies making a snowman because there has been a sudden snowfall. Without turning the light on, she picks out individual gloves at random from the box. Even though she will be out in the dark, she is so fashion conscious that she still requires the two gloves to be matching in colour. How many gloves does she need to take out of the box to be sure that she obtains a matching pair?

2 Which of the following numbers can be evenly divided in two?

41 56 83 111 164

3 I wanted to place a bet of £20 on the outcome of a football match. The odds were 2–1 (including return of the bet) if I predicted the result correctly. A friend of mine offered to predict the score of the match before it started for a fee of £5. He claims that his predictions have been 100% accurate during the previous five matches. Do you think I should take him up on the offer?

4 How can you add a single line to 'IX' (the Roman numeral for nine) to make it an even number?

5 A tank 20cm long by 10cm wide by 10cm high (8in × 4in × 4in) is half-filled with mercury. Seventeen steel cubes, each with 3cm (1¼ in) sides, are placed in the tank. How many will be completely covered by the mercury?

6 What are the next two numbers in this sequence?

36, 91, 21, 51, 82, 12, 42, ?, ?

7 According to my digital clock. something very rare happened soon after half past twelve on Tuesday, August 7, 1990. What was it?

4 CHILDREN'S MISCELLANY

Here's some lateral fun for younger readers.

1 How many times can you take 3 from 96?

2 Which side of a cat contains the greater amount of hair?

3 I want to chop down a fir tree 2m high to use as my Christmas tree. However, there is a peacock resting in the upper branches of the tree. How can I chop down the tree without disturbing the peacock at all?

4 Answer these questions:
a) In the famous Disney animated film, which girl befriends the Seven Dwarfs?
b) What colour is ivory?
c) What do cows drink?

5 I thread five doughnuts onto a piece of rope then tie both ends of the rope together to form a tasty doughnut necklace. Without eating the doughnuts off the rope or cutting the rope, I was able to eat one of the tasty treats. How did I do it?

6 Pistol Pete the cowboy boasted that he could hang up a Stetson, walk half a mile, then fire a bullet through the Stetson every time using nothing more than his pistol. How did he achieve this?

7 A dog is tied to a rope 10m long. There is a large, juicy bone 15m away. How can the dog get the bone without the assistance of anybody or anything else?

8 What is impossible to hold for an hour, even though it barely weighs anything?

9 Would you rather a rhinoceros attack you or an elephant?

10 A group of people get on a train, knowing that they are going to arrive at the same place from which they began their journey. There are no stops along the way, and the paying passengers aren't going to see anything of local interest. The train service only runs during certain times of the year. Despite this, many people use the service several times in the same day. What's going on?

Here are two puzzles you can try using simple household objects and a little cunning. Once you have solved them, use them as party pieces to drive your friends mad.

5 Sprinkle some salt on a piece of paper. Then sprinkle some pepper over the top. The challenge is to separate the salt and pepper using a plastic comb.

6 How can you suspend a bottle in mid-air for more than ten seconds using nothing more than a normal drinking straw?

Your task is to solve as many of these lateral puzzles as you can. And remember: the sensible answer is always wrong.

LEVEL 1: 1 to 5
LEVEL 2: 6 to 8
LEVEL 3: 9 or more

7 Clock it

With one stroke of the pen turn the number below into a time...

10 10 10

9 This way to exit

A group of people at a New Year's Day concert in 1900 couldn't get out of the concert hall doors. The doors were not locked and opened easily. Nor were they too small – after all the crowd had entered by them. What was the difficulty?

8 Hold on

What can you hold in your left hand but not in your right hand?

10 Sibling rivalry

The James twins are always quarrelling. In the end, their mother gets them to stand freely on the same sheet of newspaper in such a way that they can just about see each other but can't possibly touch each other. How is this done?

11 The long and short of it

Two brothers, both of whom were very short, used to leave the key to their apartment on the top of the door frame. Whenever they had to put it up or take it down Alf always stood on the shoulders of Bert, even though Bert was smaller. This hardly seems fair. So why did they do it that way?

12 Judge a book...

Constance Reader took down a big book from the top shelf of her bookshelf. On the spine it said *How to Jog*. But when she opened it, she found it had nothing to do with running. How come?

19 Spoken Impish 1
LEVEL 2

Can you use a bit of lateral thinking to work out which words the imp on this page and those on the pages that follow are depicting?

20 Cube it   **LEVEL 3**

Add three more unbroken matches so that a cube is formed. Remember that this is a lateral puzzle, so the answer might not be as straightforward as you think.

13 Auto rewind

As I was driving along one night, the tape I was listening to came to the end of side one. I pressed the 'eject' button and the tape shot out on to the floor where it got mixed up with many other similar-looking and similarly unlabelled tapes. Nevertheless, I reached down and after a little while I managed to pick up the right tape. How did I do that?

14 Fast work

Fred assembled a device containing thousands of moving parts, yet it took him only a few minutes. What might it have been?

15 Heave-ho...ping!

Two tug-of-war teams are testing an experimental new rope. There are six men pulling away on each end, trying to snap it. But they can't. To test the rope to breaking point would require ten men at each end. How can they snap the rope merely by pulling it?

17 Junk and disorderly

On entering a dark attic a collector with 20:20 vision spotted a vase amid all the junk. He at first read the date inscribed on it as being exactly 330 years later than it actually was. When he got up close he saw he was mistaken, although the date was carved in large (Arabic) numerals and very clearly at that. How might his mistake have been caused?

16 Losing your head

A man's head travelled about 10m (30ft) more than his feet but he was unharmed. How come?

18 Food for thought

The food in the restaurant was of the best quality and there was certainly nothing wrong with it. Nevertheless, large numbers of the diners became quite ill and even started to vomit. They had not been overeating. They were not allergic to the food. What was going on?

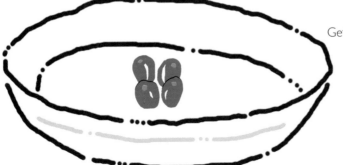

21 Nouvelle cuisine LEVEL 2

Get a soup dish and four olives (cherries also work). Without touching the olives in any way, how can you make them move to the outside of the dish so that they are roughly equidistant from each other?

Each of these two-player games presents a double challenge. First, play the game logically with a family member or friend. Then use some lateral thinking to work out how you could be sure to win the game every single time.

22 The pyramid game LEVEL 3

In the pyramid game, you need a pack of playing cards with all the cards above 9 taken out. Aces count as ones. Deal out four cards and place them in a row. Then on each of the next three rows, place the card that is equal to the sum of the two cards below it. If this number is 10 or above, add both digits together to get a single digit number.

The game can be played on two levels. In each case, the four bottom cards are dealt out, then the race begins to work out what the top card will be. Children can use pencil and paper to work through the stages. Adults should see it as a test of memory and arithmetic. But there is a third way that beats either of these methods. What is it?

> 2
>
> 3 8
>
> 7 5 3   3 + 9 = 1 2
>   1 + 2 = 3
> 5 2 3 9

23 Cornered LEVEL 1

In this game two players start a coin at square S and take alternate turns to move the coin either right or down any number of squares. The winner is the player who moves the coin to the finish at square F. A game is already in progress here – what move must be made by the next player in order to guarantee a win? And what's the right strategy to win the game every time?

24 The last coin LEVEL 2

For this game you'll need 12 coins, which should be arranged in a circle. It doesn't matter if the coins are not identical.

On your turn, you may take either one coin or two touching coins. Two players take turns until no coins are left. The number of coins you have doesn't matter – the winner is the person who takes the final coin.

What is the winning strategy?

25 X marks the spot LEVEL 3

In this game, players take alternate turns to place coins on the board. A player loses if his or her opponent can identify a square whose mid-point is exactly half-way between the coin just played and one of the other coins.

Here's a game in progress. The next player can't place a coin on square A, because square X is exactly half-way between A and the coin on the right-hand side. What moves can the next player make? And what about the move after that? What is the winning strategy? And why isn't this a very good game?

26 The conjuring trick LEVEL 2

For this game you'll need three tumblers and a coin.

Player 1 looks away while player 2 places the coin under one of the tumblers and remembers its location. Player 1 can now look, and is invited to choose one of the three tumblers. Player 2 then shows player 1 that one of the other two tumblers is empty. So, for example, if player 1 chose B then player 2 must show that A is empty (he or she cannot show C as that would give away the location of the coin). Player 1 can either stay with the original choice or go for the other tumbler. Player 1 wins the game if he can identify the tumbler which contains the coin. First answer this: if you were player 1, what would the winning strategy be? Or do you think that it's all luck and it doesn't really matter what happens?

Now try playing the game for real as many times as you like (20 goes should suffice). See how often the guessing player wins.

The term lateral thinking was coined in 1967 by Edward de Bono. He has been developing the idea and preaching the lateral gospel ever since.

The theory sets out to challenge the illusion that in every situation we are in possession of all the facts and factors. Real-life problems, say lateral thinkers, are not like a game of chess – which has a limited board, a finite set of rules and a fixed number of pieces. In life, it is permissible to invent original rules, create new pieces with new moves and draw extra squares on the board. The point

Thinking round corners

of lateral thinking is that it liberates the mind and allows the rooks and pawns to run riot.

But is lateral thinking really that radical? One might argue that inventors and thinkers have made great leaps and achieved great insights without the benefit of de Bono's philosophy. Perhaps lateral thinking is no more than a description of imagination or inspiration?

It is, at the very least, a good game. If someone said to you 'A man pushed his car. He stopped when he reached a hotel, at which point he knew he was bankrupt,' would you know the answer is that he was playing Monopoly?

ARCHITECTURE TURNED INSIDE-OUT

Why should lifts, pipes and escalators take up precious space on the inside of a building, when they could just as easily be located on the outside? No reason. Hence the striking exterior of the Pompidou Centre in Paris, where large interior expanses have been freed up for exhibitions. The same technique was used to create large trading floors at the Lloyd's Building in London.

Charles Duell, who was the Commissioner at the US Patents Office, is credited with remarking that 'Everything that can be invented has been invented'. It was 1899, and he was recommending the abolition of his own office.

Dr Dionysius Lardner (1793-1859) asserted that passengers in trains would surely suffocate because they would not be able to draw air into their lungs when travelling at speed.

Wishful thinking is one of the many enemies of lateral thinking. Leon Trotsky did no good for the Bolshevik cause when in 1924 he declared that 'England is ripe for revolution'.

In 1977 Ken Olson, head of American electronics company DEC, declared that 'there is no reason anyone would want a computer in their home'.

FOUNDER MEMBER

For Edward de Bono (left) and his admirers, lateral thinking is far more than a puzzle or a parlour game. It is an entirely new tool for thought, the first new mode of thinking to be invented since ancient times, and it can be applied to everything from strategies for nuclear disarmament to the right way of tying a balloon. To de Bono, the founding fathers of Western philosophy – Socrates, Plato and Aristotle – are the 'Greek Gang of Three'. He holds them responsible for the adversarial method of problem-solving into which the Western world has been locked for two millennia: you propose an idea, knock it down, propose a better idea, knock that one down, and so on, fruitlessly, for ever.

THE SAGE OF BAKER STREET

Sherlock Holmes is often held to be a kind of patron saint of lateral thinking. Certainly his deductions often depended on seeing beyond the facts, on noticing things that were invisible to plodding thinkers such as Dr Watson. Holmes's insight in *Hounds of the Baskervilles* is a classic lateral thought '"…the curious incident of the dog in the nighttime" "The dog did nothing in the nighttime". "That was the curious incident," remarked Holmes.' But Holmes was also guilty of closed thinking when he said that 'When you have eliminated the impossible, whatever remains, however improbable, must be the truth'. To lateral thinkers this is a ridiculous remark: you cannot whittle away the possibilities until only one remains, because possibilities are infinite. There are always more scenarios to be explored.

THE TICK-TOCK OF IMAGINATION

You are concerned about the spread of disease in Africa. You know education is the key to preventative medicine, but how do you get information to the people who need it? Newspapers and leaflets are impossible to distribute because of the distances involved; no one can afford a television and in any case there's no electricity available; batteries are out of the question. What do you do?
Trevor Bayliss (right) solved it. He imagined a radio that could be wound up like an old-fashioned alarm. Its clockwork mechanism meant that the radio's owner was also its energy supply. It took Bayliss years of work to produce and market his invention, but the vital lateral leap had been made right at the start: obsolete technology plus modern problem equals brilliant solution.

Rebuses offer an alternative to using words alone as a way of getting your point across. Try to work out the message in each of these images or combination of images, and find out if it's true that a picture's worth a thousand words.

Where on earth am I?
Name the places depicted below.

27 LEVEL 1

28 LEVEL 1

29 LEVEL 2

30 LEVEL 2

31 LEVEL 2

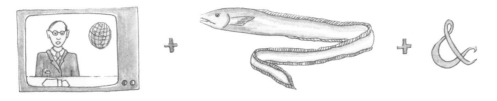

32 LEVEL 2

Cinema greats

Can you identify these Hollywood figures from the pictures below?

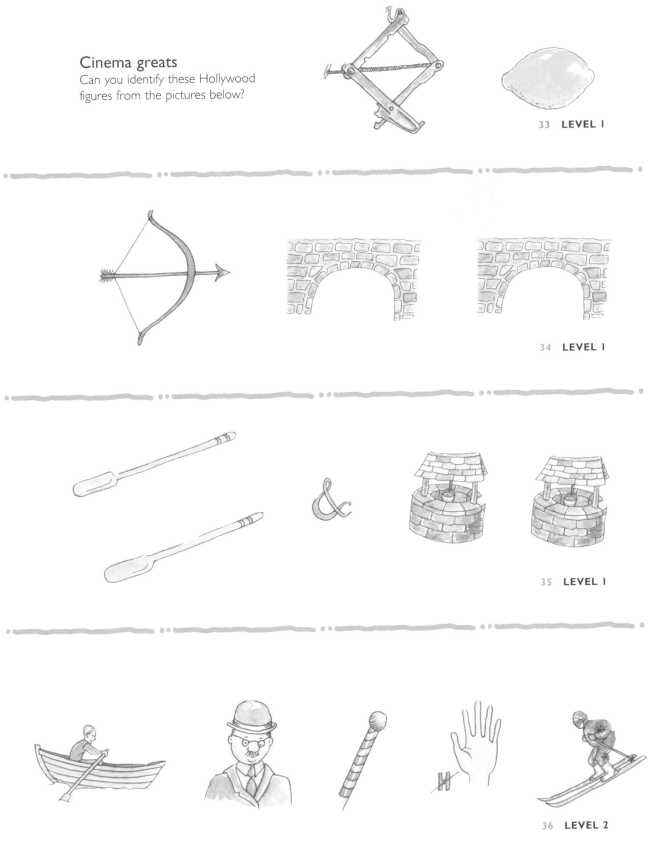

33 **LEVEL 1**

34 **LEVEL 1**

35 **LEVEL 1**

36 **LEVEL 2**

Riddles are the most ancient form of word game. Some of those below are as old as the hills — others are more modern, but are none the easier for that.

LEVEL 1:   up to 6 right
LEVEL 2:   6 to 9 right
LEVEL 3:   10 or more right

37 The riddle of the Sphinx

This riddle was set the Greek hero Oedipus by the Sphinx, a creature that was part woman, part bird and part lion. When Oedipus solved it the Sphinx jumped into an abyss out of frustration.

What goes on four legs in the morning, two legs at noon and three legs in the evening?

38 A fishy tale

Legend says that the Greek poet Homer died of frustration at not being able to solve this riddle, posed by fishermen on the island of Ios. Can you do better than Homer?

What we caught we threw away; what we couldn't catch we kept.

39 A Biblical poser

Samson proposed the following riddle to the Philistines (Judges 14:14):

Out of the eater came forth meat*
Out of the strong came forth sweet.

They solved it with the help of Delilah. What is the answer?

*meat here means 'something to eat'

40 A weighty problem

Forward I'm heavy, backwards I'm not. What am I?

41 Most curious beast

What has eight legs, three heads, two arms and two wings?

42 Creepy-crawlie

What has 20 legs, one head and four backs?

43 New for old

Though I am the third
I am called the second;
Though I am not old
I do not sound new.

What am I?

44 Call me Quin

I am one of five identical brothers
The others go around in all weather
I follow them around
Asleep in the dark,
Waiting until called upon
In times of trouble.

What am I?

45 All tied up

Tied up we wander around all day
At night we are let loose
And lie still with our tongues hanging out.

What are we?

46 Precious metal

Gold I am or silver, with a big head and thin body. All day long I walk about on my head.

What am I?

47 All things to all men

I am male, add a letter and I am female. Add another letter and I am male again. Add three more letters and I am female again.

What am I?

48 Striptease

Take away my first four letters and I remain unchanged.

What am I?

49 Less is…no less

Take away my first letter and I am unchanged. Take away my second letter and I am unchanged. Take away all my remaining letters and I am still unchanged.

What am I?

50 Spoken Impish II
LEVEL 1
What word is depicted here?

52 To catch a thief
A true story...

A man came back to his car one day to find that it had been broken into. All the valuables inside had been stolen: his wallet and keys, stereo radio, pager, a laptop computer, some money and jewellery. However, he hatched a plan to capture the culprit.

Without coming to any personal harm, he was able to hand over the thief to the police despite the absence of any clues towards the thief's identity. How did the thief get his come-uppance?

51 CHILDREN'S TEST

A If you have three grapefruit in one hand and five in the other, what have you got?

B Why is rain not like Monday?

C Will February March?

D Why is B hot?

53 Spoken Impish III
LEVEL 1
Another word from the Impish dictionary.

Fur balls
What words are these feline friends helping to identify?

54 LEVEL 1

55 LEVEL 2

By now you should be getting good at thinking like a crab walks. So now take a sideways glance at these puzzlers.

56 Colloquial Impish
LEVEL 1

Which imp word is being depicted in this court scene?

57 Wood you believe it?
LEVEL 2

How many planks are visible below?

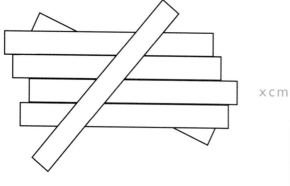

58 Crystal
LEVEL 3

What is the volume of this prism?

1 cm   2 cm

◀3 cm▶

x cm   x cm   x cm

1 cm   2 cm

3 cm

59 Whatever next? LEVEL 3

What is the next number?

1 2 , 2 1 5 , 3 0 8 , 5 2 3 , 3 4 5 , 9 1 6

60 Is that Danish? LEVEL 2

What single letter has been omitted from the following?

T B E R N T T B E

61 The odd couple LEVEL 2

Which pair of letters does not belong in this series?

S A   E R   F I   E S

62 Polyominoes LEVEL 2

What is the next figure in this 'curious' sequence?

?

63 Missing card LEVEL 3

Below are some lettered cards. Why does the letter K appear on the missing card?

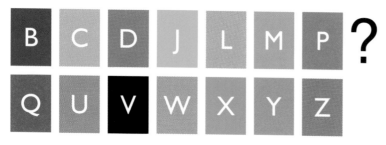

?

64 Letter grid LEVEL 3

Can you place the letter Z in the following grid so that every letter of the alphabet appears only once?

F	G	E	P	O	I
K			B	R	
M		X	S	Q	
Y	U	H	W	N	
J	D	V	L	C	A

65 Missing square
LEVEL 3
Can you find the missing square?

I	T	C
S	U	A
L	M	?

A	B	C
N	L	I

D	E	F
S	R	Y

66 Tower   LEVEL 2
In which city is this tower found?

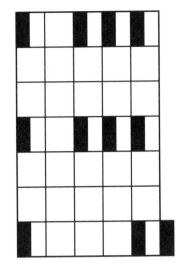

67 Think globally   LEVEL 2
Can you fill in the missing letters?

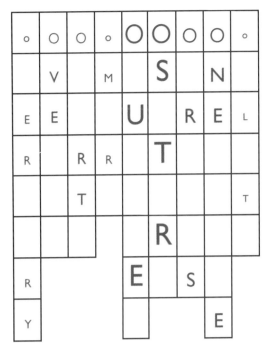

CHILDREN'S FUN

68 Password
To open the security door you must enter a specific five-letter password (indicated below) by pressing the buttons. What is the password?

To open the door ▶

A	C	E
G	H	L
M	N	R

69 Briefcase
LEVEL 2
In which case are the top secrets below: upper or lower?

70 Old Impish
LEVEL 1
A final imp word for you to decipher.

71 On the make   LEVEL 3
A car goes from A to Y and then back to A. What make of car is it?

A .... Y

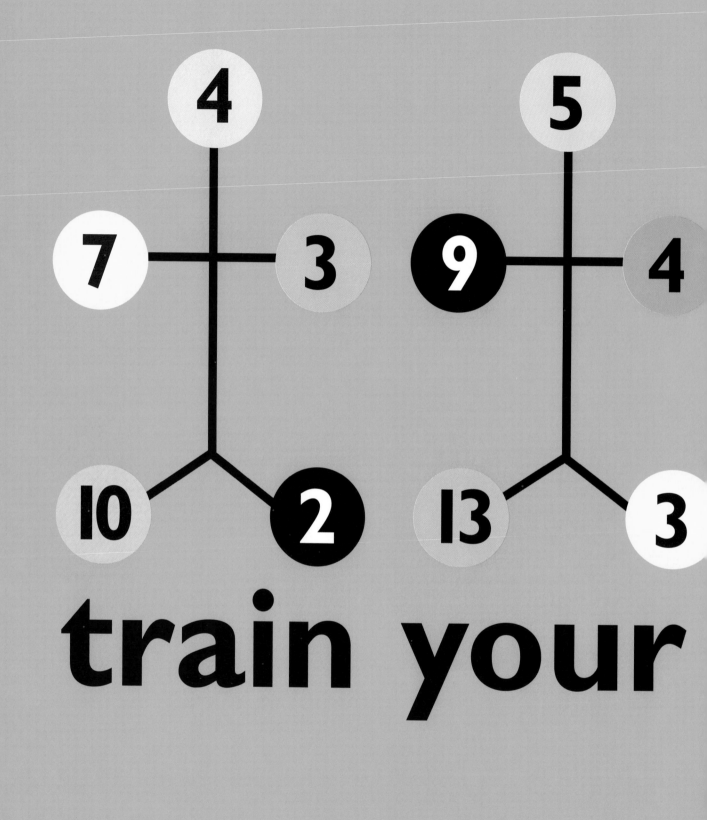

train your

brain

The puzzles in this chapter are a kind of cerebral assault course. Push yourself to the limit as you stretch your mental agility, visual reasoning and abstract cognition. And remember: when the going gets tough, the tough get their thinking caps on.

Take a look at the sets of images on these pages and overleaf. Your task is to deduce which of the four options given in each case completes the set.

1 Easy as ABC LEVEL 1

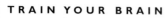

A
B
C
D

2 Poly-gone LEVEL 1

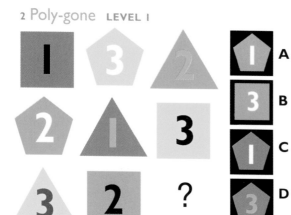

A
B
C
D

3 Star sign LEVEL 2

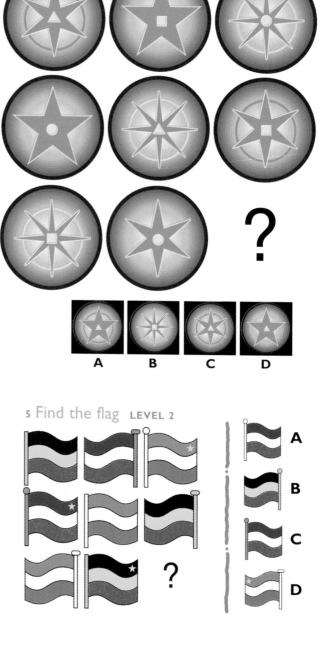

A   B   C   D

4 Jumping for joy? LEVEL 1

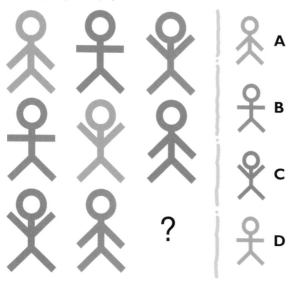

A
B
C
D

5 Find the flag LEVEL 2

A
B
C
D

6 Square off LEVEL 2

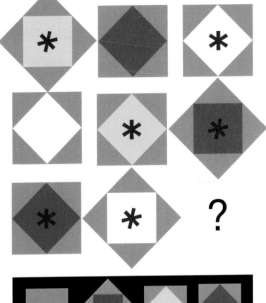

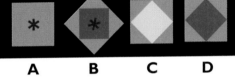

A   B   C   D

7 Where are you @? LEVEL 2

A
B
C
D

8 Sun spot LEVEL 2

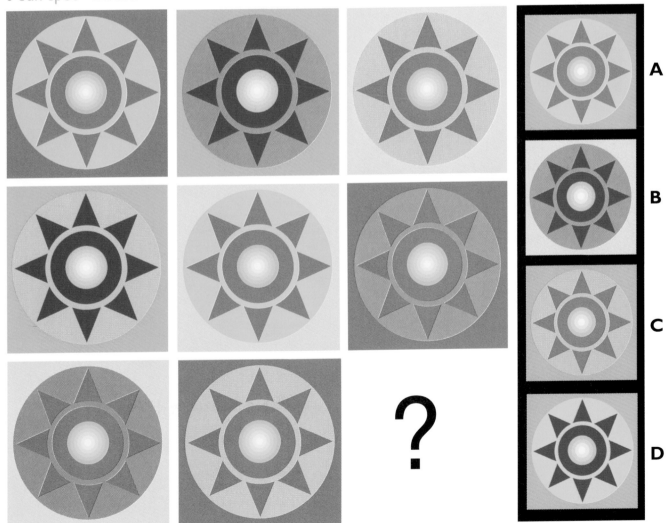

A
B
C
D

9 I say LEVEL 2

10 Crack this LEVEL 3

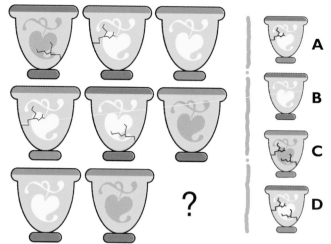

11 Geometric gap LEVEL 3

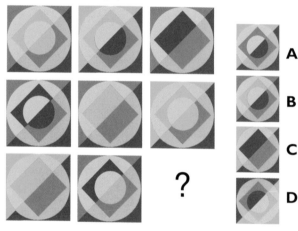

12 On target LEVEL 2

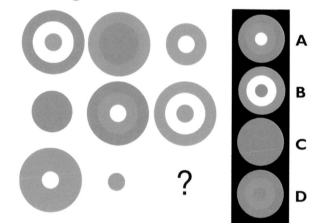

13 Joust about LEVEL 3

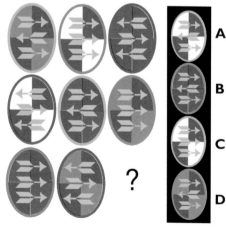

14 Fly away Peter LEVEL 3

Again, find the missing element – but you may have to think a bit harder about this puzzle.

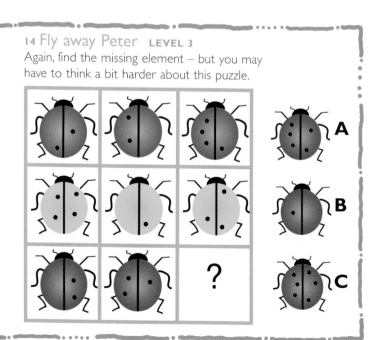

CREATIVE THINKING CHALLENGES

These puzzles are a new and increasingly popular way of having fun while training your brain to think in different ways.

When we're trying to answer questions, we normally think in logical terms to find a practical solution, particularly one that seems acceptable to people around us. The idea of the challenges below is to avoid the obvious answers and instead to think creatively. In this context, what is a 'creative' solution? It may be, for example, surreal, illogical, funny, surprising, incongruous, ingenious, witty or disconcerting.

For each question, give yourself around 10 to 15 minutes to come up with as many possible answers as you can, thinking in different ways for each one. It's impossible to predict what answers you'll come up with, but in the answers section we have listed a few creative solutions to give you some ideas (most of them silly). Don't concern yourself with how closely your answers match the ones we've listed – the main purpose of these questions is to have fun.

15 Canny thinking LEVEL 1

Nowadays companies fix the tabs of drinks cans onto the can. But this has resulted in a stockpile of detachable ring-pull tabs. With a little thought can you come up with some suggestions for uses to which the redundant ring-pulls could be put?

Avoid obvious answers such as 'recycle them to make new cans' and 'throw them in the bin'. The main feature of the ring-pull is the hole. Think about other things with holes. How about a spaghetti measurer? But the hole in the ring-pull is really small – so perhaps this is only useful as a spaghetti measurer for someone who's not too hungry. And so we have our first answer.

See if you can come up with some other ideas.

17 A hole lotta trouble LEVEL 1

Consider this: why are manhole covers round?

There are a few obvious technical reasons: round manholes don't have any sharp corners, don't need to be put back in any particular position, and can't fall though the hole (unlike square manholes, which can fall though the diagonal of a square hole).

What more creative solutions can you come up with?

16 Mona Lisa teaser LEVEL 1

The *Mona Lisa* is the most famous painting in the world, and the main topic of conversation when people look at the painting is what the Mona Lisa is thinking.

That's the question we'd like you to consider: what is the Mona Lisa thinking? Remember that your answers need to be creative and not necessarily sensible.

18 Compu-less LEVEL 1

For all the problems that they cause, computers also bring countless benefits. They enable us to create elaborate documents and perform complex calculations – while, thanks to the Internet, they spread information around the world faster than ever before.

What would the world be like today if we didn't have computers?

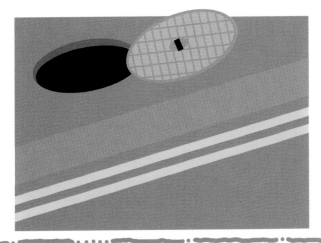

You have an hour to complete these two pages, the first of five mental workouts. These puzzles test your language skills: how wide is your vocabulary, and how good are you at guessing the meaning of obscure words? How aware are you of the deep patterns in language?

Words and meaning LEVEL 2

19

Of the words below, which two are closest in meaning?

MELLOW, MAUNDER, MANIPULATE, RAMBLE, COMPLAIN, INTRUDE

20

What is the meaning of gingival?

a A fish
b A tree
c Ginger beer
d Of the gums
e A ring of bells

21

BIG, CRAB, LOVE, PINE

Choose a word below that has something in common with each of the words above.

CAKE, TOFFEE, PEANUT, MINCE, GARLIC

22

A hertz is a unit of...

a Frequency
b Power
c Sound
d Pressure
e Heat

23

Which word in brackets is opposite in meaning to the word in capitals?

ERUDITE
(itinerant, ignorant, fallacious, recumbent, extraneous)

24

Advantageous is to beneficial as commendable is to...

REPUTABLE, LAUDABLE, SALUTARY, PERFECT, GOOD

25

'Susceptible to attack or damage'

Which of the following words most closely fits the above definition?

DEBILITATED, VULNERABLE, UNSTABLE, EMASCULATED, UNPREPARED

26

What is the meaning of angst?

a BRAVADO
b COMPASSION
c ANXIETY
d SURPRISE
e ANGER

27

What is the opposite of raillery?

a PUNGENT
b HARASSMENT
c SMARTNESS
d ANIMATED
e GENIALITY

28

Which of the following two words are opposite in meaning?

COMPLEX, SPOILT, UPSET, RUDE, COMPOSED, HAPPY

29

Which of the word-parts below, when joined to 'mania', means the fear of motion?

a OIKO
b HEDONO
c KINESO
d HODO
e TREMO

Letters and sequences LEVEL 1

30

Create two words from the following ten letters, using each letter once only:

DEOKBLURAC

(clue: fair weather)

31

Change just one letter in each of the following words to form a familiar phrase.

BE TIE WAS

32

Place two letters in each bracket so that they finish the word on the left and start the word on the right. The letters in the brackets, read downwards, will spell out a six-letter word.

(clue: a chip off the old block)

LO (_ _) IN
TH (_ _) LE
FU (_ _) SE

33

The following well-known quotation from the English playwright William Shakespeare has had all of the vowels removed, and the remaining consonants have been broken up into groups of five. Replace the vowels and find the quotation.

WHTSN NMTHT WHCHW CLLRS
BYNYT HRNMW LDSML LSSWT

34

Each group below forms part of a word that may or may not be hyphenated. Find the three words.

FSC GHHE USSAK

35

Only one set of the letters below can be arranged into a five-letter English word. Can you find the word?

ANDGE, GURSM, SGPRE,
ERLBS, MOHYA, TRINC, ALTNS,
RSLON, MECDN, ASPDN

36

What word can be placed between the brackets in order to finish the first word and start the second?

PUT (_ _ _) DEN

37

What four-letter word can be placed in front of the following words to make five new words or compounds?

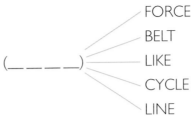

(_ _ _ _) — FORCE
— BELT
— LIKE
— CYCLE
— LINE

38

What six-letter word can be made from the following four letters?

E N
J T

39

Place two of these four-letter combinations together to make an eight-letter word (without changing the order of the letters):

MUSH OVER HELM SEAT
MORE ROMO ISOT

40

Find three islands or island groups in the sequence below:

_ O _ O _ O _
_ U _ A _ R _
_ A _ E _ R _

41 Turn again LEVEL 3

Start at one of the corner squares and spiral clockwise round the perimeter, finishing at the centre square to spell out a nine-letter word. You must provide the missing letters.

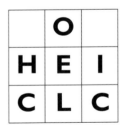

		O
H	E	I
C	L	C

42 Lost beauty LEVEL 3

What name can be placed on the bottom line to complete the three-letter words reading downwards?

T	P	S	F	P	N	R	S	A
I	A	K	E	E	I	U	A	S

This second challenge is about numbers. Studies show that even babies can count: almost from birth we keep a tally of the objects around us. Arithmetic, it seems, is in our genes.

The problem with numbers LEVEL 2

43

If a cat has two legs and a leopard has six legs and a hippopotamus has ten legs, how many legs has a stallion?

44

A cricketer averaged 22 runs for his first 10 innings. After a further 20 innings his average increased to 34 runs. What was his average for his second 20 innings?

45

All of the mathematical signs in the following equation have been omitted – your task is to put them in.

33 ? 11 ? 3 ? 6 = 115

46

Multiply all of the numbers from -6 to 6 in increments of one. That is:

-6 × -5 × -4 × ... 4 × 5 × 6

What is the total?

47

How many different combinations of 11, consisting of six men and five women, can be made out of teams of eight men and eight women?

48

Which number is the odd one out?

1553
1892
2137
3649
6397
4085
2464
4585
4868
4276

49

Using standard mathematical rules, find the value of this fraction:

$$\frac{6 - 9 \times 7}{6 + 4 \times 3} = ?$$

50

Simplify $\frac{7}{22} \div \frac{14}{44}$

51

7598123 is to 8239517 as 4139652 is to which of these:

9523164, 9253146, 5932614, 9532164

52

My son opened his piggy bank and found he had the same number of 10p, 20p and 50p coins, totalling £25.60. How many coins were in the piggy bank?

53

6 apples and 9 bananas cost £1.17
5 apples and 11 bananas cost £1.29

How much is one banana?
How much is one apple?

54

At a recent by-election a total of 29,642 votes were cast for the four candidates, the winner exceeding his three opponents by 696, 2968 and 7158 votes respectively.

How many votes were received by each candidate?

55

In an 8-a-side game of football lasting 45 minutes, two reserves substitute each player, so that all the players, including the reserves, are on the pitch for the same length of time. How long is each player on the pitch?

Missing, please find LEVEL 2

56
What is the missing number?

57
Complete this colourful grid.

58
What number should replace the question mark?

68, 64, 32, 28, 14, 10, 5 ?

59
What is the missing number?

436 : 18
862 : 50
643 : ?

60
What number is missing from the bottom row?

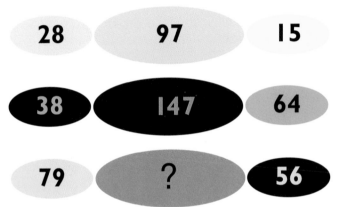

61
What number should replace the question mark?

62
What number is absent from our mixed-up number parade?

16	13	17	1
28	27	19	4
44	29	23	9
66	35	29	16
72	49	?	25

63
Find the number that completes the sequence.

18, 20, 21, 22, 24, 25, 26, 27, 28, 30, ?

64
Fill the gap in the pink circle.

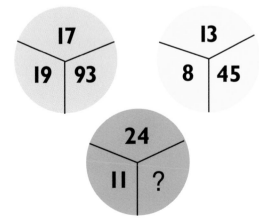

65
Find the missing numbers in these mathematical matchstick men.

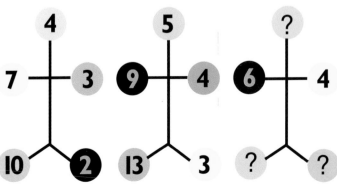

An aptitude for visual tests indicates an analytical mind. If you like these puzzles, it implies that you are a logical person who thinks things through.

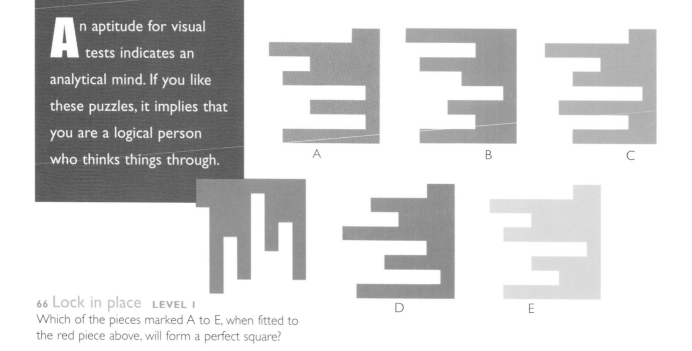

A   B   C

D   E

66 Lock in place LEVEL 1

Which of the pieces marked A to E, when fitted to the red piece above, will form a perfect square?

67 Patchwork LEVEL 2

Which of the following can be folded to form a cube?

C

E

A

B

D

68 Wedges LEVEL 2

Which four of the pieces below can be fitted together to form a perfect square?

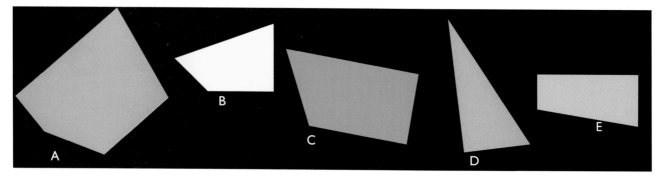

A   B   C   D   E

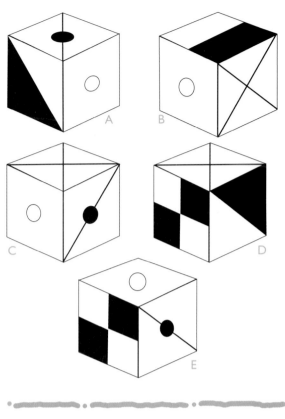

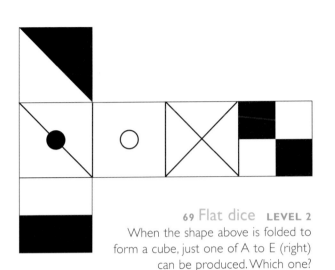

69 Flat dice LEVEL 2
When the shape above is folded to form a cube, just one of A to E (right) can be produced. Which one?

70 Measle puzzle LEVEL 2
What is the largest circle that can be drawn within this box so that it does not touch any of the other circles and does not touch the sides of the rectangle?

71 Triangle wrangle LEVEL 2
How many triangles appear in the diagram above?

72 Vision only LEVEL 3
Relying on sight alone, decide which three of the four pieces below can be fitted together to form a cube?

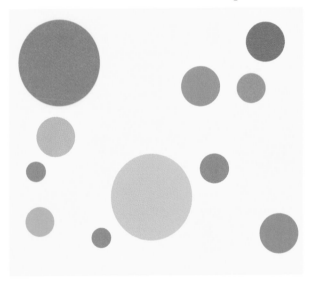

These challenges test technical reasoning. The key thing here is not to lose sight of how things work in the real world.

75 Points north LEVEL 2
There are 32 points of the compass. How many of these commence with N?

73 Round and round LEVEL 2
Four cog wheels are in constant mesh.

The 1st cog has 25 teeth

The 2nd cog has 20 teeth

The 3rd cog has 15 teeth

The 4th cog has 10 teeth

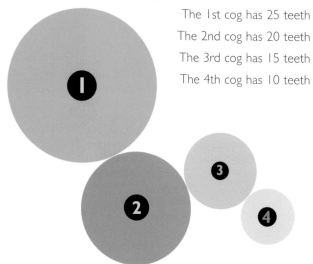

How many revolutions must the large cog make to return all of the cogs to their starting positions?

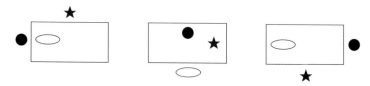

76 Designer flag LEVEL 2
Which option below continues the above sequence?

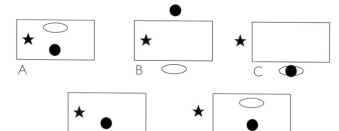

74 Went to mow LEVEL 2
Three men can each mow a cricket pitch in the following time:

One man takes three hours

One man takes four hours

One man takes six hours.

Working together at this rate, how long would it take all three of them to mow the cricket pitch together?

77 Cool eggs LEVEL 3
Which option below continues the above sequence?

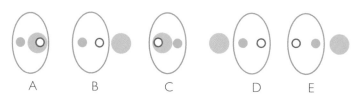

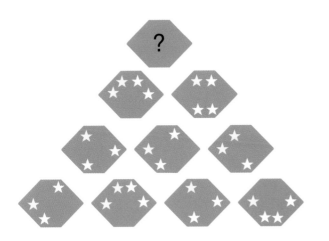

78 Star-crossed LEVEL 3
Which option below should replace the question mark at the top of the pyramid?

A   B   C   D   E

79 Whorls LEVEL 3
Which is the odd one out?

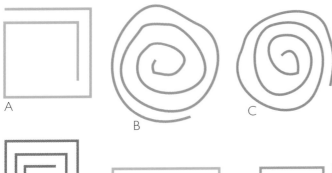

80 Computer talk LEVEL 2
What number in the decimal system is represented by the following binary notation?

I I 0 I I 0 I I 0 I I 0

81 Spot the amoeba LEVEL 2

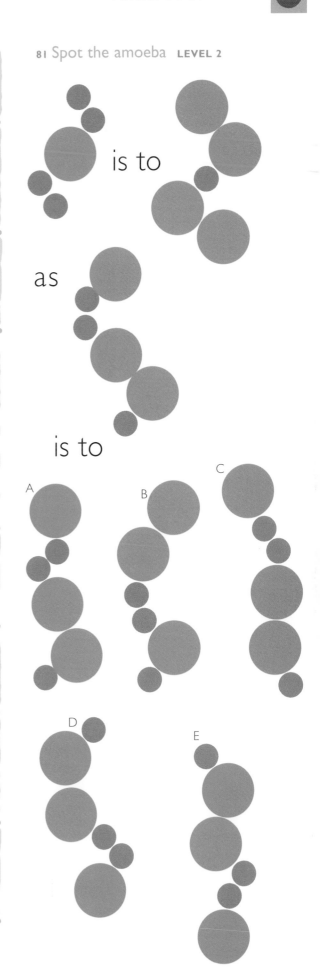

These challenges are a mix of logic, spatial awareness, technical reasoning, arithmetic and visual acuity. They are a kind of pentathlon that you do in your own armchair.

82 Beach souvenir
LEVEL 2
A bag of sand weighs 17.5kg + ⅞ of its total weight. How much does the bag of sand weigh?

83 Easy reading LEVEL 1
In how many ways can the word EASY be read?

Start at the central letter E and move to an adjacent letter up, down, backwards or forward, in and out in any direction.

84 Fruit corner LEVEL 2
If 6 apples + 3 bananas cost 43½p and 5 apples + 7 bananas cost 61p, what is the value of 1 apple + 1 banana?

86 Unfinished work LEVEL 2
How many more blocks are required to turn this incomplete construction into a solid cube, assuming that all blocks are the same size as those already placed and that none of the blocks already placed is moved?

85 Dice tower LEVEL 1
Four dice are stacked one on top of each other. What is the total value of the three pairs of hidden faces in the stack, given that the top face is a 6 and the bottom face is a 3?

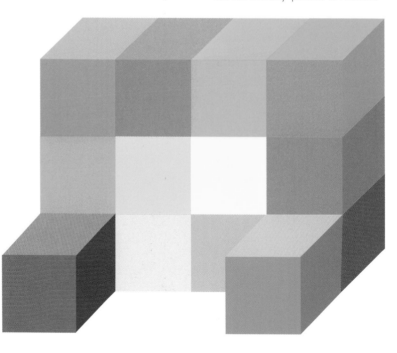

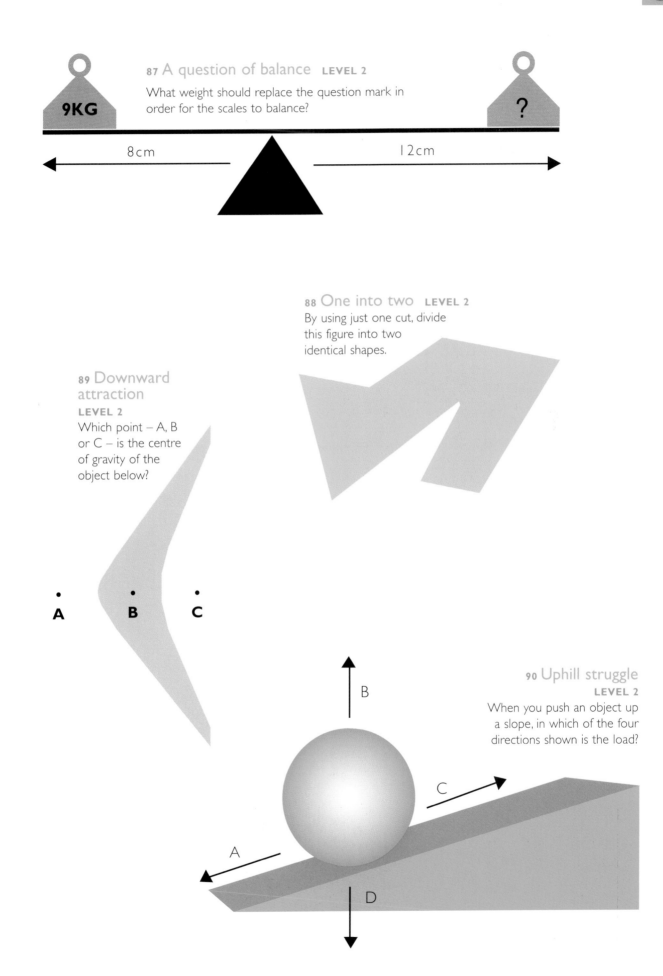

87 A question of balance LEVEL 2

What weight should replace the question mark in order for the scales to balance?

9KG

?

8cm

12cm

88 One into two LEVEL 2

By using just one cut, divide this figure into two identical shapes.

89 Downward attraction

LEVEL 2

Which point – A, B or C – is the centre of gravity of the object below?

A

B

C

90 Uphill struggle

LEVEL 2

When you push an object up a slope, in which of the four directions shown is the load?

B

C

A

D

91 Under Pressure LEVEL 2

You have exactly 3 minutes to complete the following puzzle. We recommend that you read it through quickly, then have a go at answering the questions.

A

Place a tick in this box ☐ if E is the last letter of this sentence. If the reverse sides of the dice in figure A would total 10, write ZEBRA in this space _____. If the plural of mouse is mice, write MICE in this space _____, if it isn't, write NICE. How many of the words in this sentence have not been spelt innkorrektly? ____ . Tick this box if you can spell the word iguana from the letters in figure B ☐. If the circle in figure C has a greater area than the triangle, cross out the word in the previous sentence that contains the most vowels. If the triangle has a greater area, cross out the word lobster here. If Bill Clinton's middle name is the same as the last name of a former US president, write IT IS here _____, unless Ronald Reagan's middle name is the same as a former British Prime Minister's, in which case write NO instead. If the flags of three European countries are contained in figure D, write SUPER under this line ----------. If Norway is one of them, write DUPER above the line, unless the name of a South American country can be found in the previous sentence, in which case write SUPER. Circle the word in this puzzle that contains the most letters, unless it is spelt incorrectly, in which case circle the word that contains the second largest number of letters.

B

G U
U A
A I N

C

D

92 Just say yes or no LEVEL 2

Don't think about these questions too hard. Trust your instincts and see how many you answer correctly.

1 Are these colours in alphabetical order?

BASHFUL	HAPPY
SNOOZY	DOPEY

2 Are these four of the Seven Dwarfs?

PARAGUAY	GUYANA
SURINAM	ECUADOR

3 Are these countries all in South America?

4 Are these colours in rainbow order?

5 Are these red lines all the same length?

1980	1936
1908	1930

6 Were these all Olympic years?

51	261
327	123

7 Are these numbers all divisible by 3?

HYGIENE	ACCEED
PHIAL	CRUETT

8 Are any of these words correctly spelt?

93 Lost property office LEVEL 1

It's time for the annual audit of the lost property office and as you can see it's rather untidy. How many of these questions can you answer correctly in 10 minutes to help the job go a bit quicker?

1 How many scarves can you find strewn about the office?

2 What is sitting on top of the computer keyboard?

3 How many timepieces can you locate?

4 How many umbrellas are facing point downwards?

5 There are two abandoned walking sticks – one has the head of a creature on top. Name it.

6 How many keys can you find? Add that to the number of balls.

7 Other than the gnome's fishing rod, what other item might help you catch a fish?

8 What colour is the lost teapot?

9 The phones are ringing – but where are they?

10 Oh dear, how embarrassing! How many items of underwear can you spot?

For these puzzles you need a clock with a second hand – and a book to cover the page. These are tests of mental agility: do you already have a mind like a mountain goat? Or do you need to take your brain on a bracing hike?

You have 3 minutes to prepare before each challenge. You must use this time to memorize a diagram or test yourself at a particular mental skill. Write your answers on a piece of paper or, using the acetate, in the empty box at the bottom right of the page.

You must answer each question in turn, and although you may pass on a question you cannot return to it later or change a previous answer. The answers are the only thing you write down – taking notes or writing out calculations is not allowed.

LEVEL 1   40 correct answers in total
LEVEL 2   41–50 correct answers in total
LEVEL 3   51+ correct answers in total

RAINBOW

94 After the storm

Look at the rainbow sequence above and memorize it as best you can in 3 minutes. (For the benefit of colour-blind readers, the sequence of colours is: red, yellow, pink, green, orange, purple, blue.) You will be asked a series of questions about this diagram, such as:

Q Fourth letter from the left   (Answer: N)

Q Colour of the W   (Answer: blue)

When the 3 minutes have expired, cover up the diagram. You now have a maximum of 2 minutes to write down your answers to as many of these questions as you can:

1 Second letter from the left.
2 Colour of the R.
3 Name the orange letter.
4 Number of letters in the penultimate letter's colour.
5 Middle letter.
6 Colour of letter six from the right.
7 Number of consonants on rounded rectangles.
8 Colour of the letter before N.
9 Letter between two rounded rectangles.
10 Letter halfway between R and B.
11 Total number of vowels.
12 Letter halfway between the yellow and purple letters.
13 Letter two places after the letter before N.
14 Colour of letter three places before the letter after B.
15 Number of letters with half-turn symmetry.

95 Touch-tone test

Look carefully at the illustration of ordinary telephone keypad and memorize it as best you can in 3 minutes. You will then be asked a series of questions about this diagram, such as:

Q First key in third row   (Answer: 7)
Q Key below 3   (Answer: 6)

When the 3 minutes have expired, cover up the diagram. You now have a maximum of 2 minutes to write down your answers to as many of these questions as you can:

1 Second key in third column.
2 Key in far bottom-right.
3 Key two keys below 1.
4 Key in fourth row and second column.
5 Key between 5 and 0.
6 Sum of keys in third row.
7 Key between 3 and 7.
8 Total of numbers in middle column.
9 Key in same row as 9 and same column as 2.
10 Number of keys bearing prime numbers.
11 Key in same column as # and same row as 8.
12 Key between 6 and *.
13 Key one above the key that's two to the right of 4.
14 Number of letters in number of the key that's two places to the left of 9.
15 Key two places above the key that's one to the left of 0.

96 Count your cards

Look at the illustration of playing cards and memorize it as best you can in 3 minutes. The letters J, Q and K stand for Jack, Queen and King respectively, and for the purposes of this test they are each worth 10. You will be asked a series of questions about this diagram, such as:

Q Suit of card below the 3
   (Answer: hearts)

Q Value of card above the 8
   (Answer: 4)

When the 3 minutes have expired, cover up the diagram. You now have a further 3 minutes to write down the answers to as many of these questions as you can:

1 Name of card in top-right corner.
2 Name of card above the 10.
3 Suit of the 4 card.
4 Suit of card below the 7.
5 Suit of card two to the left of the 9.
6 Highest-ranking card with the suit of hearts.
7 Value of card one above and three to the right of the 10.
8 Suit of card two places from the left in the top row.
9 Number of cards that have a value above 7 and/or are red.
10 Suit that does not appear in second column.
11 Number of card one place above card two places to left of the King.
12 Total value of all cards with suit of diamonds.
13 Highest black card bearing an odd number.
14 Total numeric value of all six black cards.
15 Total numeric value of the six cards in middle row and/or third column.

97 Image-conscious

Look at the illustrations above and their associated numbers, and memorize them as best you can in 3 minutes. You will be asked a series of questions about this diagram, such as:

Q Object in box 4   (Answer: cat)

Q Number of box above the padlock   (Answer: 2)

When the 3 minutes have expired, cover up the diagram. You now have a further 3 minutes to write down the answers to as many of these questions as you can:

1   Object below the key.
2   Object three to the left of the heart.
3   Number of letters in the name of the object in box 1.
4   Box containing the spider.
5   Value of box above the clock.
6   Value of box that contains an anagram of EARTH.
7   Number of object that sounds like the ninth letter of the alphabet.
8   Object in box one below and two to the right of the star.
9   Object in same row as the cat and same column as the padlock.
10 Total value of boxes containing the two parts of the body.
11 (Value of cat) + (value of heart).
12 (Value of key) × (value of clock).
13 (Value of eye) × (value of object below star) × (value of spider).
14 (Value of object two to the left of heart) − (value of object one to the left of cat).
15 Total value of eye, heart, clock, cat and spider.

ANSWERS		
	8	
1	9	
2	10	
3	11	
4	12	
5	13	
6	14	
7	15	

Memory is a phenomenon about which we know very little. We assume that memories are stored in the neurons of the hippocampus (right). This organ, deep in the brain, is sometimes larger in taxi drivers, who exercise their memories daily in their work. We also know that memorization has three stages, iconic, short-term and long-term.

Iconic memory is a snapshot of what your senses are perceiving at any given instant. Most

Remember, remember

of these memories — the colour of the car you just passed, the sequence of advertisements in a commercial break — are discarded as mental garbage within a few moments.

Short-term memory is a kind of waiting room for events that may yet prove significant: what you had for lunch, the name of a person you met last week, a telephone number.

Long-term memory stores facts that have been reinforced (usually by repetition or emotional impact) and can last a lifetime: your home address, knowledge of a foreign language, your wedding day. Sometimes entirely unremarkable iconic images stow away for ever in long-term memory. We all have these gatecrashers in our minds: a snatch of conversation from childhood, a moment spent staring out the window at school, a few bars of music heard once on the radio.

IN THE MINDS OF BABES AND SUCKLINGS
The greatest feat of memory ever performed belongs to a child – or rather to all children. Babies' acquisition of language is an epic achievement of recall. Word learning begins at about a year old, and experiments have shown that the average 18-year-old knows about 60,000 words. This means that every child picks up a new word every 90 minutes, storing it permanently in memory: 10 new words a day, every day without fail, right through childhood. This workrate is truly remarkable since toddlers are not simply soaking up the separate words, they are simultaneously analysing the language, subconsciously working out its grammar, and making intuitive guesses about the exact meaning of words. This analysis is an astonishing intellectual undertaking, one that almost every person takes on and completes before the age of three.

RICHARD OF YORK GAINED BATTLE IN VAIN

The rainbow mnemonic is a famous memory aid. But to recall the colours from the inside out try this mnemonic: **Vikings In Britain Gave Yoyos Out Readily.**

Memory marathon

The world memory championships were inaugurated in 1991. Events include recalling an unpublished poem (including punctuation) and memorizing a random series of ones and zeroes. Memory Grand Masters must be able to recall 713 numbers in one hour, 365 cards in one hour, and the sequence of a full deck of cards in under 3 minutes.

Train your memory

The memory is like a muscle: the more you use it the stronger it gets. There are many techniques you can use to strengthen your recall, or to give your memory a helping hand. Here are some of them:

Word association is good for learning vocabulary in a foreign language. For example, French for a drink is boisson, which sounds like bison — so imagine a bison at a watering hole. The same imaginative technique, mixed with some mental exaggeration can be used for remembering names, such as Mr Smiley (left).

Mnemonics are phrases formed from the first letters of the series you are trying to remember. If you are inventing a mnemonic for yourself, make it memorable by making it funny:

'Attlee's cat eats my dinner; Wilson heard we call that moggie Blair' is a mnemonic (with a few signposts) to help you remember post-war British prime ministers.

The Room System requires you to imagine you are in a building where each room contains a visual reminder. In the first room, for example, there is a big red telephone ringing loudly: it is to remind you to pay your bill: in the next room is a large mooing cow: you have to buy milk. You recall the list by wandering back through the house, ticking off the tasks as you go.

The Link System means creating images that link key ideas. Say you want to remember to go to the library, to buy a new pen and to buy some coffee: imagine a fountain pen with brown ink writing in a book.

98 Colourful memories **LEVEL 2**

In a variation of the traditional and much loved parlour game we've collected a colourful plateful of 15 objects that we want you to commit to memory. Study the objects for 3 minutes then cover the page. How many can you recall? Do any of the colours stick in your mind? Do they help or distract you? Now sketch the plate and try to position the objects from memory. (For tips on improving your memory, see the feature on pages 212 and 213.)

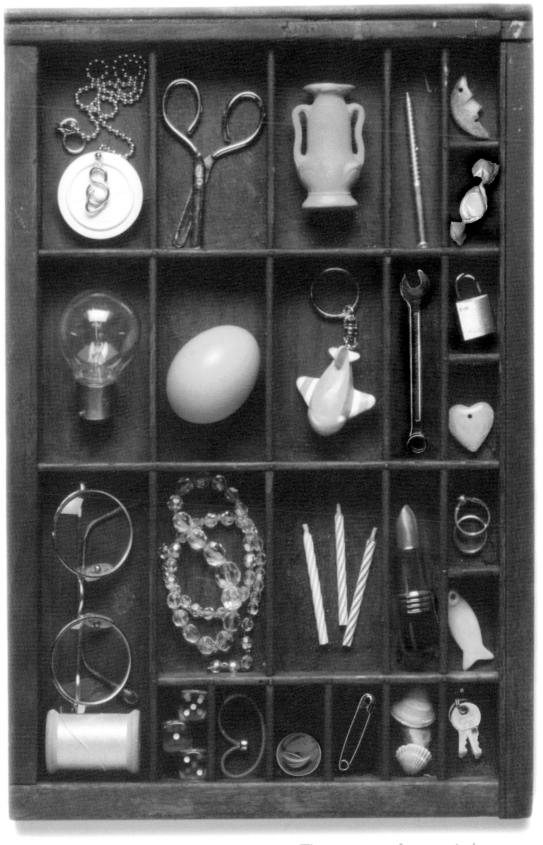

99 The corners of your mind **LEVEL 3**
Here you'll see 25 unconnected objects arranged in random order.
As before, study the page for just 3 minutes before closing the
book. How many can you remember?

Are you absent minded, or can you remember every number in your phone book? Test your powers of recall with the following tall stories. Read each one through, then turn over the page and try to answer the questions without having to look back at the originals. Good luck!

101 The old man and the whale LEVEL 1

There is an old man by the Iztacalco gate who will tell you his story for a peseta. Half a century ago he was a fisherman in Tuxpan, working the Gulf of Mexico for red snapper and barracuda. One May dawn he set out with the bearded Carlos and Pedro with the gold tooth. As his boat, the *Tula*, cut through the purple water, Carlos scanned the sea while the others prepared the nets and bait. Suddenly Carlos cried out. A shape, 10 feet across, was moving slowly off the starboard bow. Hoping for a shoal of snapper, Pedro and Carlos ran to the huge rod that hung from the prow. As they bent feverishly to their task, the surface behind them broke with a crash like summer thunder. The man stood still, as a giant black and white body soared slowly over his head, reaching for the Pole star. It was an orca, in a place where no whale should have been. It hung in the air, the dawn turning its skin into an impossible rainbow. Then, with a slow flick of its massive tail, it ploughed back into the sea. When the water had settled, the man turned to his friends. They were soaked. They talked of a tsunami, a tidal wave. They had seen nothing. They did not believe him.

100 Jack Brady, Private Investigator LEVEL 2

Brady pulled his red 1957 Plymouth up to the sidewalk on the corner of 31st and Main and cut the engine. His watch read 9.54. Up at his office window (third floor, second from the right) the light was on. In 2 minutes he was outside the frosted glass of a door marked JACK BRADEY PI, eyeing the silhouette of a woman. He went in. 'Excuse me,' he said, 'this is my office.' The woman – blonde, 26, green eyes – looked up. 'You're excused, but next time rent a bigger one.' Brady dropped into his oak chair, opened the lower left-hand drawer of his teak desk, took out a bottle and glasses. He poured, they drank. 'So,' said Jack, 'you're looking for your husband.' 'How d'ya know?' she asked. 'I'm a detective. Can you describe him?' 'Six foot tall, 30 years old. Last seen wearing tan chinos, blue shirt, orange tie, sports jacket and a crooked grin.' Jack nodded. 'I've seen him around.' She drained her glass, got up, headed for the door. 'If you find him, tell him he's late for dinner at Roxy's.' Jack smiled crookedly. 'I will. And thanks a million for dropping by, Mrs Brady.'

102 The race LEVEL 3

Bill slid the blue slip into his pocket and raised his binoculars as the horses came into the home strait. The tannoy squeaked: '…it's Gamegirl in the lead, with Last Straw a length behind, Gamegirl ridden by Sean Casey in yellow, just in front of Last Straw ridden by Mike Stack in blue and white… and oh my goodness Banana Skin is down! He's down but his rider Steve Leary is unhurt … and Last Straw's gaining on Gamegirl, and now Snail's Pace is making a break! It's Snail's Pace coming up on the inside, past First Gear and Lazy Bones, and he's into third place, that's Snail's Pace ridden by Pete Broad, and Mike Stack's looking back, he's seen the danger, can he keep the pressure on Gamegirl… and they're into the final furlong, and it's Last Straw at 4 to 1 neck and neck with Gamegirl at 7 to 2, with Snail's Pace in third place, there's only a few lengths to go! And as they pass the post Last Straw wins, followed by Gamegirl and Snail's Pace, and behind them come Idle One, Dozy Lad, Sleepwalk…' Bill sighed, reached for the blue slip and tore it up.

103 The mission LEVEL 2

The man slipped the black cassette into his car stereo, opened the brown file and took out a photograph. 'The man you're looking at,' said the tape, 'is Colonel Igor Gregorovich Ivanov, head of S.P.R.A. and wanted in 37 countries.' The man extracted a second photo. 'And this is Ivana Karpenko, his assistant, a.k.a. Freya Berga, Mathilde Masseuse and Tracy Boggins.' The man opened a small white envelope and took out three items. 'The passport belonged to Glenda Norse, a 40-year-old croupier from Maine, found dead yesterday in Washington Park. On her body were that playing card – the six of clubs – the ruby brooch and the book of matches from the Kool Kat Klub.' The man looked at his right hand. 'The blood on your fingers is hers. We believe the two S.P.R.A operatives spilt it. Your mission is to prove it. Good luck. This cassette will self-destruct in 10 seconds.' The man, Jon Phipps, a.k.a Igor Ivanov, laughed cruelly. 'Quicker than that, I think.' He wrenched open the door and ran for cover as the car blew into a thousand pieces.

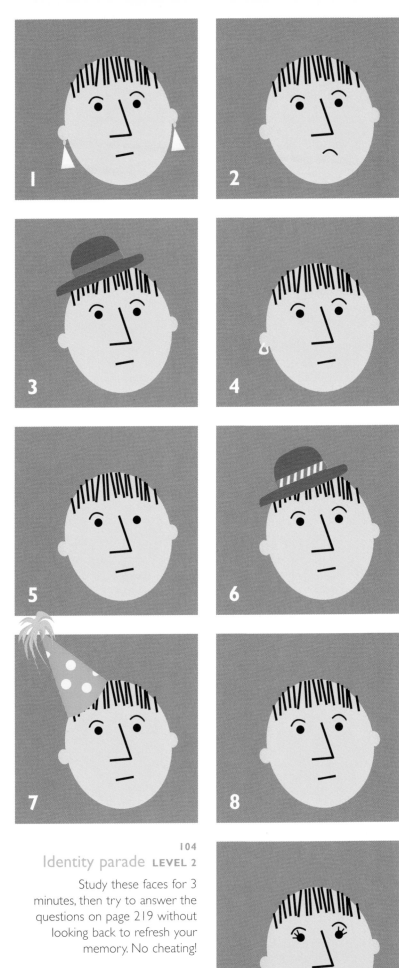

Identity parade **LEVEL 2**

Study these faces for 3 minutes, then try to answer the questions on page 219 without looking back to refresh your memory. No cheating!

105
Matching symbols grid
Ignore this grid until you've had a chance to look at the puzzle on page 219. Then try answering the questions below, marking your answers in the grid. Then look back to page 219 to see if you're right.

1 Position the blue circles.

2 Where are the two green triangles?

3 Where are the purple squares?

4 A blue triangle sits next to a purple circle somewhere in the grid. Can you locate them?

5 Where are the green circles?

6 Where does a green triangle sit below a purple triangle?

7 Position the green squares.

8 Where are the blue squares?

9 Which symbols sit in the bottom row?

10 Which symbols sit in the right-hand column?

The questions below relate to the tall tales on page 216, which tested your memory for facts and figures. How many of these can you answer without looking back at the text?

100 Jack Brady, Private Investigator LEVEL 1

1 What colour, year and make was Jack's car?
2 What colour shirt was Jack wearing?
3 In which drawer of his desk was the bottle?
4 What's wrong with the wording on Jack's door?
5 What kind of wood is Jack's chair?
6 On the corner of which two streets is Jack's office?
7 What colour is the woman's hair?
8 What is the difference in their ages?
9 What did the woman do before getting up and leaving?
10 What type of trousers is Jack wearing?

101 The old man and the whale
LEVEL 2

1 By which gate does the old man sit? (spell it!)
2 Where was he a fisherman?
3 Which of his friends had a gold tooth?
4 What was his boat called?
5 How wide was the shape Carlos saw in the water?
6 On which side of the boat was it, left or right?
7 What kind of fish were they hoping it might be?
8 When the whale surfaced, how was the crash described?
9 Where was the whale 'reaching for'?
10 What did they call a tidal wave? (spell it!)

103 The mission LEVEL 2

1 What colour is the cassette?
2 What is Colonel Ivanov's middle name?
3 Name two of Ivana Karpenko's aliases.
4 What colour is the envelope?
5 Where was the croupier found?
6 Which playing card was found on her?
7 Where did the matches come from?
8 Which hand did Jon Phipps look at?
9 What did Phipps say?
10 What did the voice on the tape say after 'Good luck, Jon'?

102 The race LEVEL 3

1 At the start of the commentary, which horse was in the lead?
2 Who was riding this horse?
3 Which horse was Steve Leary riding?
4 What were the odds on Last Straw winning?
5 Who was riding Snail's Pace?
6 When Snail's Pace first came up on the inside, he passed two horses. Name one of them.
7 Which rider won the race?
8 What are Mike Stack's colours?
9 Which horses came fourth, fifth and sixth?
10 What are Sean Casey's colours?

104

Identity parade LEVEL 1

On page 217 you'll find a series of faces that look similar but have characteristics that make each unique. After you've studied them, try to answer the questions below from memory alone.

1 Three people are wearing hats – which three?

2 Which is the unhappy face?

3 Which person is minus an eyebrow?

4 Whose hat has a striped band?

5 ... and whose hat has a plain band?

6 ... and what colour is the plain band?

7 Who's wearing too much mascara?

8 Who's wearing the party hat?

9 ... and what colour are the dots on the party hat?

10 Who likes to wear a single earring?

11 On which side (from the wearer's viewpoint) is the single earring worn?

12 What shape are the earrings on the person who is wearing a pair?

105

Matching symbols LEVEL 2

Study the position of these symbols for 3 minutes, then visit the grid on page 217 for a series of questions to test your visual memory.

tricky

Doing general knowledge
quizzes is a kind of mental
librarianship. It does not
matter how much you
know; the only important
thing is: how fast can you
retrieve trivia files from
the dusty filing cabinet of
the brain. So fingers on
buzzers – question one...

trivia

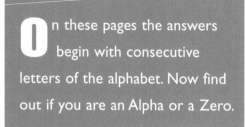

On these pages the answers begin with consecutive letters of the alphabet. Now find out if you are an Alpha or a Zero.

1 Brought to book   LEVEL 3

If you're not good with names, you might find this a bit of a struggle! We've given clues to famous characters from literature. How many can you recall?

A Name of the lion befriended by the children in C. S. Lewis's series of Narnia stories

B The eponymous Hobbit

C Hero on a quest to reach the Celestial City in *The Pilgrim's Progress*

D Surname of Eliza, Professor Higgins's student in *Pygmalion*

E Gypsy girl in *The Hunchback of Notre Dame*

F In *Watership Down*, the rabbits were Hazel, Bigwig, General Wormwort and…?

G The third 'man in a boat', in addition to Harris, J. and Montmorency the dog

H Man who marries the mother of Lolita in order to be near to Lolita herself

I The narrator and survivor in *Moby Dick*

J The narrator in *Treasure Island*

K George Smiley's adversary in *Tinker, Tailor, Soldier, Spy*

L Central character in Dickens's *The Old Curiosity Shop*

M The slave girl in *Ali Baba and the 40 Thieves*

N The pig who leads the other characters in *Animal Farm*

O Willy Wonka's small helpers in *Charlie and the Chocolate Factory*

P Phileas Fogg's valet in *Around the World in 80 Days*

Q The name of the captain in *The Caine Mutiny*

R The horse of *Don Quixote*

S Tiger in *The Jungle Book*

T The Famous Five's dog

U Vagabond in Victor Hugo's *L'Homme qui Rit*

V Surname of the central character in *Les Misérables*

W Character with poor time-keeping in *Alice in Wonderland*

X Surname of the priest in *Anthony Adverse*, set during the Napoleonic Wars

Y Name of the Captain who is caught in a *Catch-22* situation

Z Heathcliff's servant in *Wuthering Heights*

2 The wild alphabet   LEVEL 2

Here's a real menagerie of living things to identify. How many can you bag?

A Fruit of the oak tree

B Breed of domestic dog that does not bark

C As well as its eponymous location, this finch is also native to Madeira and the Azores

D Herb, member of the parsley family, chiefly used in pickles and preserves

E Egg-laying mammal, also called the spiny anteater

F Plant from which linen is made

G Small burrowing mammal whose name means 'honeycomb' in French because it 'honeycombs' the soil

H The pungent roots of this perennial herb are used as a condiment

I 'Bird-hipped' dinosaur from the early Cretaceous period

J Plant used to flavour gin

K The story goes that this was accidentally named after the Aboriginal word for 'I don't understand'

L Beetle that feeds on aphids, and is named after the Virgin Mary

M Small carnivore famous for its ability to kill snakes

N Genus of herbs of which the daffodil is the most well-known member

O The largest living bird, now found wild only in Africa but increasingly farmed elsewhere for its meat

P Alternative name for the papaya fruit

Q Type of zebra with a brown body, white legs and stripes over its upper body that became extinct in 1883

R Double-crested American bird noted for its high sprinting speed, as immortalized in a series of cartoons

S The young of the pilchard, used for canned food

T Giant spider that can live for up to 30 years

U Generic term for any animal with hoofs

V Surprisingly, this plant, whose pods are dried out to be used as a flavouring, is a member of the orchid family

W Species of aconite, often quoted in literature as a poison

X Woody tissue that provides plants with support, water and salts

Y The Tibetan ox

Z Variety of cattle, noted for its humped back and resistance to heat and disease

3 Name the author LEVEL 3

Not all quotations come from great works of literature. Although there are some literary quotes here, you'll also find famous attributed sayings from many other spheres of human activity. Who said or wrote each one (note that it's the author we're looking for, not the character)?

A 'The Answer to the Great Question Of Life, the Universe and Everything is Forty-two'

B 'There's a sucker born every minute'

C 'All I need to make comedy is a park, a policeman and a pretty girl'

D *'Cogito, ergo sum'*

E 'If A is the success in life, then A equals x plus y plus z. Work is x; y is play; and z is keeping your mouth shut'

F 'A medium Vodka dry Martini – with a slice of lemon peel. Shaken and not stirred'

G 'A verbal contract isn't worth the paper it's written on'

H 'Purple haze is in my brain, Lately things don't seem the same'

I 'Castles in the air – they are so easy to take refuge in. And easy to build, too'

J 'Our Federal Union: it must be preserved'

K 'I keep six honest serving-men (They taught me all I knew); Their names are What and Why and When and How and Where and Who'

L 'When the reviews are bad I tell my staff that they can join me as I cry all the way to the bank'

M 'After all, tomorrow is another day'

N 'There can be no whitewash at the White House'

O 'Four legs good, two legs bad'

P 'Men seldom make passes, At girls who wear glasses'

Q 'Simple this tale! – but delicately perfumed, As the sweet roadside honeysuckle. That's why, Difficult though its metre was to tackle, I'm glad I wrote it'

R *'Le client n'a jamais tort'* (The customer is never wrong)

S 'Dr Livingstone, I presume?'

T 'One Ring to rule them all, One Ring to find them. One Ring to bring them all and in the darkness bind them'

U 'I do not believe that friends are necessarily the people who you like best, they are merely the people who got there first'

V *'Fuimus Troes, fuit Ilium et ingens Gloria Teucrorum'* (We Trojans are at an end, Ilium has ended and the vast glory of the Trojans)

W 'Give a man a free hand and he'll try to put it all over you'

X 'The sea! The sea!'

Y 'The ghost of Roger Casement is beating on the door'

Z 'Rock journalism is people who can't write interviewing people who can't talk for people who can't read'

You can use the acetate to fill in the answers for each set of A to Z questions in the grid below. Good luck!

A to Z answer grid

A _____

B _____

C _____

D _____

E _____

F _____

G _____

H _____

I _____

J _____

K _____

L _____

M _____

N _____

O _____

P _____

Q _____

R _____

S _____

T _____

U _____

V _____

W _____

X _____

Y _____

Z _____

4 Wish you were here? LEVEL 2

Here are details of some of the most famous landmarks in the world. Can you identify the buildings? Extra points if you can name the location of each.

5 Completely barking LEVEL 2

Can you correctly identify the breed of these dogs? It's not as easy as it might appear because some of the dogs look slightly out of the ordinary.

This family quiz has questions for everyone. Children get extra points for blues and reds.

ORANGE For all the family
BLUE For grown-ups
RED For grown-up know-it-alls

6 Science

1 Which scientist is famous for his theories of relativity?

2 What was the name of the project, headed by J. Robert Oppenheimer, to create the first atomic bomb?

3 Who discovered the antibiotic drug penicillin?

4 What is the name of the amplifying semi-conductor device contained in all modern electronic devices?

5 In 1990 a space telescope named after an American astronomer was launched. What is its name?

6 Early scientists longed to be able to transmute base metals such as lead into gold. What was the name of their profession?

7 Who is credited with the invention of the concertina?

8 Which 19th-century English mathematician invented a 'difference engine' that anticipated the computer?

9 One substance – said to have been invented by the Chinese – has been responsible for the deaths of millions, but has also produced wonderful night-time displays. What is it?

10 In the 1930s chemists led by Wallace H. Carothers at the US Du Pont Company invented a substance that changed clothing for ever. What was it?

8 Record breakers

1 Which is the longest species of snake?

2 Name the world's highest mountain.

3 One species of whale is the largest of all extant animals, measuring 33m (110ft) in length. Which one?

4 Which planet is the largest in the solar system – more than 1300 times the volume of the Earth?

5 Which animal has an eye that can grow to over 38cm (15in) in diameter?

6 Name the largest country in South America.

7 What is the longest river in Asia?

8 What is the hottest country in the world?

9 A BBC radio show about country folk is the longest-running daily radio serial. Which one?

10 What is the smallest bird in the world?

7 Literature

1 What was the name of the 19th-century US writer whose novels about family life, such as *Little Women*, caused a sensation when first published?

2 What is the name of the young hero raised by wolves in Rudyard Kipling's *Jungle Book* volumes?

3 In his 15th-century account of the life of King Arthur, Sir Thomas Malory described the archetypal wizard. What is the wizard's name?

4 Scarlett O'Hara is the heroine of Margaret Mitchell's epic *Gone With the Wind*. Name the period of American history that provides the backdrop for the novel.

5 Which Russian writer gave us the novel *Dead Souls*?

6 Who is the hero of J. M. Barrie's story of pirates and red Indians in Never Never Land – the boy who will not grow up?

7 Who wrote the novel *Tom Jones*?

8 One of the characters in Shakespeare's play *A Midsummer Night's Dream* is the victim of a spell that puts a donkey's head on his shoulders. What is his name?

9 *The Catcher in the Rye* is a novel detailing the trials of adolescence. Who wrote it?

10 Which US-born British poet, critic, playwright and editor wrote the poems 'Four Quartets' and 'The Waste Land'?

9 The Olympics

1 Which 100m champion was stripped of his gold medal at the 1988 games after failing a drugs test?

2 Which Roman emperor banned the Olympic Games?

3 Which city hosted the 1928 games?

4 An Olympic biathlon tests which two sporting disciplines?

5 Britain's Sebastian Coe won gold medals in the 1500m in 1980 and 1984. Who was his arch rival?

6 The Olympic Games were not held during the Second World War. Where were the 1948 games, the first following the conflict, held?

7 At the Atlanta Olympic Games in 1996 a two-year-old record for the 100m was beaten with a 9.84 second performance. Name the athlete who beat the record.

8 Which city will host the 2004 Olympic Games?

9 What is the name of the Greek city commemorated in a running event over 26 miles 385yd?

10 At the 1936 Berlin Olympics, German leader Adolf Hitler walked out of the games when a black American athlete won his fourth gold medal. What was the athlete's name?

10 Empires

1 Edward Gibbon chronicled the decline and fall of which ancient empire?

2 Constantinople (modern Istanbul) was at the heart of the empire ruled by Justinian the Great in 527–565. What was the empire's name?

3 The pyramids were burial chambers for the kings and queens of which North African empire?

4 The empire based at Troy in Asia Minor was brought down when a Greek army overwhelmed the city. What device did the Greeks use to breach Troy's defences?

5 At the end of the First World War, which empire extended over a quarter of the world's land surface?

6 The South American Inca empire centred on Peru ruled for 400 years until about 1530. Who or what brought the empire to an end?

7 In the film *Star Wars*, Luke Skywalker is pitted against the leader of the 'Evil Empire'. What is the name of Luke's adversary?

8 What was the name of the 13th and 14th-century empire that controlled most of the eastern world?

9 The Ottoman Empire endured for more than 600 years and at its height included most of south-east Europe. What is the name of the new republic that replaced it when it came to an end in 1922?

10 The Mughal Empire a huge territory between the years of 1556 to 1707. Which modern country comprises much of that same area?

11 Hollywood

1 Actress Tippi Hedren was discovered by Alfred Hitchcock. What was the first Hitchcock film in which she starred?

2 Which Hollywood personality and sometime actress, when asked 'How many husbands have you had?' replied 'You mean, apart from my own?'

3 The film *Some Like it Hot* starred Marilyn Monroe, Tony Curtis and Jack Lemmon. But who played the part of the gangster Spats Colombo?

4 In 1975 an unlikely tale of a giant shark called *Jaws* broke all previous box-office records. Who directed the film?

5 This British-born comic actor and film-maker was once described as the 'single most important artist produced by the cinema', but in the 1950s his permit to enter the USA was revoked. Who was he?

6 Humphrey Bogart starred as Rick Blaine in the 1942 film *Casablanca*. Who played his ex-lover Ilsa Lund?

7 Which director of slapstick comedies helped make the name of early Hollywood stars such as Fatty Arbuckle and Harold Lloyd?

8 Elizabeth Taylor had a tempestuous relationship with her co-star in the 1963 film *Cleopatra*. Who was he?

9 Female fans adored the star of the 1921 silent weepy *The Sheik*. What was his name?

10 Marion Michael Morrison was the real name of one of Hollywood's greatest stars, an all-American hero who personified the frontier spirit. What was his screen name?

12 Music

1 Which composer suffered from progressive deafness and near the end of his career was almost totally deaf?

2 Name the singer-songwriter and founder member of the Beatles who was assassinated in 1980.

3 *The Marriage of Figaro*, *The Magic Flute* and *Don Giovanni* are operas by which Austrian composer?

4 In 1899 Scott Joplin developed a distinctive style of jazz which took the USA by storm. What was it called?

5 Bandleader and singer Louis Armstrong was jazz's foremost virtuoso on which instrument?

6 The 'Wall of Sound' was created by an American record producer who worked with groups such as the Ronettes and the Crystals. What was his name?

7 Two British composers produced a celebrated series of comic operas, including *The Pirates of Penzance*, between 1871 and 1896. Who were they?

8 Which blockbuster movie starring Julie Andrews was an adaptation of a Richard Rogers stage musical?

9 Which popular singer was called 'The King'?

10 With what style of music was the American rock band Nirvana associated?

13 Animal world

1 Which amphibious Australian mammal lays eggs?

2 Which mammal is the swiftest runner over short distances?

3 The ears of the African elephant can be over 1m (about 3ft) wide. Apart from improving the elephant's hearing, what other purpose do they serve?

4 Which animal, found throughout Africa, Asia, parts of Europe and South America, is covered with protective quills?

5 Is the dolphin a fish or a mammal?

6 Are bats blind?

7 Which flightless bird lives on the open plains of Africa and can lay up to eight 1.1kg (2½lb) eggs?

8 Scientists have found fossil remains of a fish that was alive 350 million years ago. At first they thought it had died out, but living specimens have now been caught. What is the name of the fish?

9 In winter, animals such as bears and squirrels slow down their bodies to a permanent state of drowsiness. What is this condition called?

10 Which bird has eyesight 100 times more acute than that of a human being and has the ability to turn its head through 270 degrees?

14 Game facts LEVEL 2
A bunch of sporting teasers to test your mental muscle...

1 Who was the first gymnast to score a perfect 10 at the Olympic Games?
2 How old was tennis player Boris Becker when he first won the Wimbledon Men's Singles title?
3 What's the height of the crossbar on the goalposts of a rugby pitch?
4 Put these field events in order of world record distance, starting with the longest:

hammer   shot   javelin triple jump   discus

5 In which sport was Marc Girardelli a five times world champion?
6 When did women's pole vault become an officially recognized athletic event?
7 The score – Iraq 251, Yemen 33. What was the sport and why was it special?
8 Which is the only team to win the football World Cup four times?
9 Who is the only golfer to win all four Majors at least three times each?
10 Why is the Indianapolis 500 so called?

15 Sporting chance LEVEL 2
Can you name the major sport that is played in each of these famous sporting venues?

1 Louisiana Superdome
2 Crucible Theatre, Sheffield
3 Recreation Ground
4 Augusta National
5 SCG
6 Belmont Park
7 Flushing Meadows
8 Spa
9 Murrayfield
10 Neu Camp

16 Motor mania LEVEL 2
Four-wheeled fun.

1 What was the racing number of Herbie, the 'Love Bug'?
2 . . . and which fruit do you associate with Herbie?
3 What breakthrough was made by a car called Thrust SSC in Nevada in 1997?
4 Which car manufacturer's name means 'I Roll' in Latin?
5 Which car did James Bond drive in *Goldfinger*?
6 Which TV cop drove a red Ford Torino?
7 Which was the first car to sell a million?
8 What was the first name of the original Mr Benz?
9 Which sports car featured in the movie *Back to the Future*?
10 Who designed the Mini?

17 Hobby horse LEVEL 2
A few pastime posers.

1 What do astronomers call the point directly overhead in the sky?
2 What do gardeners mean by 'topiary'?
3 What is the proper term for a coin collector?
4 In which sport might you use a Brunswick Command Zone?
5 Who would use a 'Hot Shoe' to connect what to what?
6 In which craft is 'Entrelac' a recognized variant?
7 What single word might magicians use to describe sleight of hand?
8 Which well-known board game came to western Europe from India via Persia and Muslim Spain?
9 Which world surfing venue has the biggest waves?
10 Which oriental art might teach you how to make a paper frog?

All the questions below relate to eating and drinking. Try them to test your culinary know-how and vinous vocabulary.

18 Then add a pinch of... LEVEL 2

1 What are: lovage, burnet, oregano, summer savory?

2 What are: gunpowder, lapsang souchong, orange pekoe and jasmine?

3 What are: angel hair, conchiglie, pappardelle, penne, ziti and tortelloni?

4 What do vanilla, cocoa and tofu have in common?

5 What are: Scotch bonnet, cayenne, jalopeño, birdseye and guajillo?

6 What are: ink cap, shaggy cap, death cap, Jew's ear, cloud ear, lawyer's wig, wood woolly-foot, horn of plenty, shiitake?

7 What are: Yukon Gold, Cara, Belle de Fontenay, Bintje, Ratte, Desirée?

8 What are the UK equivalents of the following American terms:

i	biscuits	ii	broil	iii	blackstrap molasses
iv	chips	v	shrimp	vi	cilantro
vii	eggplant	viii	crackers	ix	scallion
x	romaine	xi	confectioner's sugar		

9 What is the spice saffron?

10 What do these fish have in common?

alevins	smolt
fry	grilse
parr	kelts

20 Mainly wine LEVEL 3

1 Which fortified wine is produced in the Douro region?

2 Which is NOT a grape variety?

Palomino	Tinta Barroca
Len de l'Ell	Gewurztraminer
Riesling	Soave

3 Of which useful piece of wine-cellar equipment are these examples:

foudre	tonneau
tun	pipe
barrique	

4 Give alternative names for these grapes:
  i Pinot Bianco ii Shiraz
  iii Cot iv Garnacha
  v Muskateller

5 What fruits are used in the production of these alcoholic drinks:
  i kirsch ii perry
  iii calvados iv crème de cassis

19 Eat locally LEVEL 3

1 Match the food with the country or region of origin:

i	crêpes suzette	India
ii	bobotie	United States
iii	blueberry slump	Italy
iv	tempura	Thailand
v	moussaka	Scotland
vi	nam pla	Spain
vii	shrikhaind	Japan
viii	panna cotta	France
ix	rumbledethumps	Morocco
x	yabby	South Africa
xi	tarte flambée	Russia
xii	arroz con pollo	Alsace
xiii	kulebyaka	Australia
xiv	cheese fondue	Switzerland
xv	harira	England
xvi	fat rascal	Greece

2 Match each classic French sauce with its essential ingredient:

i	florentine	apple
ii	maltaise	tomato
iii	provençale	onion
iv	soubise	truffle
v	duxelles	cream
vi	Crécy	carrot
vii	normande	spinach
viii	Chantilly	blood-orange juice
ix	Périgueux	mushroom

3 Match the same word to each of these place names to make four sweet treats:

Eccles Genoa Madeira Dundee

6 What kind of wine are these:
  crémant
  spumante
  frizzante
  mousseux

7 Which, if any, of the following are wine faults?
  oxidation
  autolysis
  carbonization
  botrytis

8 How have these ingredients been used in wine-making over the years:
  dried ox blood
  egg whites
  fish swim-bladders
  milk

21 Who was who LEVEL 2

The names below might not instantly ring a bell because all of these people became famous under a different name. See how many future stars you can spot.

1 HARRY WEBB

2 ROBERT ZIMMERMAN

3 WILLIAM CLAUDE DUKENFIELD

4 ARCHIBALD ALEXANDER LEACH

5 ROY SCHERER

6 BERNARD SCHWARZ

7 FREDERICK AUSTERLITZ

8 DINI CROCETTI

9 ANNIE MAE BULLOCK

10 JULIA ELIZABETH WELLS

22 The name's Smith... LEVEL 2

Most of us have harboured a secret desire to be as suave and enigmatic as super-spy James Bond, but how much do you actually know about the man with the golden gun?

1 How many James Bond titles did Ian Fleming write?

2 Which was the first one published?

3 Which famous children's book did he also write?

4 True or False: Kim Basinger was a Bond girl?

5 Which character did Desmond Llewelyn play?

6 Which Bond movie theme did Sheryl Crow sing?

7 In which film did Oddjob make his debut?

8 ...and what was his weapon of choice?

9 Which Bond movie starred Superman's girlfriend?

10 What was special about Bond girl Tracy Draco?

whose eyes?

whose nose?

whose mouth?

whose hair?

whose chin?

whose top half?

whose bottom half?

23 It's a great part
LEVEL 2

The strange-looking celebrity above is a film director's worst nightmare. Can you work out which parts of which stars have combined to form this fantastical creature?

24 Relatively close LEVEL 2
These stars can be linked to one of the
others in some way. First identify
the faces, and then try to figure out
what their relationship is.

25 Marvellous mammals LEVEL 1
How much do you know about the kingdom of the warm-blooded.

1 What is the name of the toothed nocturnal animal, native to Africa, that lives in burrows and feeds mainly on ants and termites?
2 The term 'cetacean' is used to describe what type of mammal?
3 Which animal spends virtually its entire existence hanging by its legs from the boughs of trees?
4 Which is the largest type of bear?
5 What term is applied to mammals such as the kangaroo who carry their young in a pouch?
6 The mouflon, varieties of which inhabit the mountains of south-west Asia, and Corsica and Sardinia, is what kind of animal?
7 Bengal, Chinese, Sumatran and Siberian are all subspecies of what type of creature native to south and south-east Asia?
8 Apart from human beings, which is the only animal to have unique 'fingerprints'?
9 Which is the only mammal capable of sustained flight?
10 Name the mammal, genus *Procyon* and native to North and Central America, that is grey in appearance with a dark band around its tail, a pale face and a band across its eyes.

26 Dinoquiz LEVEL 2
You may need to bone up on some natural history before tackling this quiz about the lost race of dinosaurs.

1 What was the predominant diet of the four-legged sauropod dinosaurs that included the Diplodocus?
2 Who wrote the novel on which the 1993 film *Jurassic Park* was based?
3 What was the largest variety of flesh-eating dinosaur?
4 *Compsognathus* was a genus of tiny carnivorous dinosaur that lived during the late Jurassic period. Which familiar creatures did they most closely resemble in appearance?
5 Nobel prize winning American scientist Luis Walter Alvarez published a controversial theory about the cause of the dinosaurs' extinction. What was it?
6 Name the 1948 film musical starring Frank Sinatra and Gene Kelly in which the skeleton of a dinosaur is knocked over and reduced to a pile of bones.
7 What is the meaning of the Greek word *bronte* in the name of the huge dinosaur brontosaurus, which implies that the animal shook the ground when it walked?
8 Dinosaurs dominated life on land for 140 million years from the late Triassic period until their extinction during which period (64 million years ago)?
9 In which country is Dinosaur Provincial Park where, in the early 20th century, fossil remains of 60 different species of dinosaur were discovered?
10 What was the name of Fred Flintstone's pet dinosaur?

27 In your garden – and beyond
LEVEL 2
How familiar are you with the world of plants?

1 Commonly found in arid regions, which is the largest family of succulent plants, which have fleshy stems and leaves swollen with water-storage tissues?
2 What is the common name of the late-flowering perennial garden plant, genus *Solidago*, which has long-pointed, lance-shaped leaves and numerous tiny, deep yellow-shaded flower heads arranged in a dense pyramid shape?
3 Hybrid tea, floribunda, miniature and climbing are all species of which garden plant?
4 What word describes the study of plants, including the classification, structure, physiology and ecology?
5 In *The Winter's Tale*, which plant did Shakespeare describe as 'the fairest flowers o' the season'?
6 What type of plants are sorrel, angelica and hyssop?
7 Which parasitic plant was venerated by the Druids, who cut it ceremonially from their sacred oak with a golden knife?
8 'Gros Vert de Laon', 'green globe' and 'Jerusalem' are all types of which vegetable?
9 On its mutinous voyage, the *Bounty* had spent five months in Tahiti where it had been sent to gather what type of plants for the West Indies?
10 *Calluna*, *erica* and *daboecia* are three genera of which small, bushy evergreen shrub?

28 Woofers and mousers LEVEL 2
Test your pet-friendliness with these questions about man's best friend and his worst enemy.

1 In which city can you see a statue of a skye terrier named Greyfriars Bobby?
2 Which US president owned cats called Tiger, Blacky and Smokey?
3 Which breed of dog stars in the film *Beethoven*?
4 What is the comparative human age of maturity of a one-year-old cat?
5 Which breed of dog can give evidence in an American court?
6 What is the name of Garfield's rubber chicken?
7 True or false: male dogs bite more often than females?
8 Who is Tweety Pie's stalker?
9 What is the name of the bulldog in the *Tom and Jerry* cartoons?
10 Cats can see in total darkness. True or false?

29 Doctor, doctor LEVEL 3

Don your white coat and test your knowledge of bones, diseases and life-saving treatments.

1 The fibula, tibia and femur are all bones in which part of the human body?

2 Name the US doctor who developed a vaccine against polio.

3 Rubella is a highly infectious, short-lived disease that affects older children and young adults. What is its more common name?

4 Which system of treatment uses massage, manipulation and the stretching of joints to treat backache and pain in the legs, neck and head?

5 Which part of the human body contains the pineal body, the parietal lobe and the frontal lobe?

6 What familiar piece of a doctor's equipment was invented by the French physician René Théophile Hyacinthe Laënnec in 1819?

7 Which highly infectious disease was declared in 1979 to have been completely eradicated?

8 What is the name of the curved bone, also known as the collarbone, that lies horizontally at the base of the neck between the sternum (breastbone) and the scapula (shoulder bone)?

9 What word, used to describe a technique for limiting addictive behaviour and relieving anxiety, was coined by British surgeon James Braid?

10 Which lifesaving device was developed as a result of research combining engineering with medical electronics carried out by Wilson Greatbatch?

31 Technical pursuit LEVEL 3

Calling all boffins...

1 Name the German physicist who, in 1913, invented a device for measuring radioactivity?

2 Name the camera invented by Edwin Land in 1948.

3 The Epson HX-20, introduced in 1982, was the first of its kind. What was it?

4 In which film was the technology available to allow audiences to hear the spoken voice for the first time, and whose voice was it?

5 Registered in 1879 as patent number 223,898, what was Thomas Alva Edison's most famous invention?

6 Who was the British aeronautical engineer who, in 1941, successfully developed the jet engine for aircraft?

7 Which German engineer designed and built the first internal combustion automobile?

8 Who first succeeded in transmitting a radio signal across the Atlantic Ocean?

9 What did British computer specialist Tim Berners-Lee develop in 1989?

10 Types of what were discovered by Christian Hulsmeyer, Germany, 1904; Gregory Breit and Mark Tuve, USA, 1925; and Sir Robert Watson-Watt, UK, 1934–5?

30 Pluses and minuses LEVEL 3

Does your mathematical know-how add up?

1 The ratio of the circumference of a circle to its diameter is denoted by which Greek letter?

2 Which British philosopher and mathematician said: 'mathematics may be defined as the subject in which we never know what we are talking about, nor whether what we are saying is true'?

3 How many faces has a dodecahedron?

4 Which German mathematician gave his name to a one-sided surface that he created by giving a strip of paper a half-twist then fastening the ends together?

5 What type of algebra, in which logical operations are replaced by symbols, is also known as symbolic logic?

6 What is the better known name of Charles Lutwidge Dodgson, a lecturer in mathematics at Oxford University in the 19th century, who compiled a series of mathematical brain teasers known as 'pillow problems'?

7 In 1665, shortly before his death, a French mathematician created a celebrated theorem by claiming to have discovered the proof that there are no instances in which the sum of two cube numbers is equal to another cube number. Who was he?

8 Name the 3rd-century BC Greek mathematician who wrote *Elements of Geometry*, which remained a standard textbook until the 19th century?

9 Which Scottish mathematician invented logarithms and devised a set of graduated bones used as an aid to multiplication?

10 Which French mathematician, physicist and theologian invented the first calculating machine in 1641?

32 In the stars LEVEL 3

Limber up for our space programme.

1 Name the first satellite sent into space in 1957?

2 Name the area of the Moon where Armstrong, Aldrin and Collins make their landing on July 20, 1969?

3 Name the Polish astronomer whose 1530 treatise *On the Revolution of the Celestial Sphere* angered the Church because it was at odds with the official view that the Earth was at the centre of the universe.

4 Discovered between Mars and Jupiter, of what are Ceres, Pellas, Juno, Vesta and Cybele examples?

5 Titan, Mimas, Rhea and Dione are just 4 of the 20 known moons of which planet?

6 In 1929, who propounded the big bang theory?

7 What is the name of the US spacecraft that arrived at Venus in 1990?

8 Which planet has a red spot as wide as the Earth, a feature that has been observed for 300 years?

9 Which comet visited our solar system during 1997, but will not return until the year 6000?

10 Visible in the constellation Canis Major, what is the name of the brightest star in the night sky?

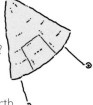

33 In the pipeline

The rectangular grid in the bottom right shows both ends of three pipelines. On its left is a list of 20 scientific terms, each of which is primarily used or discussed in one of the following sciences:

DIFFICULTY:
LEVEL 1   10 minutes
LEVEL 2   7 minutes
LEVEL 3   5 minutes

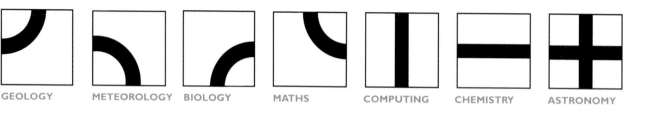

GEOLOGY   METEOROLOGY   BIOLOGY   MATHS   COMPUTING   CHEMISTRY   ASTRONOMY

For each item in the list, draw the appropriate component in the numbered square. For example, item 5 is Mistral, a meteorological term for a cold northerly wind that blows through France, so the component corresponding to METEOROLOGY has been drawn in square 5.

If you correctly repeat this for the other 19 squares, the diagram will show you how the pipe ends connect together. We want to know which ends connect to which. The three pipes never join, but may cross over other pipes. Reconsider your answers if the diagram appears to be wrong.

1   Modem
2   Protozoa
3   Isotope
4   Pulsar
5   Mistral
6   Abscissa
7   Nebula
8   Doldrums
9   Routine
10   Mainframe
11   Amino acid
12   Red shift
13   Corona
14   Nephrite
15   Nonagon
16   Apogee
17   Jade
18   Hypotenuse
19   Catalyst
20   Amalgam

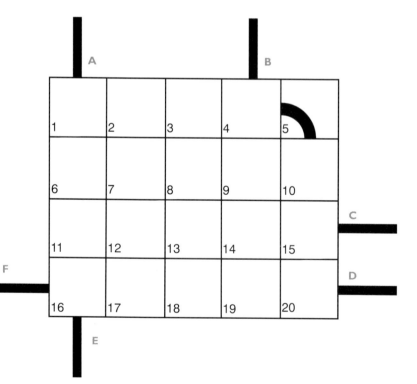

34 Trivia trail   LEVEL 2

Your objective is to find the correct route through this quizzical maze. Each intersection contains a question, the answer to which contains either NORTH, EAST, SOUTH or WEST. This tells you which exit you must take to move to the next question. If you go off the left or right side of the grid, you emerge at the box on the opposite side of the same row. If you have used the correct route, you should find that two boxes were not used. Which two?

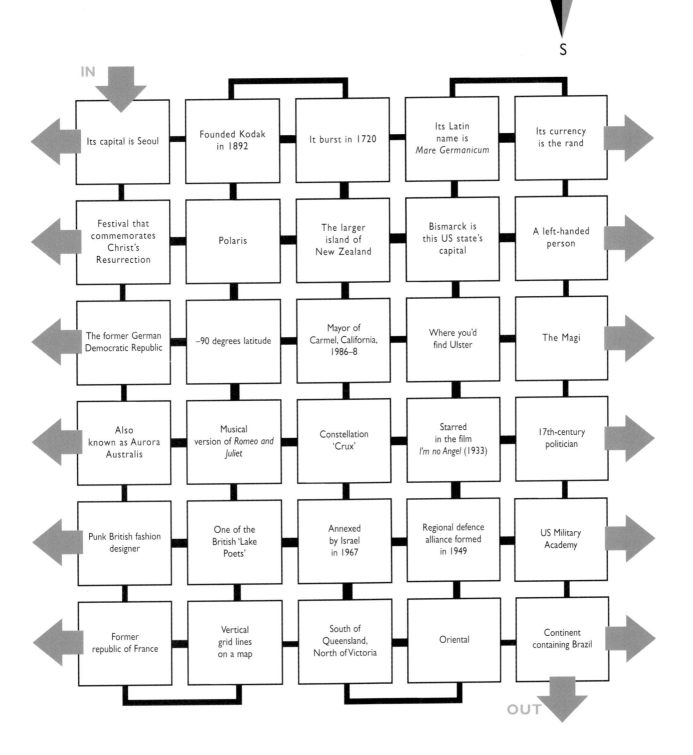

Where on Earth? Test your knowledge of the planet with these 30 geography questions. How well do you know your way around the world?

35 Place these names
LEVEL 1

1 Which two countries' names include the letter 'x'?

2 What are the modern names of the African countries once called Northern Rhodesia and Southern Rhodesia?

3 Name four states of the USA beginning with the letter 'I'.

4 Insert four three-letter words into the gaps to make the names of four countries:

F***ce

S***en

B***ei

C***

5 These countries are known locally as Eire, Ellas and Suomi. What are they called in English?

36 Watch your language
LEVEL 1

6 In which country is Magyar spoken?

7 Which country contains the largest number of Portuguese speakers?

8 How many official languages are spoken in Switzerland?

9 Name two countries beginning with 'C' that have both French and English as official languages.

10 Which dialect of Chinese is spoken in Hong Kong?

37 Neighbours LEVEL 2

11 Name the nine countries that have borders with Germany.

12 The longest continuous border in the world is between which two countries?

13 Which country is bounded by Iran, Afghanistan, China and India?

14 Apart from a short Atlantic coastline, one African country is almost completely surrounded by another. Name them both.

15 Which international border is crossed most frequently?

38 Common places LEVEL 2

16 What do these have in common, geographically: Beaver, Raccoon, Skunk, Seal, Snake, Salmon?

17 What do these have in common: Edward, Victoria, Tanganyika, Nakuru, Turkana?

18 What do these have in common: McKinley, Aconagua, Kilimanjaro, Kosciusko?

19 What do these have in common: Bridgetown, Port of Spain, Castries, Port-au-Prince, Kingston?

20 What do these have in common: Gozo, Pantelleria, Skiros, Kefallonia, Menorca?

39 Biggest, smallest, tallest
LEVEL 3

21 Which is the world's largest country by area?

22 ...and the second largest?

23 In which country is the world's highest waterfall – the Angel Falls?

24 Where is the world's largest active volcano?

25 Which is the world's smallest independent country?

26 Which of the world's freshwater lakes has the largest surface area?

27 Which is Europe's highest mountain?

28 What's special about the Challenger Deep in the Mariana Trench?

29 The Sahara is the largest desert by far. Which is second largest?

30 Alphabetically, which are the first and last states of the USA?

40 Movie Location quiz
LEVEL 1

In each of the following movies the principal action took place in a particular country of the world.

Can you name the country?

1 *Evita*

2 *Schindler's List*

3 *The Emerald Forest*

4 *Doctor Zhivago*

5 *Casablanca*

6 *Viva Zapata!*

7 *Ryan's Daughter*

8 *The Last Emperor*

9 *Frantic*

10 *Strictly Ballroom*

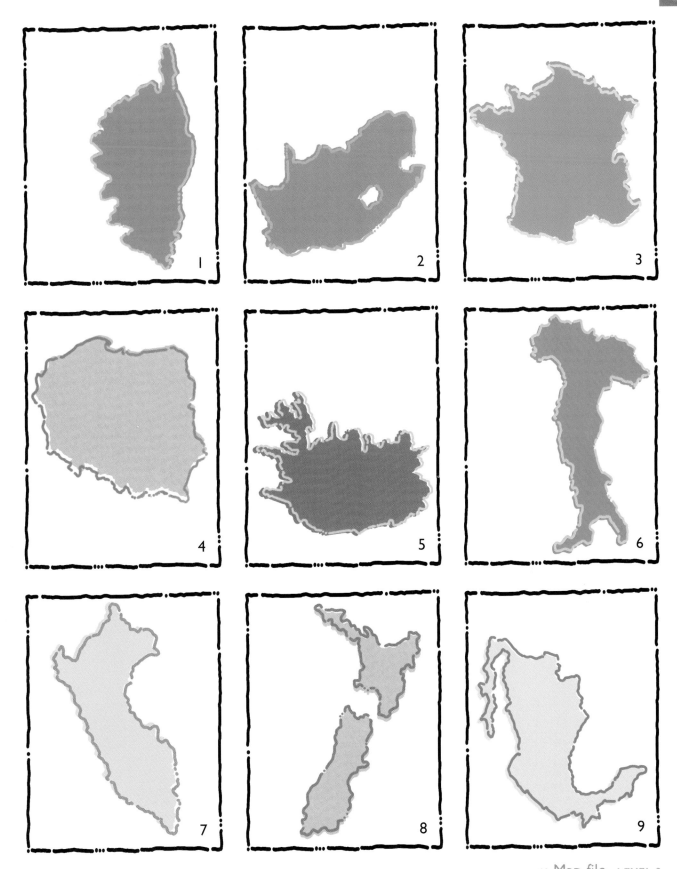

Can you match the listed countries and regions with the outlines shown above? Some are definitely more difficult than others: none is drawn to scale and north is not always to the top.

MEXICO   **NEW ZEALAND**   **POLAND**
ICELAND   **CORSICA**   **FRANCE**
ITALY   **SOUTH AFRICA**   **PERU**

Quizzes come in all shapes and sizes. Some are played for fun, some for prestige, some for big money. They can be deadly serious, or just a way of whiling away an hour in the pub. But whatever form they take, quizzes are good mental exercise. They test not just your stock of knowledge, but your speed of reaction and recall, and your powers of estimation, logic and guesswork.

A starter for ten

Where did quizzes come from?

The origin of the word 'quiz' is completely obscure. Legend has it that in the 1780s a theatre manager in Dublin wagered that he could introduce a new word into the lexicon within a day. By writing the mysterious word QUIZ on the walls of the city, he soon had everyone talking and won the bet: from graffiti to dictionary in under 24 hours. The word was subsequently used as a description of anything odd (as in 'quizzical'). How it then came to mean a knowledge-based test is not known, but that sense was established by the 1860s. What is certain is that it is a very fitting word, looking as it does like a strange amalgam of question, query, quip and quest.

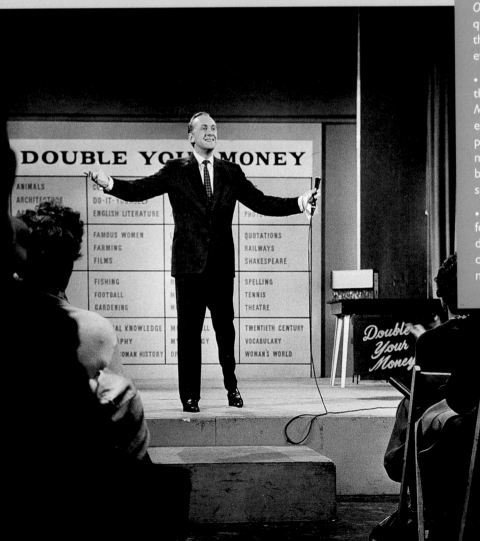

Did you know that...

• In 1998, producers of the TV quiz *100%* had to change their rules after contestant Ian Lygo won 75 shows in a row. They felt viewers were getting bored with his invincibility.

• The largest ever TV quiz was Japan's *Ultra Quiz*, which involved 5000 contestants. The prizes for the winner included a racehorse and a helicopter.

• The world's first TV quiz show was broadcast on May 31, 1938. It was called *Spelling Bee*, and a panel of guests were invited to spell a series of words, scoring one point for each correct answer.

• The greediest television quiz in terms of questions is *Fifteen To One*, which gets through about 120 questions per half-hour episode – that is around 8000 questions in every series.

• Bill Wright, the creator of the intimidating BBC series *Mastermind*, was inspired by his experiences of interrogation as a prisoner of war. The military mantra 'Name, rank and number' became 'name, occupation and specialized subject'.

• David Briggs, who had the idea for *Who Wants To Be A Millionaire?*, developed the concept over a cup of coffee with two partners in a motorway service station.

YOUR LUCKY DAY
Quizzing is a spectator sport, especially when there are prizes to be won. *Double Your Money* was one of the first British TV shows to offer cash for questions.

Biggest ever quiz cheats

The worst scandal ever to hit a quiz happened in 1958 on the American TV show *Twenty-One*. The reigning champion, Herb Stempel, was proving unpopular with the commercial sponsor of the programme, so the producer approached Charles Van Doren, an English lecturer, about becoming a player on *Twenty-One*. It was hoped that the personable Van Doren would knock Stempel off his throne.

The scandal broke when it transpired that Van Doren was supplied with questions by the producer before the programme went on air. The fact that Stempel got the questions too did not matter: the integrity of the show was compromised, and it was soon dropped. It did, however, provide the inspiration for a hit film, *Quiz Show*, in 1994.

And in 1998, on a Swiss TV quiz, a student named Tommaso Ramundo caused viewers to jam a TV channel's phone lines when he suspiciously gave the answer to a question that had not yet been asked. It turned out that a friend of his had attended rehearsals and provided him with the answers.

What makes a good quiz?

- **Pitch it right**: most people should be able to answer most questions. The point of a quiz is not to show how much the setter knows.

- **Keep it simple**: the system that works best for social occasions is a written quiz in which teams record their answers on paper. That way, everyone gets a chance to contribute.

- **Make it clear**: the host should have a confident attitude, a clear voice and an idea of how to pronounce any difficult words such as crannog, Solzhenitsyn or Dadaism. The host should at least read through the questions beforehand.

- **Do your research** and ensure your facts are up to date: for example, Lagos is no longer the capital of Nigeria, even though some reference books might say so.

- **Take it slowly**: the questions should be read out at the rate of about one a minute. Competitors appreciate a short gap between each round to allow thinking time and to take notes.

- **Don't be obscure**: the exact height of Big Ben is not something that everyone has at their fingertips, and it is not, on its own, a very interesting fact.

- **Assume nothing**, no matter how obvious the answer seems: the author Margaret Drabble was asked to set specialist questions about her own books for *Mastermind* – she made several mistakes.

Break it up by having a picture or music round half-way through the competition: if you are using electronic equipment, make sure it works before you start.

42 Take your pick LEVEL 2

To make life easier for you, we're showing you the answers to this quiz. But to make sure that life is not too easy we've supplied twice as many wrong answers as right ones. Can you identify the right answers?

WORKS OF ART

1 Who painted the ceiling of the Sistine Chapel in Rome?
  a Reubens
  b Leonardo da Vinci
  c Michelangelo

2 The *Mona Lisa* is also known as...?
  a La Gioconda
  b La Giocasta
  c La Giocosa

3 Who painted *The Laughing Cavalier*?
  a Rembrandt
  b Frans Hals
  c Van Dyck

4 Which of these painters was a Surrealist?
  a Edgar Degas
  b Salvador Dalí
  c Paul Cézanne

5 Who painted *The Scream*?
  a Edvard Munch
  b Claude Monet
  c Henri Matisse

6 In Botticelli's *Birth of Venus*, what is Venus standing on?
  a the beach
  b a dolphin
  c a seashell

7 Who created pictures of Marilyn Monroe and Campbell's soup tins?
  a David Hockney
  b Andy Warhol
  c Ben Nicholson

8 Who painted *The Fighting Temeraire*?
  a Canaletto
  b Hogarth
  c Turner

9 Which of these painters was not an Impressionist?
  a Pissaro
  b Picasso
  c Monet

10 Who painted *Flatford Mill*?
  a Constable
  b Sargent
  c Inspector

CLASSICAL MUSIC

11 Who composed *Madame Butterfly*?
  a Verdi
  b Rossini
  c Puccini

12 How many symphonies did Beethoven write?
  a eight
  b nine
  c ten

13 To which family of instruments does the cor anglais belong?
  a brass
  b woodwind
  c percussion

14 Which of these is not a choral work by Handel?
  a Messiah
  b Samson
  c Methuselah

15 What nationality was Gustav Holst?
  a Swedish
  b Danish
  c British

16 Who composed the ballet *Swan Lake*?
  a Tchaikovsky
  b Mendelssohn
  c Verdi

17 With which instrument is Nicolò Paganini associated?
  a piano
  b violin
  c trombone

18 Complete the title of Saint-Saëns' best-known work: *Carnival of the _____*?
  a Gods
  b Mardi Gras
  c Animals

19 What was Arturo Toscanini's profession?
  a conductor
  b composer
  c pianist

20 What does *adagio* mean?
  a lively
  b slowly
  c sadly

FOLKLORE AND LEGEND

21 Which fire-breathing monster has a lion's head, a goat's body and a dragon's tail?
  a Chimera
  b Sphinx
  c Gryphon

22 Where would you find a banshee?
  a Iceland
  b Ireland
  c Israel

23 Witches supposedly revel on Walpurgis Night. When is that?
  a the Eve of May Day
  b the Eve of All Saints' Day
  c Christmas Eve

24 Which dog guarded the gates of Hades?
  a Styx
  b Cerberus
  c Pluto

25 In Egypt, how was the god Anubis represented?
  a as a jackal
  b as a hyena
  c as a crocodile

26 What was the Phoenix?
  a a lion
  b a dragon
  c a bird

27 In medieval English folklore, another name for Puck was...
  a Hobgoblin
  b Robin Goodfellow
  c Robin Hood

28 In Norse mythology, what is the paradise for slain warriors called?
  a Valkyrie
  b Valhalla
  c Valencia

29 Who had an affair with Guinevere?
  a Sir Gawain
  b Sir Galahad
  c Sir Lancelot

30 Which magical root is said to shriek when pulled up?
  a mangrove
  b mandrake
  c mangel-wurzel

43 Treasure hunt LEVEL 2

Two teams of treasure hunters are searching through old catacombs to find the X that marks the spot. Unfortunately, they do not know which is the right X. So in each cell they must decipher a clue which, if followed correctly, will lead to the treasure sites. Right answers will bring them nearer; wrong ones will take them down blind alleys.

Begin the first expedition at START 1 (bottom of page). If you think the statement in this space is correct, follow the 'TRUE' arrow,

otherwise follow the 'FALSE' arrow. Continue until you reach one of the 'X' symbols.

Then start again on the second expedition as indicated at START 2 and travel as before until you reach a different 'X' symbol. This second route is longer than the first, and neither path crosses over the other.

Once you have completed both routes, see if you have found the true locations of the treasure by checking with the answers at the back of the book.

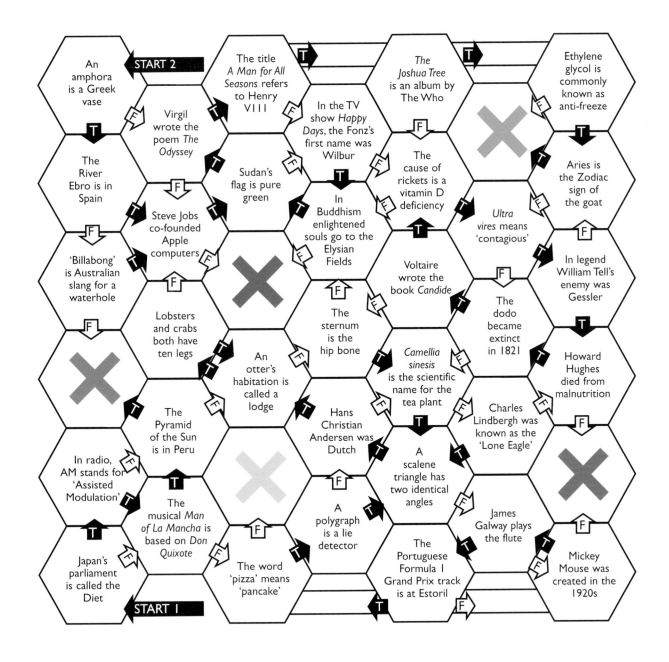

44 Images of Britain
LEVEL 1

The above montage contains images of 12 of Britain's most famous landmarks. How many can you recognize?

45 Location finder LEVEL 2

Now see if you can match the locations below with the landmarks you've identified.

Blackpool

Brighton

Bristol

Cambridge

Coalbrookdale

Gateshead

Gwynedd

Lincoln

Loch Duich

London

North Yorkshire

Uffington

46 Dates to remember LEVEL 3

Identify the completion date of each landmark using this list of possibilities.

c. 3000 BC	1726	1864
c. 1260	1779	1894
1400	1822	1991
Late 13th century	1831	1997

A re you wise to the ways of Britain? See if you really know who's what and what's where in this sceptered isle.

47 Who?

LEVEL 1

1 Who is the Patron Saint of Wales, whose feast day falls on March 1?

2 Who is Britain's First Lord of the Treasury?

3 'I have found it impossible to carry the heavy burden of responsibility and to discharge my duties as king as I would wish to do without the help and support of the woman I love.' Which woman is being referred to here?

4 Which singer, born in Pontypridd in 1940, was inspired by the energetic style of Elvis Presley?

5 Who in the 1970s earned the malicious nickname 'Milk Snatcher'?

6 Who in the 1990s spiced up the world of pop music with a very short Union Jack mini-dress?

LEVEL 2

7 Who was the first woman to receive the Order of Merit? She is best known for her humanitarian efforts during the Crimean War.

8 Who, collectively, were the six farm workers from Dorset sentenced in 1834 to seven years in an Australian penal colony?

9 Which protest singer and ex-soldier wrote a song containing the line 'I don't want to change the world, I'm not looking for a new England.'?

10 Who wrote *Brighton Rock*?

11 Name the Scottish architect who designed the Glasgow School of Art in 1896, and established a distinctive British style of *art nouveau*.

LEVEL 3

12 Name the architect responsible for the new headquarters of MI6, as well as many other new buildings along the River Thames.

13 Name the six categories of citizen who are not allowed to stand as Members of Parliament.

48 What?

LEVEL 1

1 Name the block of stone used in the coronation of Scottish kings until it was taken to Westminster Abbey by Edward I. (It was returned to Scotland in 1996.)

2 According to the nursery rhyme, what objects did Old King Cole, the 'merry old soul', call for?

3 Name the four flowers that are the traditional emblems of England, Ireland, Scotland and Wales?

LEVEL 2

4 According to an Act of 1908, what plots of land are officially set at one-quarter of an acre in size?

5 From 1865, what had to proceed steam carriages by a distance of at least 60 yards (55m)? The repeal of this regulation is commemorated annually by the Brighton Run.

LEVEL 3

6 On what might you find one of the following: a leopard's head, an anchor, a rose and a castle?

7 What unconventional obituary appeared in the *Sporting Times* in 1882, giving rise to a sporting tradition that is still observed?

49 Why?

LEVEL 1

1 Why did King John *not* sign the Magna Carta at Runnymede?

2 According to legend, why did Lady Godiva ride naked through the marketplace in Coventry?

3 What issue drove Britain to wage a (largely diplomatic) war with Iceland between 1959 and 1976?

4 Why is the 'Bloody Tower' in the Tower of London so called?

LEVEL 2

5 Why, in 1913, did the British Government introduce an Act allowing certain ailing prisoners to be released from prison, only to be re-arrested as soon as they were well? And how was the bill known?

6 Why, thanks to William Henry Fox Talbot, is a window of the south gallery of Lacock Abbey, Wiltshire, photographically famous?

LEVEL 3

7 Between 1837 and 1844, Charles Dickens published his first works. How was he able to tailor his stories to public taste as he went along?

8 Why is the strange symbol '£' used to represent pounds sterling?

50 Where?

LEVEL 1

1 Which two parliaments were united by the Act of Union of 1707?

2 Name the city which is the birthplace of David Hockney and is the home of the National Museum of Film, Photography and Television.

3 Which village in Wales provided the location for the 1960s television series *The Prisoner*?

4 In which town is the National Library of Wales?

LEVEL 2

5 Name London's main airport from 1920 to 1946 (before the advent of Heathrow).

6 The National Eisteddfod changes its location each year, but the International Music Eisteddfod always takes place in the same Denbighshire town. Name the town.

LEVEL 3

7 Where, at the height of the English Civil War between 1642 and 1645, did Charles I base his Royalist headquarters?

8 Where in Britain would you be if you found yourself visiting the Goose Fair, the Lace Market and the Trent Bridge cricket ground?

9 Where in Britain can you admire six concrete cows standing in the middle of an open field?

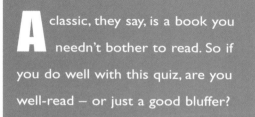

A classic, they say, is a book you needn't bother to read. So if you do well with this quiz, are you well-read – or just a good bluffer?

51 Matchmakers LEVEL 1

Can you match the items on the left with the famous story in which they appear, listed on the right?

THE OBJECTS	THE STORIES
Bottle labelled 'Drink Me'	*Legend of King Arthur*
Golden Fleece	*Treasure Island*
Apple	*The Rime of the Ancient Mariner*
Sword named 'Excalibur'	*William Tell*
Submarine named *Nautilus*	*The Importance of Being Earnest*
Albatross	*Cinderella*
Persian slipper	*Jason and the Argonauts*
Pieces of eight	*Adventures of Sherlock Holmes*
Glass slipper	*Alice in Wonderland*
Handbag	*20,000 Leagues Under the Sea*

52 Famous first lines LEVEL 2

Can you name the works of literature that open with the following lines? (Extra points for the author.)

1 'Now is the winter of our discontent made glorious summer by this sun of York.'

2 'Someone must have been telling lies about Joseph K., for without having done anything wrong he was arrested one fine morning.'

3 'Last night I dreamt I went to Manderley again.'

4 'Season of mists and mellow fruitfulness, Close-bosomed friend of the maturing sun.'

5 'It was the best of times, it was the worst of times.'

6 'Except for the Marabar Caves – and they are twenty miles off – the city of Chandrapore presents nothing extraordinary.'

7 *'Longtemps je me suis couché de bonne heure* [for a long time I used to go to bed early].'

8 ''Twas brillig, and the slithy toves /Did gyre and gimble in the wabe.'

9 'Dr Iannis had enjoyed a satisfactory day in which none of his patients had died or got any worse.'

10 'This book is largely concerned with Hobbits.'

53 What's in a name? LEVEL 2

Can you match the real names in the list on the left with the writers' pen names in the list on the right?
Clue: even if you don't know the answer, there is quite often some connection between authors' real names and the *nom de plume* they choose for themselves.

REAL NAME	PEN NAME
Samuel Clemens	Currer Bell
Hiraoka Kimitake	Catherine Marchant
Eric Blair	George Eliot
François-Marie Arouet	George Orwell
Alexei Maximovich Peshkov	Mark Twain
Catherine Cookson	Mary Westmacott
Charlotte Brontë	Maxim Gorky
Agatha Christie	Yukio Mishima
Mary Ann Evans	Lewis Carroll
Charles Lutwidge Dodgson	Voltaire

54 Famous last lines LEVEL 2

Can you name the works of literature which close with the following lines? If you don't actually know the answer, there may be a clue in the text. (Extra points for the author.)

1 'The tranquil waterway leading to the uttermost ends of the earth flowed sombre under an overcast sky – seemed to lead into the heart of an immense darkness.'

2 'I leave this manuscript, I do not know for whom; I no longer know what it is about: *stat rosa pristina nomine, nomina nuda tenemus*.'

3 'The creatures outside looked from pig to man, and from man to pig, and from pig to man again; but already it was impossible to say which was which.'

4 'And in truth, who would not make the circuit of the world for less than that?'

5 'And a police inspector is on his way here – to ask some – questions – .'

6 'Yet stands the Church clock at ten to three? And is there honey still for tea?'

7 'Here then, as I lay down the pen, and proceed to seal up my confession, I bring the life of that unhappy Henry Jekyll to an end.'

8 'Yours is the earth and everything that's in it, And – which is more – you'll be a Man, my son!'

9 'So thanks to all at once and to each one Whom we invite to see us crowned at Scone.'

10 'He loved Big Brother.'

55 Who said it? LEVEL 1
Which fictional characters said the following lines?
(Extra points if you can name their creators too.)

1 'Be but sworn my love, and I'll no longer be
   a Capulet.'
2 'I am well aware that I am the 'umblest person
   going. My mother is likewise a very 'umble person.'
3 '*Tous pour un, un pour tous*
   [All for one, one for all]!'
4 'O Lovely Pussy! O Pussy my love, What a
   beautiful Pussy you are.'
5 'I always heard, Sancho, that to do good to rogues
   is to throw water into the sea.'
6 'Give me a girl at an impressionable age and she
   is mine for life.'
7 'It happened one day, about noon, going towards
   my boat, I was exceedingly surprised with the print
   of a man's naked foot on the shore.'
8 'It was a blonde. A blonde to make a bishop kick
   a hole in a stained glass window.'
9 'Reader, I married him.'
10 'Tabaqui came to me not long ago with some rude
   talk that I was a naked man's cub and not fit to
   dig pig-nuts.'

57 Whose line LEVEL 3
Do you know the titles of the poems from which the
following lines come? There may be a clue in the text.
(Extra points for the poets too.)

1 'Should auld acquaintance be forgot,
   And never brought to mind.'
2 'When people call this beast to mind,
   They marvel more and more
   At such a little tail behind,
   So large a trunk before.'
3 'Abandon all hope, you who enter!'
4 'From the waterfall he named her,
   Minnehaha, Laughing Water'
5 'If I should die, think only this of me:
   That there's some corner of a foreign field
   That is for ever England.'
6 'Though Nature, red in tooth and claw
   With ravine, shrieked against his creed.'
7 'The Moving Finger writes; and, having writ,
   Moves on.'
8 'Each in his narrow cell for ever laid,
   The rude forefathers of the hamlet sleep.'
9 'Nobody heard him, the dead man,
   But still he lay moaning;
   And I was much further out than you thought.'
10 'One end is moo, the other milk.'

56 Children's favourites LEVEL 1
Here is a collection of crafty questions from the
world of children's fiction. (Extra points if you
can name the authors involved.)

1 Where did Peter Pan and the Lost Boys live?
2 What happens to Pinocchio when he lies?
3 Before Dorothy was whisked off to the Land
   of Oz, in which American state did she live?
4 Why did the Princess have to sleep on a pile
   of mattresses and feather beds placed on
   top of a single pea?
5 What was the name of the murderer
   encountered by Tom Sawyer?
6 When a group of children walked through a
   magic wardrobe into a wintry land, where
   had they arrived?
7 Who found a cottage 'made of bread and cakes,
   and the window panes were of clear sugar'?
8 In which European country do Asterix and
   Obelix battle against the Roman invaders?
9 What is the name of the school for wizards
   where Harry Potter studies?
10 In *Watership Down*, what kind of
   creature is Kehaar?

58 Fictional females LEVEL 2
Can you work out the names of these famous
fictional females from the short descriptions?
(Extra points for their creators.)

1 A shrewd elderly spinster with an endless
   fascination for murder.
2 High-spirited heroine who falls in love
   (eventually) with Mr Darcy.
3 Sulky fairy who swallows poison intended for
   Peter Pan.
4 Flower-seller given elocution lessons by
   Professor Henry Higgins.
5 Curious little girl who falls foul of the Queen
   of Hearts.
6 Married Southern belle loved tragically by
   Jay Gatsby.
7 Upper-class woman who falls for her
   game-keeper Oliver Mellors.
8 Domineering wife of the Bishop of Barchester.
9 Nineteenth-century French doctor's wife
   who seeks romance through adultery.
10 Former slave who charts her own
   memories of survival.

59 Hit the headlines

Here you'll find a series of newspaper-style headlines relating to particular historical and cultural events. First work out the subject of the story then try the following:

LEVEL 1 Identify the century
LEVEL 2 Identify the decade
LEVEL 3 Identify the exact year

1 St Bernadette, a 14-year-old peasant, experiences a series of visions in a grotto.

2 Talk show *A.M. Chicago* changes its title to include the name of the host.

3 The 'Little Wonder', Charles Blondin, crosses a tightrope 50m (165ft) in the air.

4 Dag Hammarskjöld, Secretary General of the United Nations, goes missing.

5 Louise Brown is born at Oldham General Hospital, England, creating a world first.

6 Tom Morris of Prestwick, Scotland, becomes the lucky first man to achieve this feat.

7 King Camp Gillette launches his new invention, which people are supposed to throw away.

8 Karol Wojtyla, former goalkeeper and quarry worker, gets top job in global firm.

9 Queen commits suicide using poison – but later theories suggest a different means.

10 Linda Eastman marries fiancé Paul, breaking the hearts of many teenage girls.

11 Pocket-sized magazine publishes first highly readable edition.

12 Husband and wife team make an elemental, but ultimately fatal, discovery.

13 Final score in this inaugural match: Uruguay 4, Argentina 2.

14 The *New York World* publishes Arthur Wynne's new game – much frustration follows.

15 Frenchmen Jacques and Joseph Montgolfier take to the air in their invention.

60 Battle stations   LEVEL 2

Here are clues to ten military engagements that changed the course of history. They may all be familiar to you – but can you put a name to each battle, and say when it took place? (Hint: the battles are listed here in chronological order, earliest first.) Award yourself one point for each part of each answer you get right.

1 William of Normandy invaded England and defeated King Harold by the seaside.
Supply (a) the name of the battle; (b) the year it happened.

2 The decisive battle of the 100 Years' War: King Henry V's archers defeated the French near Calais.
Supply (a) the name of the battle; (b) the century in which it took place.

3 Admiral Lord Nelson defeated the French fleet near Cadiz, but was fatally wounded by a sniper.
Supply (a) the name of the naval battle; (b) the year it took place.

4 Napoleon met his final defeat, beaten by the Duke of Wellington near a village in Belgium.
Supply (a) the village that gives its name to the battle; (b) the year it took place.

5 180 volunteers, including Jim Bowie and Davy Crockett, were overwhelmed by the Mexican army in San Antonio, Texas.
Supply (a) the name of the fort they were defending; (b) the decade in which the siege took place.

6 Colonel George Custer and his 200 cavalrymen were killed by the Sioux led by Chief Sitting Bull.
Supply (a) the name of the battle; (b) the decade in which it took place.

7 The Japanese air force made a surprise attack on the home base of the US Pacific Fleet in Hawaii.
Supply (a) the name of the naval base; (b) the month and year of the attack.

8 Allied troops invaded German-occupied France, landing on the beaches of Normandy.
Supply (a) the code name for the day of the landings; (b) the month and year they took place.

9 British paratroopers defeated Argentine forces in the first land battle of the Falklands War.
Supply (a) the site of the battle; (b) the month and year.

10 USA, Britain and the Saudis launched an air and missile attack on Iraq in the first Gulf War.
Supply (a) the name of the campaign; (b) the month and year it began.

61 Those were the days   LEVEL 2

How much do you know about the 20th century? Perhaps you weren't even around for some of these decades, but the 40 events below all left their mark on the world. Try to make your own impression with 40 right answers.

1920s

1 In which year was the Wall Street Crash?

2 Which leader became leader of the Italian state in 1922?

3 Name the Scotsman who invented television.

4 Who made the first solo transatlantic flight?

5 Which Swedish actress was the seductive star of the film *Flesh and the Devil*?

1930s

6 In which year did the Spanish Civil War end?

7 Name the German parliament building that was set on fire in 1933.

8 Which epic retreat ended in 1935?

9 Name the actor who terrified the USA with a radio dramatization of *The War of the Worlds*.

10 In 1938 a British locomotive set a world speed record for steam engines. What was the name of the locomotive?

1940s

11 In which year was the state of Israel established?

12 Which former leader of the Russian revolution was assassinated in Mexico?

13 Name the swing-band leader who disappeared on a flight to France in 1944.

14 Who succeeded Winston Churchill as Prime Minister of Britain in 1945?

15 Who wrote *Nineteen Eighty-Four*, published in 1949?

1950s

16 In which year did Hungary revolt against Soviet domination?

17 Name the first athlete to run a mile in under 4 minutes.

18 Who was elected US President for a second term in 1956?

19 Name the man who emerged as Soviet leader following the death of Stalin.

20 Who were the first two men to reach the summit of Everest?

1960s

21 In which year was the Berlin Wall erected?

22 Who was the second man to set foot on the Moon?

23 Who became The Beatles' manager in 1961?

24 Which 1966 film starring Paul Scofield won six Oscars?

25 Name the surgeon who conducted the world's first heart transplant operation.

1970s

26 In which year did Elvis Presley die?

27 Name the military dictator who expelled 50,000 Asians from Uganda in 1972.

28 Whom did Princess Anne marry in 1973?

29 Who became the British Poet Laureate in 1972?

30 Who became leader of Iran after the Shah was driven into exile?

1980s

31 In which year was 'Black Monday', when stock exchanges crashed in London and New York?

32 Name the Romanian dictator who was summarily executed by firing squad on Christmas Day 1989.

33 Which 1987 film directed by Bernardo Bertolucci won nine Oscars?

34 Who became the youngest man ever to win the Wimbledon singles title?

35 Who was the former secret agent whose book *Spycatcher* was banned in Britain?

1990s

36 In which year was Nelson Mandela released from prison?

37 Whom did Michael Jackson marry in 1994?

38 In April 1998 a federal judge dismissed a sexual harassment case against President Clinton: who was the woman involved?

39 In which city were the 1992 Olympic Games held?

40 Which record became the biggest-selling single of all time in 1997?

62 They made history LEVEL 3

Here is a set of pictures of some of the most famous
figures in world history. Your task is simply to name them,
but you get an extra point if you can identify which of
them was tutored by the great philosopher Aristotle.

63 Wet afternoon medley   LEVEL I

Can you match the following rain-related tunes to
the singers who recorded them? For extra points, name
the year in which each song had its debut.

It Keeps Rainin'	Frankie Laine
Crying in the Rain	Neil Sedaka
Tell it to the Rain	Tina Turner
Don't Let the Rain Come Down	B. J. Thomas
Raindrops Keep Falling on my Head	The Four Seasons
I Can't Stand the Rain	Fats Domino
Rain Rain Rain	Randy Crawford
Laughter in the Rain	The Everly Brothers
Just Walkin' in the Rain	Ronnie Hilton
Rainy Night in Georgia	Johnnie Ray

64 Summer songs   LEVEL I

Can you match the following sunny tunes to the
recording artists? Name the year for added points.

The Sun Ain't Gonna Shine Anymore	Frank Sinatra
Sunny Afternoon	Elton John
Summer is Over	The Animals
Summertime Blues	Cream
House of the Rising Sun	Stevie Wonder
Summer Holiday	Eddie Cochran
Sunshine of Your Love	Walker Brothers
Don't Let the Sun Go Down on Me	Frank Ifield
Summer Wind	The Kinks
You are the Sunshine of My Life	Cliff Richard

66 War effort   LEVEL 2

Can you match the following tunes, all of which became
popular during the Second World War, with the artists who
recorded them? Some of the songs were of course recorded
by more than one artist, in which case we want the most
successful version. Extra points awarded for the songwriters.

The White Cliffs of Dover	Marlene Dietrich
Run Rabbit Run	Glenn Miller
Wish Me Luck	Noël Coward
Boogie Woogie Bugle Boy	Doris Day
Lili Marlene	Vera Lynn
I'll Be Seeing You	The Andrews Sisters
In the Mood	Flanagan and Allen
Sentimental Journey	Dinah Shore
One For My Baby	Gracie Fields
Don't Let's Be Beastly to the Germans	Frank Sinatra

65 Rainbow rhapsody   LEVEL 2

Here we've listed some of the artists who've recorded
these colourful songs on the right. Put each song back
with the right singer or band.

Yellow Submarine	David Essex
Green, Green Grass of Home	Alannah Myles
Red, Red Wine	Bing Crosby
Blue Monday	REM
Black Velvet	The Stranglers
White Christmas	The Beatles
Pink Cadillac	UB40
Silver Dream Machine	Tom Jones
Golden Brown	Natalie Cole
Orange Crush	New Order

67 Technicolor test   LEVEL 2

Now see if you can match these groups and artists of
various hues to their respective hit songs.

Red Hot Chilli Peppers	Paranoid
Pink Floyd	Real Gone Kid
Yello	Give it Away
Deacon Blue	Let's Stay Together
Black Sabbath	Another Brick in the Wall
Barry White	The Race
Bobby Goldsboro	You Sexy Thing
Al Green	Two Can Play That Game
Bobby Brown	Honey
Hot Chocolate	You're the First the Last My Everything

68 Classical oddities

There are all manner of bizarre stories to be found in the world of classical music, as this quiz proves.

LEVEL 1

1 Which Tchaikovsky work, written in 1880, employs real cannons as part of the percussion section? It depicts the retreat of Napoleon's army from Moscow.

2 What happens 840 times during Satie's piano chorale *Vexations*?

3 Which *avant-garde* composer incorporated silence as an element in his work, most infamously in his composition *4'33"* (1952) in which the 'performers' sit in complete silence for 4 minutes and 33 seconds?

4 Why are there only seven movements in Holst's suite *The Planets* , when there are nine planets in the solar system?

LEVEL 2

5 What did Liszt pay women to do during his concerts?

6 What was remarkable about Arturo Toscanini's conducting?

7 Which composer was supported for 14 years by a wealthy patron called Madam Nadezhda von Meck, whom he was not allowed to meet?

8 Who composed a musical work named *The Trout*?

LEVEL 3

9 Which American composer, a self-styled 'bad boy of music', composed the *Ballet Mécanique*, the score for which requires the use of aeroplane propellers, car horns and electric bells?

10 What performer dances to Stravinsky's *Circus Polka*?

69 It's instrumental

This quiz tests your knowledge of musical instruments.

LEVEL 1

1 It has 46 strings and 7 pedals. What is it?

2 Which musical instrument is similar to the flute, except that it is smaller and its pitch is one octave higher?

3 Which two woodwind instruments have double reeds?

4 What is the technical term for the piece of plastic, ivory, metal or wood in the shape of a rounded triangle, with which the strings of guitars and other stringed instruments are plucked?

LEVEL 2

5 What name is given to a traditional Indonesian orchestra in which the musicians play a variety of drums, xylophones and gongs?

6 Which steam-operated keyboard instrument shares its name with the Greek muse of epic poetry?

7 Which ceramic egg-shaped hollow instrument, invented by an Italian musician called Giuseppe Donati in the 1800s, contains a mouthpiece and up to eight finger-holes?

8 The balalaika is a triangular stringed instrument used in Russian folk music. How many strings does it have?

LEVEL 3

9 What links a large type of tuba with *Monty Python's Flying Circus*?

10 Complete the analogy: piano is to pianoforte as cello is to _____?

70 The works

This quiz concentrates on particular musical works and events surrounding their composition.

LEVEL 1

1 Which part of Wagner's *Lohengrin* can you hear performed in church hundreds of times every year?

2 Why does Beethoven's ninth symphony also represent a major musical first?

3 Which Verdi opera was first performed in Egypt, to celebrate the opening of the Suez Canal?

4 What connects Mahler's tenth symphony, Puccini's opera *Turandot*, Borodin's opera *Prince Igor* and Schubert's *Symphony No. 8 in B Minor*?

LEVEL 2

5 Which of Beethoven's symphonies carried a dedication to Napoleon that was later revoked?

6 Two well-known operas have a central character called Figaro. Name them.

7 Which well-known work by Ravel was originally written for the dancer Ida Rubenstein?

8 The celesta, an instrument that consists of a glockenspiel played by a keyboard mechanism, was first used orchestrally in which Tchaikovsky ballet?

LEVEL 3

9 Unconventional choreography and orchestration caused the audience to riot at the première of which Stravinsky ballet in 1913?

10 Whose symphonies include the *London*, the *Clock*, the *Surprise* and the *Military*?

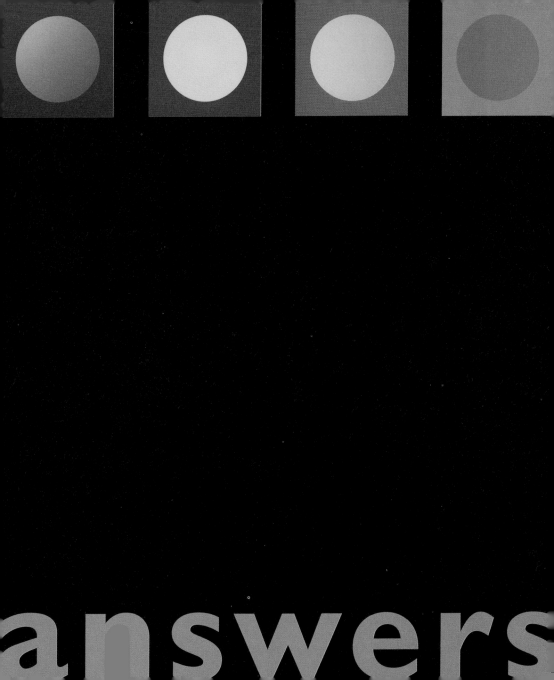

answers

1 Wonky donkey
C is the odd one out. The pattern on its understrap is missing.

2 Potty pottery
Vase D is the odd one out. The third square in the bottom row has a different-coloured middle.

3 Hitching a lift
There are 15 differences, as shown below.

4 Spot the dog
The identical dogs are D and F.

5 Soup's up!
The identical bowls are D and I.

6 Life's a beach
The figure skater on the left-hand side of the picture is the interloper.

7 Scene of the crime
The pictures should be in this order: F, H, B, E, I, A, C, G and D.

8 The impossible room
Working from **left** to **right** the errors are:

I love NY shows a picture of the Eiffel Tower.
Telephone (banana handset).
Cushion on left of couch is made of concrete.
Lampshade has no base.
Window – shed is upside down; flower is too big; curtain has no tie.
Wall switch has no button.
Photo album is back to front.
Tumbler on table is upside down.
Bunch of grapes contains both green and black grapes.
Glass top of table has only three supporting legs.
Table is touching the floor at the back and floating at the front.
Calendar shows Feb 31 – Feb has only 28 or 29 days.
Chair has no wheels on its legs.
Clock – back to front and has three hands.
Computer mouse is a cartoon mouse.
Wall map shows South America joined to Africa.
Shadow of lampshade does not match shape of lamp.
Book case – *Romeo and Jeff; War and Peas;* different door handles.

(Don't be fooled by the picture in the top left-hand corner: this an accurate representation of a famous optical illusion – see page 54 – so it's not wrong as such.)

9 Lost in squares

12 Kaleidomaze

10 Maddening maze

13 Tiny circles

14 Spy relay
Character A hid the
papers in the windmill.

C gave them to B;
B gave them to D;
D gave them to A.

11 Disco lights

15 The tomb
of the pharaohs

16 Computer bug

◯ = value of monitors

The first figure shows the highest-scoring route through the maze. The second figure (below) shows the lowest-scoring route through the maze.

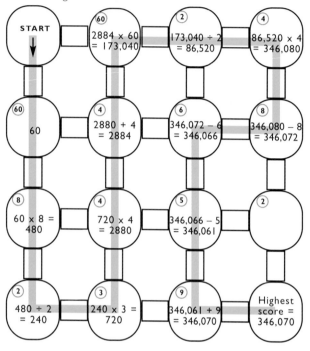

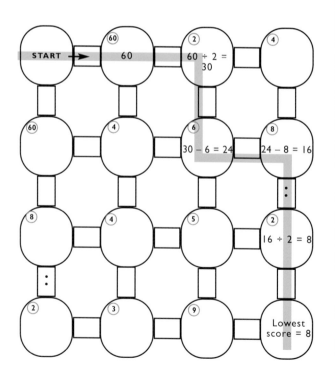

17 Escape plan

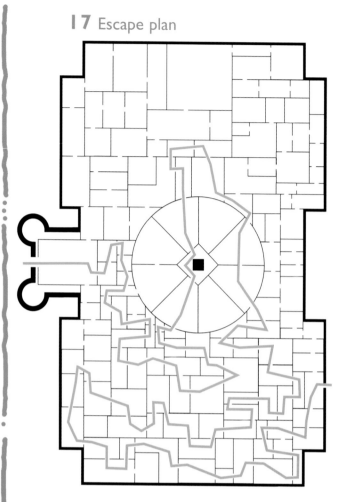

18 Paradise and purgatory

You selected the correct route if you picked the following objects.

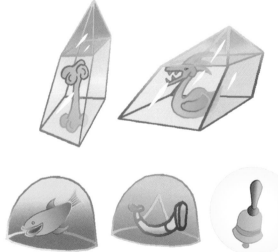

19 Treasure Island express

If you've followed the clues correctly you should have destroyed the track as shown in red, in the order 1–7 (did you realize that a 'giant scull' is the oar, and not the giant skull?). This leaves the brown route shown as the only possible route to the treasure, marking the X circled in the top right-hand corner as the spot.

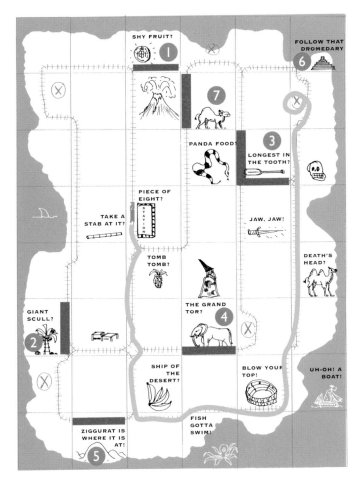

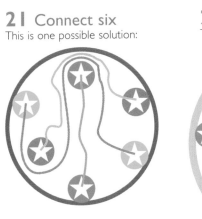

20 The Kempe Castle kidnappers

If you've followed the clues you should have reached the professor by this route.

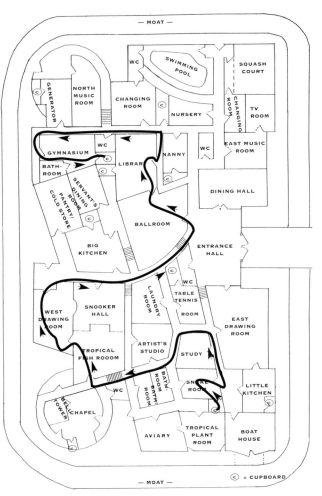

21 Connect six
This is one possible solution:

22 Relate eight
This is one possible solution:

23 Five to five
This is one possible solution:

24 Three-way freeway

1 Route avoiding the pink squares:

2 Route avoiding the green squares:

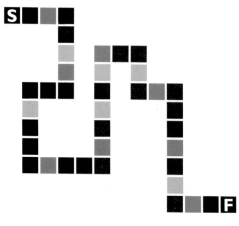

3 Route avoiding the blue squares:

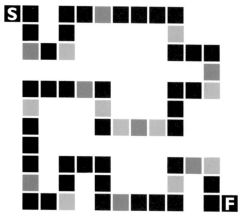

25 Constellation

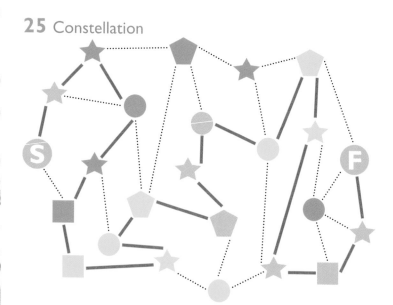

26 Fit the pieces

27 Lock together

28 Hex-agony

29 Time for colour

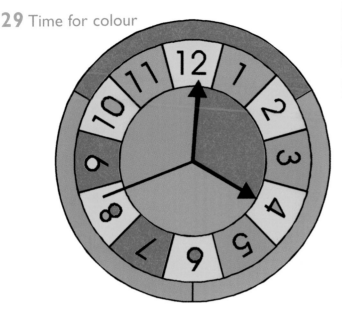

30 Band width 1
There is just one band.

31 Band width 2
There are two separate bands.

32 Bee's-eye view
There are five occurrences of the pattern.

33 Psychedelic chess
There are six occurrences of the pattern.

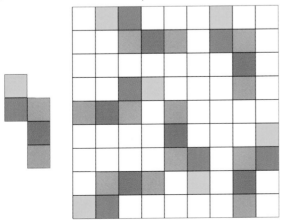

34 Know the ropes
1 No – this is easily seen to be a simple loop if you imagine the right-hand end moved across to the left.
2 Yes – this is the simplest knot possible and is called a 'trefoil knot'.
3 Yes – this is another trefoil knot. However, notice that the knot is oriented differently to the previous knot. Knots, like people, are 'right-handed' or 'left-handed'.
4 No – the large loop at the bottom will slip through the hole in the middle, and this will become a straight piece of rope.
5 Yes.
6 No.
7 No.
8 Yes.
9 No.

35 Loop the loops 1
The yellow pieces make a complete loop.

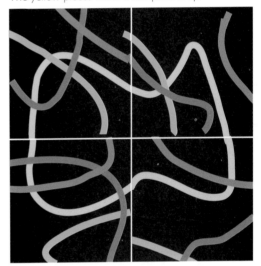

36 Loop the loops 2
The blue pieces make a complete loop.

37 Rotation vexation

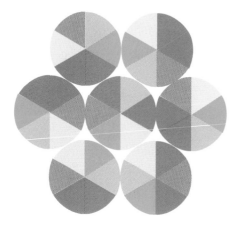

38 Flag jigsaw 1
Piece C is correct.

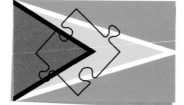

39 Flag jigsaw 2
Piece B is correct.

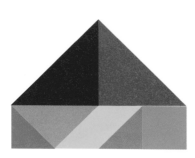

40 On the campsite

41 Formal chair

42 Farmer Giles's barn

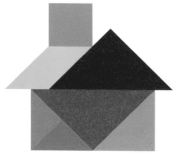

43 Home sweet home

44 Bust in profile

45
Light my
fire

46 Top hat for Ascot

50 Tangrams count

47 Time for a rest

48 On the run

49 Rabbit flees from a fox

51 A chip off the old block
There are 33 cubes missing.

52 Cube-odd
The quickest method goes as follows:
total volume of cuboid if complete = 6 x 6 x 5 = 180
volume of each small cuboid = 2
number of small cuboids in complete cuboid = 180/2 = 90.

However, we can count that six small cuboids have been removed from the large cuboid. Therefore, there must be 90 – 6 = 84 small cuboids in the figure.

53 Warehouse clearance
Start with crate 1. The sokoban (X) moves up one space, then right one, pushing crate 1 one space to the right; then X moves left one, up four, right two and down all the way until he reaches the top side of crate 1; then he pushes crate 1 out of the exit. Now X moves crate 3 one to the right, enabling him to access crate 2 from the bottom side. Pushing from beneath, X moves crate 2 up one space; then X himself moves right one, up two, left one and pushes crate 2 down one space; X himself then moves right one and down one then pushes crate 2 two spaces to the left. Now X goes the long way round (using the now cleared passage on the left) to move crate 2 out of the warehouse. From here, it is easy to remove crate 3, followed by the others.

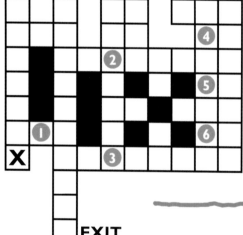

54 Arrow point
84. The lowest number divisible by 6, 7, 8 and 9 is 504. A movement of 504 teeth results in 84 revolutions of the 6-toothed cog, 72 revolutions of the 7-toothed cog, 63 revolutions of the 8-toothed cog, and 56 revolutions of the 9-toothed cog, leaving all the cogs the right way up again.

55 Classicist's pastime
7. A movement of 42 teeth will see the 'T' revolve completely seven times and the 'R' revolve completely six times, with the 'O' being unaffected. The 'Y' will turn 4⅔ times round – and as the 'Y' reads correctly every third of a turn, it will still read as a 'Y'.

56 Fisherman's delight
3. Three revolutions of the 8-toothed cog will result in a movement of 24 teeth. The 'O' will be unaffected, the 'Y' will turn 2⅔ times, the 'S' will turn 1½ times (it reads the same upside down), the 'T' and 'E' will revolve completely four times each and the 'R' will revolve completely twice.

57 A revolutionary problem
2. A double revolution of the first cog will result in a movement of 20 cog teeth. The triangle cog will have moved around 1⅔ revolutions, making the triangle the right way up. The circle is unaffected and the star will have turned round twice to get to its current position.

58 Leonardo's teapot
Handle A must be turned anticlockwise and handle B clockwise to make the tray descend.

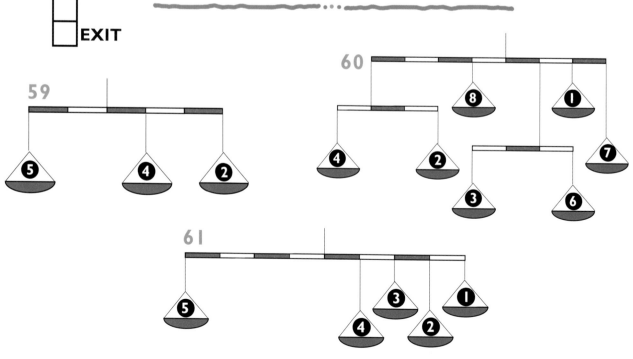

62

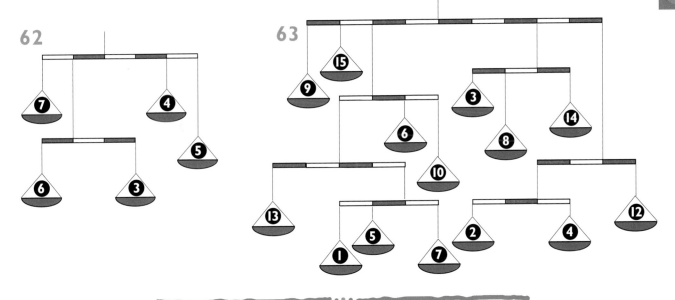

63

---

64 In the tub
The water level falls.
When the metal is taken out of the bowl, the bowl displaces less water, hence the water level falls by an amount corresponding to the volume of water equal to the weight of the metal.
When the metal is dropped in the water, it displaces its own volume of water and the water level rises. The amount by which it rises corresponds to the volume of the metal, very much less than the volume of an equal weight of water. The net result is, therefore, a fall in water level.

65 Barrel brawl
Tip the barrel until the beer is level with the top and the liquid is still. If you cannot see any part of the bottom of the barrel, as shown, the barrel is more than half full. If, however, you can see part of the bottom of the barrel, it is less than half full.

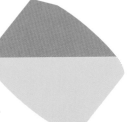

66 Temperature conversion
1 To change Fahrenheit to Celsius: substract 32° and then divide by 1.8.
77 – 32 = 45 ÷ 1.8 = 25
Therefore: 77°F = 25°C.

2 To change Celsius to Fahrenheit: multiply by 1.8 then add 32°.
15 × 1.8 = 27 + 32 = 59
Therefore: 15°C = 59°F.

Curiously, -40° is the only temperature that is the same in both Fahrenheit and Celsius.

67 Sands of time
Start both glasses running at the same time.

Turn the four-minute glass over as soon as it runs out (i.e., after four minutes). Turn the seven-minute glass over immediately that runs out (after an extra three minutes). At that moment the four-minute glass has one minute left. Turn it over when that minute is over (an extra one minute). Then turn the seven-minute glass over, which at that time has only run for one minute (an extra one minute). That makes a total of nine minutes (4 + 3 + 1 + 1).

---

68 Thick as a plank
Cut the board as shown below:

Then lay pieces A and B side by side as shown:

69 Collision course
The pink ball shoots off at 8000 km/h and the green ball stops motionless, dead in its tracks. (In real life the speed would be less than 8000 km/h due to energy lost during the collision.)

70 Focal point
Point X.

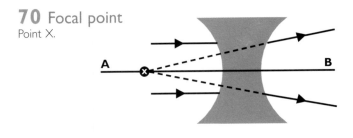

71 Planetary motion
16 months (8 times longer than planet Z). Kepler's Third Law states that the square of the time taken for one orbit is equal to the cube of the average distance from the centre of the Sun. Thus, to increase the distance from the Sun by a factor of 4 will affect the orbit period by the square root of 4^3 (8). So increasing the distance four times increases the period by eight times. Planet Z's period is two months, so Y's is 2 × 8 = 16 months.

Battle stations
72 WORKED SOLUTION
The starting position looks like this:

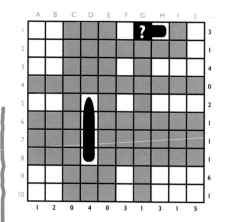

We know that all the rows and columns containing a 0 must be completely made of sea. Row 6 already contains one piece of ship and cannot have any more, so the rest of that row must be filled with sea. Because H1 is the start of a ship, G1 must be a piece of ship. (We don't know whether that's the middle or the end, so mark it with a '?' for now.) Column G contains only one piece of ship, so the rest of that column must be sea too, as must I1, F2, H2 and I2 as no ship can be adjacent. So now we have:

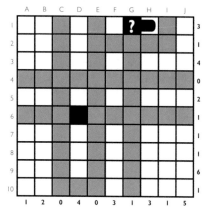

D5 must be the end of a ship, and D7 must contain a piece of ship. Row 7 has only one piece of ship, so the rest must be sea. Now you'll notice that there are no places left for the battleship to go except column D, so D8 must be the end of the battleship. Row 8 has one piece of ship, so the rest of it is filled with sea. Similarly, all four of column D's pieces have been located, so the remainder is all sea. The situation now looks like the figure at the top of the next column.

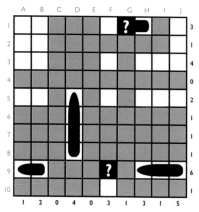

Row 9 has six pieces of ship, but only six spaces left. So they must all be ships and the space around them must be sea, except F9, which might be a submarine or a destroyer on F9 and F10.

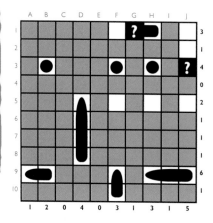

Since row 10 has one piece of ship and one space remaining, F10 must be the other half of a destroyer. We can also fill the rest of columns A and I with sea. Row 3 has four spaces for four pieces of ship. One of these spaces is B3, so column B can be filled with sea. The battle scene now looks like this:

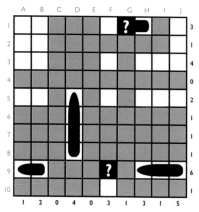

Thinking about what ships there are left to place, there must be a submarine at J5 and the final pieces of cruiser at J1 and J2, to give the final answer:

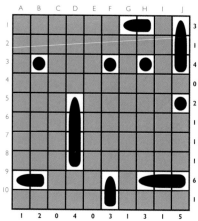

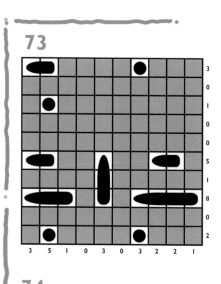

73

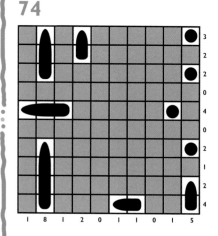

74

75

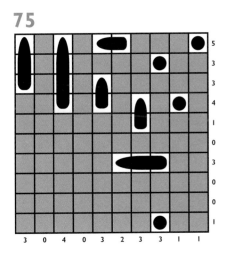

76

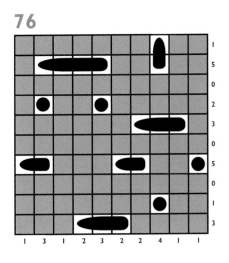

77

78 The green man
Turn the picture upside down and you'll find a man wearing a hat, with the different parts made from vegetables.

79 Trident tested
No answer needed.

80 Impossible triangle
The truth is it's in the middle. Sounds impossible? Try measuring it yourself.

81 Line weight
Both lines are exactly the same length, believe it or not.

82 Upstairs downstairs
No answer needed.

83 Spaced out
It spells AVOID – a subtle reference to the white space (a void, perhaps?) between the coloured blocks forming the letters.

84 Elegance and strength
No answer needed.

85 Shape up
A minimum of three colours is necessary.

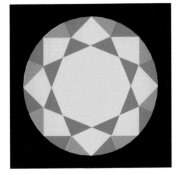

86 Odd fellows
The two pieces shown in white in this diagram are the odd ones out. The remaining pieces form the corners of four 'invisible triangle' illusions, denoted here by the four different colours.

87 Looking-glass skyscrapers
No answer needed.

88 Shoot that poison arrow
The word FLIGHT is formed, as shown.

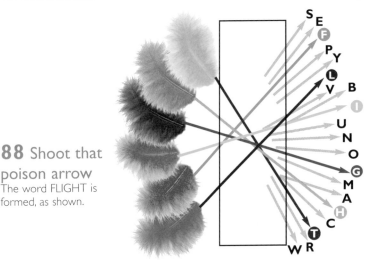

89 Pick up sticks
Yellow short; orange short; red short; lilac short; purple short; light green short; dark green short; light blue long; dark blue short; yellow long; orange long; red long; lilac long; purple long; light green long; dark green long; light blue short; dark blue long.

1 Anagram mountain

LEVEL 1	LEVEL 2	LEVEL 3
Vat	Oblique	Voyeuristic
Next	Heraldic	Rhododendron
Party	Costumier	Brainstorming
Exodus	Beefburger	Autobiographic

2 World leaders

LEVEL 1
1 Yasser Arafat
2 Willy Brandt
3 Joseph Stalin
4 Tony Blair

LEVEL 2
1 Henry Kissinger
2 Benito Mussolini
3 Mary Robinson

LEVEL 3
1 Franklin D. Roosevelt
2 President Boris Yeltsin

3 Writers and poets

LEVEL 1
1 Victor Hugo
2 Germaine Greer
3 Marcel Proust

LEVEL 2
1 Edgar Allan Poe
2 Boris Pasternak
3 Georges Simenon
4 William Shakespeare

LEVEL 3
1 Sir Arthur Conan Doyle
2 Hans Christian Andersen

4 Stop and go anagrams

LEVEL 1	LEVEL 2
Porthole	Creative, reactive
Glossary	Unloaded, duodenal
Computer	Latitude, altitude

LEVEL 3

Recounts, construe, counters, trounces
Staplers, plasters, psalters
Triangle, altering, alerting, integral, relating

5 Odd one out

1 **spied**. It contains an embedded foodstuff, pie: s(pie)d. The rest contain embedded drinks: a(gin)g, f(rum)p, s(tea)m, v(ale)t.

2 **annoy**. All of the others spell names backwards: Liam, Enid, Tessa, Dennis.

3 **brethren**. All of the others have the adjacent letters 'the' embedded in the word.

4 **elope**. All of the others have two different pronunciations and meanings.

5 **taper**. All of the others are anagram pairs: armed/dream, sited/edits, rated/trade, easel/lease, react/crate, remit/merit, ulcer/cruel.

6 **end**. All of the other three-letter words are spelt out by taking alternate letters of one of the seven-letter words: ant/magnate, apt/warpath, ape/sampled, woe/swooped, use/quashed, red/friends, ear/remarry.

7 **defamation**. All of the others contain the vowels AEIOU once each only.

8 **amen**. All of the other four-letter words are anagrams of the last four letters of one of the ten-letter words: naturalism/slim, temperable/bale, cognisance/cane, balustrade/dear, participle/pile, stalagmite/item, confidante/neat, beastliest/site.

9 **admonished**. None of the other words repeats a letter. Admonished repeats the letter D.

10 **rob**. In all the others the sum of the letters is 42 when you add up the total of their positions in the alphabet.

6 Mixed doubles

TOGA	GOAT	6 and 7
PLATES	PETALS	5 and 11
LEMON	MELON	9 and 15
LIMES	SMILE	4 and 13
FRINGE	FINGER	1 and 16
TOP HAT	HOT TAP	8 and 14
HEADLAMPS	LAMPSHADE	2 and 12
CHARIOT	HARICOT	3 and 10

7 summer   **8** password

9 overheat   **10** weightless

11 Jigsquare 1

M	I	R	E
A	R	I	D
G	O	N	G
I	N	K	Y

12 Jigsquare 2

S	L	A	B
T	Y	K	E
A	R	I	A
B	E	N	D

13 Hiawatha's secret

1 **JUPITER** – the fifth planet from the Sun.

2 **EPSILON** – the fifth letter of the Greek alphabet.

3 **PENTAGON** – a five-sided geometric shape, like that shown in the puzzle's illustration.

4 **STARFISH** – a sea creature with five arms.

5 **QUINTUPLE** – word meaning 'five-fold'.

LEVEL 2
All the words are related in some way to the number five.

LEVEL 3
The letters in the highlighted squares form the word **NATIONS**. The 'Five Nations' was a confederacy of the five Iroquois tribes who inhabited New York.

Alpha Dice

14	15	16	17
1 RESCUE	1 POLITE	1 CARBON	1 BICEPS
2 HAMMER	2 RESUME	2 OBTAIN	2 ATOMIC
3 INCOME	3 ORIENT	3 NUGGET	3 SAHARA
4 NOTICE	4 DEFECT	4 SENIOR	4 KIMONO
5 ENOUGH	5 USEFUL	5 URGENT	5 ESCUDO
6 SILENT	6 COUPLE	6 LITTLE	6 TUNDRA
7 TRENCH	7 TARGET	7 THREAD	7 BRONZE
8 OXYGEN	8 IMPURE	8 ABROAD	8 ARTERY
9 NEEDED	9 OPPOSE	9 NATION	9 LAUREL
10 EASIER	10 NARROW	10 TOMATO	10 LITANY
First column **RHINESTONE**	First column **PRODUCTION**	First column **CONSULTANT**	First column **BASKETBALL**

18 Definitely maybe…

You have CLEARLY MISUNDERSTOOD my position. I have a SMALL CROWD of people under my control – about 30 people as an EXACT ESTIMATE. I have told them to ACT NATURALLY while we are ALONE TOGETHER.

You have probably built up an ACCURATE STEREOTYPE of my psychological background. It is ALMOST EXACTLY thirty years since the end of the CIVIL WAR in which I fought for another country. It was PRETTY UGLY on the battlefield because it was difficult to avoid all the FRIENDLY FIRE. Thankfully I was on active service for only 18 months until I was FOUND MISSING by the PEACE FORCE that was drafted in. Since then I have lived here as a RESIDENT ALIEN. It is ODDLY APPROPRIATE that this military experience is useful now.

Use some MILITARY INTELLIGENCE and supply me with a crate of NON-ALCOHOLIC BEER and six PLASTIC GLASSES from which to drink it. I also demand a NON-STOP FLIGHT to Antigua. Comply or suffer the consequences – this is your only MANDATORY OPTION.

Remember my motto: ANARCHY RULES!

19 A to Z of synonyms

Merge	AMALGAMATE
Fat	BLUBBER
Lust	CONCUPISCENCE
Cheated	DIDDLED
Fizz	EFFERVESCENCE
Feathery	FLUFFY
Chuckling	GIGGLING
Tourist	HITCH-HIKER
Prime	INDIVISIBLE
Spell	JUJU
Ornament	KNICK-KNACK
Defamatory	LIBELLOUS
Least	MINIMUM
Vacuum	NOTHINGNESS
Birdwatcher	ORNITHOLOGIST
Sprinkled	PEPPERED
Embodiment	QUINTESSENCE
Cooler	REFRIGERATOR
Stupidity	SENSELESSNESS
Gossip	TITTLE-TATTLE
Dishonest	UNSCRUPULOUS
Tap	VALVE
Beaten	WHITEWASHED
Photocopying	XEROGRAPHY
Annual	YEARLY
Nap	ZIZZ

EXPLANATORY NOTES:
Prime means indivisible because a prime number is one that is indivisible by any whole number (except 1 and itself).

20 Z to A of antonyms

Modesty	RAZZMATAZZ
Monotone	POLYPHONY
Eccentric	ORTHODOX
Snooty	LOWBROW
Stall	REV
Beginner	GURU
Constant	INTERMITTENT
Trust	POSSESSIVENESS
Seller	PROCURER
Transparent	OPAQUE
Intellectual	NINCOMPOOP
Novice	AFICIONADO
Separation	INTERCONNECTION
Least	MAXIMUM
Coherent	ILLOGICAL
Electronic	CLOCKWORK
Umra	HAJJ
Ciao	ARRIVEDERCI
Overt	HUSH-HUSH
Direct	ZIGZAGGING
Elite	RIFF-RAFF
Quit	PERSEVERE
Neat	MUDDLED
Typical	UNCHARACTERISTIC
Archangel	BEELZEBUB
Prelude	CADENZA

EXPLANATORY NOTES:
1 To stall an engine means to provide so little fuel that it no longer works; providing more fuel than the minimum necessary causes the engine to 'rev' up.

2 The *umra* is a minor pilgrimage to Mecca; the main pilgrimage, which followers of Islam are expected to make once during their adult lives, is called the *hajj*.

3 A prelude is an introductory piece of music. A cadenza is heard towards the end of the performance.

21 Match this

Anchor man	Gold fish
Achilles heel	Rain bow
Chain saw	Ghost writer
Mountain goat	Kangaroo court
Fruit cocktail	Bermuda triangle
Money spinner	Crocodile tears
Queen bee	
Roman nose	(The 'unwanted' pairs:
Rubber stamp	Red herring
Wolf whistle	White elephant
Leap frog	Goose berry)

22 Letter logic 1

```
ACROBATIC   T   C   C
 E   V   L   N ARIOSO  M
GREENBACK   A   G     M
 E   R   I   E ANONYM
GARDENING   S   I     I
 L   O   O   S OFFSET
 B   C   E GEM   U A   T
ALLEGRO   ESSENCE
 C   A   O ACE   E T   E
KARATE   O   E   S     I
 S   I   I IRONSTONE
TANIST   N   J U     T
 A   E   T ACCORDION
GOTHIC   O   I     I   N
 E   S   C ABANDONED
```

23 Letter logic 2

```
BABIES   ATLANTIC
 L R O     A H E     H
ORIENT   OBSOLETE
 C G S   A L Y P     E
KOHL   EDGES   DEER
 A T A   A A B   E   S
GOODHUMOURED
 E N E   H   G M     C
   TARAMASALATA
 S F D   U L   N R   S
HEEL   SCOUT   AQUA
 I R B   T M V U     N
VIRGINIA   BOLERO
 E E L   O     T S   V
RATTLING   PERSIA
```

24 Time for tea

```
EASY   CARROT
A   O   A   O   H
R   HUNGARY   R
T   N   E   A   E
HANG   BLUE
     ENTER
BEER   OATH
A X   B T   E
K THOUGHT   A
E R   R E   R
REASON   RUST
```

25 Time for tea

```
MELT     IDEA A
I   RAPID     D
G   I   L     U
HARP SHEKEL   T
T I   I   O T
   ADVENTURE
S   E   U A   R
CIRCUS   KNEE E
E   A     E   P
N   LARGE G   L
TELL     PONY
```

26 Zoo clue

```
DORY   CHUB
O   A G Y   A
DUMBO   EEL
O     R N   D
  PELICAN
C   A L     P
HOG   LLAMA
O   L A   R
WREN   DEER
```

27 Gridlock

```
EPIC   CAPS   POSE   MAPS
COMA   UNIT   ONUS   EMIT
HOPI   STOA   LEISURELY
OPERATINGSYSTEM   TOE
   TORAH   SEMIS   BAHTS
GNU   ERE   WED   ARTY
LOOK   DRESSREHEARSED
USUAL   OPT   DAR   YTTR
TESLAS   EAVE   RIG   SAY
   AMUSEMENTPARK
FIG   ALP   PEER   LANDAU
EROS   TAB   MAG   BOILS
DAGUERREOTYPES   XMAS
   EELY   QUO   OAT   ERR
PETRI   GUTSY   LIEIN
ART   TELEPHOTOLENSES
PIECEMEAL   URGE   GINA
ECRU   META   TIER   LOIN
RASP   ASHY   HORS   ENDS
```

28 Honeycomb crossword

DAYDREAM — NEURON — MICA — ORGANZA — CURRANT — NOUGAT — GOLDRUSH

29 Crystal crossword

1 Avocados
2 Updating
3 Attracts
4 Nova
5 Strange
6 Piranha
7 Octangle
8 Arctic

The planet anagram is **Neptune**.

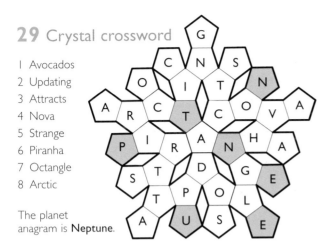

30 Giant family crossword

DANISHPASTRY SCATTERBRAIN
UNICORN WEBFOOTED SCOURGE
LEASEHOLDERS GEORGEORWELL
BAMBI FAWN BEE LENS POONA
RETRENCH RUBICON LADYBIRD
EGO GOTHAM MAP PIGEON FRO
LIGHTHEARTED MISINTERPRET
KEYPUNCH HUT CROTCHET
CALABRIA ULYSSES ROSEANNE
IMMURE LIFTINGBODY STREAM
GAZPACHO LOGICAL COURTIER
OLDNORSE BED TAPDANCE
STATENISLAND CHERRYPICKER
IRA SIGHTS EMU FENCER ICE
NEOPHYTE SPIDERS KITSCH
YES RENO CUB ROAD TAO
LEADERWRITER BENNYGOODMAN
TIPPING SCRATCHES LEAFLET
ELVISPRESLEY ROCKINGHORSE

31 Mind the gaps 1

BLOSSOM DREAM
SUTRA UPSTART
ESCAPED AHEAD
MELODY MEMBER
TENOR LETTERS
HARNESS LYING
SHEET SISTERS

32 Mind the gaps 2

AVIARY AFFAIR
TON GENDARMES
VERDI ENDURES
UNREALISTIC
EVENING HASTE
OCTAGONAL ODD
SIESTA FRAMED

33 Flying colours 1

The anagram is **Mother Teresa**.

STOLE D USAGE
LAYSISTER
ASIDE K MEETS
V INTRO N
PREEN A SNAIL
O AGITATE N
JUTS L M VELD
S ECLIPSE A
CELLO N CROWD
E WIDER N
DIANA O ESSEN
SURROGATE
EMEND R MYTHS

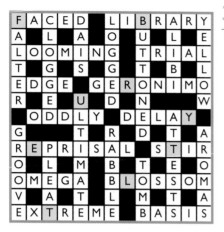

34 Flying colours 2

The anagram is **butterfly**.

The crossword grid reads:

F	A	C	E	D		L	I	B	R	A	R	Y
A		L		A		O		U		L		E
L	O	O	M	I	N	G		T	R	I	A	L
T		G		S		G		T		B		L
E	D	G	E		G	E	R	O	N	I	M	O
R		E		U		D		N				W
	O	D	D	L	Y		D	E	L	A	Y	
G				T		R		D		T		A
R	E	P	R	I	S	A	L		S	T	I	R
O		L		M		B		T		E		O
O	M	E	G	A		B	L	O	S	S	O	M
V		A		T		L		M		T		A
E	X	T	R	E	M	E		B	A	S	I	S

35 Arrow route 1

36
Four square 1

1 R U S T
2 U G L Y
3 S L A P
4 T Y P E

37
Four square 2

1 M A R K
2 A L O E
3 R O A N
4 K E N T

38 Arrow route 2

39
All square 1

1 S T A B S
2 T A M I L
3 A M P L E
4 B I L G E
5 S L E E T

40
All square 2

1 S T A L L
2 T I B I A
3 A B B E Y
4 L I E G E
5 L A Y E R

41 Warm up

LEVEL 1

1 Ace is a term used in tennis – and also means a top pilot.
2 Bend (means 'warp', you can have a U-bend or an S-bend).
3 Stow (S to W), means pack.
4 Cryptic. A crypt is the underground of a church, followed by IC – the abbreviation for 'in charge'.

LEVEL 2

1 Candle (wicked here implies 'having a wick', not 'evil').
2 Bridge (i.e., something that spans a river).
3 Enraged ('exploded' implies this is an anagram of 'angered' and means incensed).
4 Escalator (i.e., a powered flight of stairs) takes you higher.

LEVEL 3

1 Long Island.
2 Double agent (2 × 007 = twice James Bond).
3 Orchestra pits ('possibly' indicates the anagram of 'stratospheric'. 'Are airs here' implies a musical location – as in a musical air).

42 Dual clues 1

43 Dual clues 2

P	E	S	S	I	M	I	S	T
E	B	A	A	B	A	S	E	R
R	A	N	S	O	M	E	R	E
M	U	D	H	A	M	L	E	T
E	D	I	S	T	A	F	F	I
A	C	E	T	I	C	S	A	C
T	O	G	U	N	L	A	C	E
E	C	O	N	G	A	M	E	N
S	O	U	T	H	W	E	S	T

44 Quick cryptic

W	A	D	E	R		F	A	I	R	Y	T	A	L	E
A		E		E	I	N		A		B		M
L	A	B	Y	R	I	N	T	H		W	H	A	L	E
L		I		E	A	A	N		N		N		N
P	I	T	F	A	L	L		B	L	I	N	D	E	D
A		A	D		I	N	O	
P	O	L	O	S	H	I	R	T		G	E	N	E	S
E		I	S	E		I		E		E
R	A	V	E	S		R	E	D	H	A	N	D	E	D
	E	L	A		I		L	A	I		I
C	A	R	N	A	G	E		E	A	R	D	R	U	M
A		P	C	L		M	M	E		E
C	R	O	O	K		I	M	I	T	A	T	I	O	N
T		O	E	T		T	I	N		N		T
I	S	L	A	N	D	E	R	S		L	A	S	T	S

45 Double trouble 1

G	A	R	L	A	N	D		T	A	R
I		A	B		E	I		I		U
A	L	I	C	E		S	H	E	L	L
N		N	N		L	E	E		E
T	R	I	O		R	A	D	A	R
	E		A	C	T		A
B	U	R	N	S		E	M	U	S
E			C	U	T		A		A
G	L	O	V	E		R	I	G	H	T
I		D	N		E	E		E		I
N	O	D		T	R	E	A	S	O	N

46 Double trouble 2

E	D	D	Y		S	H	O	W	C	A	S	E
F		E		G		I		H		S		A
F	A	L	L	O	U	T		I	N	C	U	R
I		T		L		M		T		E		P
G	R	A	N	D	P	A	R	E	N	T	S
I			E		N		W		I		C
E	N	D	I	N	G		P	E	N	C	I	L
S		R		F		T		D			U
	W	O	R	L	D	W	I	D	E	W	E	B
D		P		E		O		I		H		B
I	S	S	U	E		B	E	N	G	A	L	I
S		I		C		I		G		L		N
C	O	N	C	E	R	T	O		D	E	N	G

47 Tile teaser

	G	R		I	N	T	E	R		C
L	A	M	E	N	T		R	U		O
	T	S		A	B	I	L	I	T	Y
V	E	N	I	A	L		D	N		O
A		S		I	C	E	B	O	A	T
R	U	S	T	I	C		N		U	E
E		T		N		S	T	A	S	E	S
S	L	A	C	K	E	N		M		G
I		R		B		A	U	B	U	R	N
D	E	V	E	L	O	P		E		E
U		E		O		P	U	R	I	S	M
E		D	O	T	T	Y		S		S

48 Eureka!

C	U	L	P	A	M	O	B	I	L	E
O	N	A	O	M	I	A	P	H	I	D
F	W	R	N	A	S	C	I	I	C	I
F	O	E	T	U	S	C	A	G	E	S
E	V	M	I	R	I	A	M	H	E	P
R	E	N	A	I	S	S	A	N	C	E
D	N	A	C	E	S	A	R	E	H	R
A	N	N	U	L	I	R	I	S	E	S
M	A	T	R	A	P	S	T	S	L	I
S	I	S	A	L	P	I	A	N	O	O
A	L	U	M	N	I	G	L	E	N	N

49 The hard stuff 1

A	U	C	O	N	T	R	A	I	R	E
E		A		O		E	L		S
S	A	P		B	U	M	B	L	E	S
I		S		L		U			E
R	A	T	H	E		S	I	O	U	X
		A						C
P	A	N	I	C		A	C	C	R	A
L				R	E	I		P
U	S	E	L	E	S	S		P	A	N
M		T		A		O		U		E
B	R	A	H	M	A	P	U	T	R	A

Here are explanations for four of the
hardest clues in puzzle 49, just in case
you're stumped.
10 across: 'Io' = satellite (of Jupiter); 'u' =
university; 'x' = unknown; 's' = south.
Dakota = Sioux (the Native American
people). Thus, io found by u, x by s =
Sioux.
12 across: There are two meanings to
'panic'. As well as scare, panic is also a
type of grass.
19 across: Flower (flow-er) =
Brampaputra; Brahma = god; put = set;
ra = sun god. Thus, Brahmaputra.
6 down: Two meanings – the county, and
Robert Devereux, Earl of Essex.

50 The hard stuff 2

R	E	C	I	P	E		S	C	O	W
U		A		O		T		O		I
L	I	T	T	L	E	W	O	M	E	N
E		E		E		M		C
R	I	P	O	S	T	E		A	S	H
		U		A	D		N
B	U	S		P	A	L	A	D	I	N
A		H		A		E			A
B	A	K	E	R	S	D	O	Z	E	N
E		I		T		E		O		N
L	E	N	T		B	E	T	O	N	Y

Simply acrostics

51

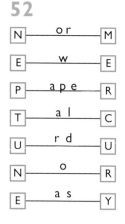

V alentine E
E rotic A
N ecta R
U ni T
S ig H

52

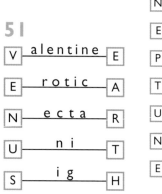

N or M
E w E
P ape R
T al C
U rd U
N o R
E as Y

53 Crystal ball

A MODERN ART   E WOEFULLY
B VENTURE   F TOFFEE
C BUNNIES   G WHITE HOUSE
D FIFA   H MARILYN

54 Expert advice

A ELEMENTARY
B WATSON
C BEHIND THE TIMES
D BLEMISH
E HEAR HEAR
F SHAMPOO
G OVERVIEW
H SUITE

I OBEDIENT
J FIB
K TOOTHY
L UVULA
M WHITHER
N MAUVE
O TOWPATH

The quotation is from Sherlock Holmes.

```
H O W   O F T E N   H A V E   I   S A
I D   T O   Y O U   T H A T   W H E N
  Y O U   H A V E   E L I M I N A T E
D   T H E   I M P O S S I B L E   W H
A T E V E R   R E M A I N S   H O W E
V E R   I M P R O B A B L E   M U S T
    B E   T H E   T R U T H
```

55 Lost in space

```
T H A T S   O N E
S M A L L   S T E P
F O R   A   M A N
O N E   G I A N T
  L E A P   F O R
  M A N K I N D
```

A PLANET   F THIN
B ARMSTRONG   G SAM
C MOON   H ALIEN
D TAKE OFF   I APES
E LAND

The quotation is from Neil Armstrong.

56 Stage secret

```
A C T I N G   I S   M E R E L Y
  T H E     A R T     O F
K E E P I N G   A   L A R G E
  G R O U P   O F   P E O P L E
  F R O M   C O U G H I N G
```

A FLAMINGO   H COY
B CASTANET   I POUR
C EMPEROR   J ONE
D EGG   K GRAPEFRUIT
E GOLF   L PIE
F HIGH
G ELK

The quotation is from Ralph Richardson.

57 Lover's plea

I	F		M	U	S	I	C		B	E		T	H	E
F	O	O	D			O	F			L	O	V	E	
P	L	A	Y		O	N		G	I	V	E		M	E
		E	X	C	E	S	S		O	F		I	T	
T	H	A	T		S	U	R	F	E	I	T	I	N	G
	T	H	E			A	P	P	E	T	I	T	E	
M	A	Y		S	I	C	K	E	N			A	N	D
S	O		D	I	E									

A SUITCASE
B DECIMAL
C IGLOO
D INDEX
E PIANISSIMO
F TOKEN
G POET
H FISH
I FED
J BEHAVE
K NYMPH
L FOREFEET
M IVY
N STATUTE
O ETC
P FOG

The quotation is from William Shakespeare.

58 Lexiconfusion

1 D. 2 A. 3 C. 4 A. 5 B. 6 D. 7 B. 8 C. 9 B. 10 C. 11 D. 12 A. 13 B. 14 D. 15 C. 16 C. 17 D. 18 A. 19 B. 20 C. 21 C. 22 B.

23 D. 24 B. 25 C. 26 B. 27 A. 28 B. 29 B. 30 D. 31 A. 32 B. 33 C. 34 D. 35 C. 36 A. 37 B. 38 A. 39 C. 40 D. 41 A. 42 A.

43 D. 44 B. 45 B. 46 D. 47 B. 48 D. 49 A. 50 D. 51 C. 52 B. 53 B. 54 D. 55 C. 56 B. 57 A. 58 B. 59 D. 60 C. 61 D. 62 B.

63 A. 64 A. 65 B. 66 D. 67 C. 68 D. 69 B. 70 C. 71 D. 72 D. 73 B. 74 B. 75 A.

Clock that
For these puzzles we list the most common answers.

59 KTSGEIPLNCAR

ARK	PACK	STACK
ASK	PARK	STAKE
CAKE	PEAK	STANK
CALK	RACK	STARK
CRANK	RACKET	STEAK
KALE	RAKE	TACK
KART	RANK	TAKE
KERATIN	SAKE	TALK
LACK	SANK	TANK
LAKE	SKATE	TASK
LANK	SLACK	TEAK
LARK	SNACK	TRACK
LEAK	SPARK	
NARK	SPEAK	

Of course, the beauty of this puzzle is that you can increase the list considerably by adding suffixes such as 'er' and 'ing' and prefixes such as 're'.

60 HNO-LARIG-T

ALIGHT	GOTH	LATHING	RATIO	THORN
ALIT	GRANT	LATIN	RATION	THRONG
ALTO	GRIT	LATINO	RIGHT	TIN
ANT	GROAT	LIGHT	RIOT	TING
ANTI	HALT	LINT	ROT	TOG
ALRIGHT	HALTING	LIT	TAG	TOGA
ARIGHT	HARLOT	LOATH	TAIL	TOIL
ART	HART	LOATHING	TAILOR	TON
GAIT	HAT	LOT	TALON	TONG
GIANT	HATING	LOTH	TAN	TOR
GILT	HILT	NIGHT	TANG	TORAH
GIRT	HINT	NIT	TANGO	TORN
GIRTH	HIT	NORTH	TAO	TRAIL
GIT	HOLT	NOT	TAR	TRAIN
GLINT	HOT	OAT	TARN	TRIAL
GLOAT	INGOT	OATH	THAI	TRIGON
GNAT	INTO	ORATING	THAN	TRIGONAL
GOAT	INTRO	RANT	THIN	TRIO
GOLIATH	IOTA	RAT	THING	
GOT	LATH	RATING	THONG	

61 INOTAWCP-E

ACE	ICE	PACE	TEN
ACNE	INCEPT	PANE	TIE
ACONITE	INEPT	PATE	TINE
AEON	LOTE	PATEN	TOE
ANEW	NAPE	PEA	TOECAP
ANTE	NEAP	PEAN	TONE
APE	NEAT	PEAT	TOPE
ATE	NET	PECAN	TWICE
ATONE	NEW	PECTIN	TWINE
AWE	NEWT	PEN	WANE
CANE	NICE	PENT	WEAN
CANOE	NOPE	PET	WEAPON
CAPE	NOTE	PEON	WENT
CENT	NOTICE	PEW	WEPT
CENTO	OCEAN	PEWIT	WET
CINE	OCTANE	PIE	WINCE
CITE	ONCE	PINE	WINE
CONE	ONE	POET	WIPE
COPE	OPEN	POETIC	WOE
EAT	OPIATE	PONCE	
ENACT	OPINE	TAPE	
EPIC	OWE	TEA	

62 DTYBNGIO-A

ADO	BAN	ION
AGO	BAT	IOTA
AID	BAY	NAB
ADIT	BANDY	NAG
ANT	BOA	NAY
ANY	BATON	OBTAIN
AND	DINGBAT	OAT
ANTE	DAINTY	TAD
ANTI	DATING	TAN
AGONY	DAB	TANGY
ANTIBODY	DAG	TOADYING
BOATING	DAN	TODAY
BAIT	DAY	TANG
BANG	GAB	TOAD
BANDIT	GAIT	TOADY
BAND	GAD	TANGO
BATING	GAIN	TOGA
BAYING	GNAT	TAB
BOAT	GOAD	TAG
BOTANY	GOAT	TAO
BAIT	GIANT	YOGA
BAD	GAY	YANG
BAG	GONAD	

Letter linking

63

ACE	COL	LACK	ORE
ACRE	COLA	LICE	PECK
ACORN	CORE	LICK	PER
ALIVE	CORED	LIMB	PERK
BECK	CORK	LIMBER	PET
BED	CORN	LIVE	PRO
BERK	DEB	LIVED	RED
BET	DECK	LIVER	REP
BICEP	DECOR	LOCI	REV
BICORN	DEVIL	LOCK	ROC
CALIBER	EVIL	LORE	ROCK
CALVE	ICE	LORN	TERN
CALVED	ICED	MICA	VET
CIVET	IMBED	MICE	VIBE
CLIMB	JERK	MICRO	VICE
CLIMBED	JET	OLIVE	VIM
CLIMBER	LACE	ORC	
COAL	LACED	ORCA	

64

BECK	JIB	THE
BEG	JIBE	THEM
BET	KEG	THIN
BIN	MET	THOR
FIB	METRO	THROW
FIN	NIB	THROWN
FURY	NIFTY	TON
GEM	NOR	TOR
GET	NORTH	TORY
GROT	NOT	TOW
GROW	NOTE	TOWN
GROWN	NOW	TRY
HECK	ORGY	TYRO
HEFTY	OWN	WHET
HEM	RHINO	WHO
HET	ROT	WON
HOT	ROTE	WORT
HOW	ROW	WORTH

65

BIN	HEAD	NOT	STORY
BINARY	HEADY	POT	TIN
BIT	HEAR	POTS	TON
BITS	LEA	RAN	TOP
BLEARY	LEAD	ROT	TOPS
DAN	LEAN	ROTS	TOR
EAR	NIB	SPOT	TORY
FURY	NIT	SPUR	UPON
FUR	NITS	STOP	

66

ACE	CADGE	FLACK	LACE	PECK
ACED	CALF	FLAT	LACED	PEDAL
ACT	CAT	FLOG	LACK	PEG
ADO	DACE	FOG	LAD	TACK
ALB	DECK	FOLD	LODE	TACKY
BLACK	DOG	GOD	LODGE	TAD
BLADE	DOGE	GOLD	LOG	
BLAT	DOLT	GOLF	ODE	
CAD	EGO	LAC	OLD	

67 Hidden cities

1	MADRID	(Crazy cast-away = Mad rid)
2	BOMBAY	(Blow up old agreement = Bomb ay)
3	ROTTERDAM	(Villain of Watergate = Rotter dam)
4	PARIS	(Equality exists! = Par is)
5	WARSAW	(Conflict perceived = War saw)
6	BUDAPEST	(Shoot a nuisance = Bud a pest)
7	SINGAPORE	(Make music a study = Sing a pore)
8	CHICAGO	(Fashionable in the past = Chic ago)
9	RANGOON	(Telephoned with nothing on! = Rang 0 on)*
10	LITTLE ROCK	(Small boulder = Little rock)

*The traditional English spelling of the city now called Yangon.

68 On with his head!

1	Hair-piece, time-piece	(LOCK/CLOCK)
2	Trivial insult	(LIGHT/SLIGHT)
3	Fish hook	(PIKE/SPIKE)
4	Summit address	(PEAK/SPEAK)
5	Ancient wrinkle	(OLD/FOLD)
6	Sick note	(ILL/BILL)
7	Hasty accident	(RASH/CRASH)
8	Money concern	(ROUBLE/TROUBLE)
9	Single single	(ONE/LONE)
10	Choose choose	(ELECT/SELECT)

69 Missing links

1	Pine	APPLE	Turnover
2	Sword	FISH	Finger
3	Spring	CHICKEN	Run
4	Short	BREAD	Basket
5	Runner	BEAN	Stalk
6	Pan	CAKE	Hole
7	Oyster	MUSHROOM	Cloud
8	Sweet	CORN	Flake
9	Cottage	PIE	Bald
10	Swiss	ROLL	Mop

A penny bun is a type of mushroom, answer number 7.

70 From A to B...

LAGOS
PARIS
ROME
PISA
BONN
RIO
SEOUL
KIEV
OSLO
CAIRO

71 Cool shades

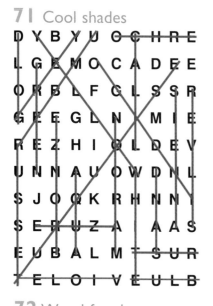

```
D Y B Y U O C H R E
L G E M O C A D E E
O R B L F G L S S R
G E E G L N M I E
R E Z H I O L D E V
U N N A U O W D N L
S J O O K R H N N
S E R U Z A A A S
E U B A L M T S U R
T E L O I V E U L B
```

72 Wood for the trees

```
B E E C H A R G L E B E
E L E P H A O C K N G
T R I N E S T B E A R S
U A A B L U R A D E C K
N M P L I N S E C T H E
L R E A M H A T C H E D
A O R S E W A B R U S O
W A M D O R E A L E A O
E A G L E B A Y X K E W
F I L L E O P E R D I D
K I T T S S E R P Y C E
W I G H I P P O P L A R
```

73 Cry havoc!

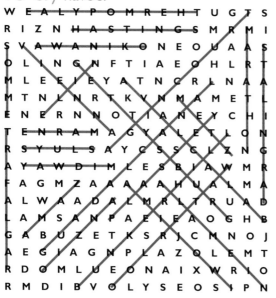

```
W E A L Y P O M R E H T U G T S
R I Z N H A S T I N G S M R M I
S V A W A N I K O N E O U A A S
O L I N G N F T I A E O H L R T
M L E E I E Y A T N G R L N A A
M T N L N R T K V N M A M E T L
E N E R N N O T I A N E Y C H I
T E N R A M A G Y A L E T L O N
R S Y U L S A Y C S S C L Z N G
A Y A W D I M L E S B I A W M R
F A G M Z A A A A A H U A L M A
A L W A A D A L M R L T R U A D
L A M S A N P A E I E A O G H B
G A B U Z E T K S R J C M N O J
A E G I A G N P L A Z O L E M T
R D O M L U E O N A I X W R I O
R M D I B V O L Y S E O S I P N
```

74 Stripes and stars

```
A W G U N L E F T P O D
S N E W J E R S E Y M E
I O W A I D O R X N A E
R T C F E V I G A K U S
O G P O L R E G S D A S
S N E R H O M R N Y L E
Z I F E R E R A M T O N
A H U G B P L I N O R N
H S I O S Y P U D H N E
T A I N R O F I L A C T
S W T A M E W R O D L U
R I M U D R Y E N I A M
```

The missing state is Delaware.

75 A place out of place

```
E F Y O D A G R L P O W S T O
W A C R E B H U M I S D E R N
O Y J E R U S A L E M X I C O
C E T S U E H G N O R A F E P
S L G A C N I B R A C D O M I
O R E V N O T G N I L L E W S
M B L A B S R E S G I J Q U A
S N E H T A D E W Y L P A L T
A D I R J I T O N K D U I T E
M I N A I R O B I H O N P O G
Y O N W R E H A M I A T E K H
S K R O C S U V E M I G L Y A
U L L T N D O N T A R H E O R
G A R T E I L P B E R L I N C
W I N O D N O L I P O W T H A
```

The places are:

Athens	London
Berlin	Manila
Buenos Aires	Moscow
Cairo	Nairobi
Copenhagen	Ottowa
Jerusalem	Sydney
Lima	Tokyo
	Wellington

The odd one out is Sydney because all the others are capital cities; Canberra is the capital of Australia.

76 Word wild web

I	T	I	N	T	I	R	N	E	I	I	I
N	E	T	T	E	N	R	E	T	N	N	I
T	R	E	N	E	T	E	N	E	T	T	N
E	N	R	E	T	N	N	N	E	U	E	T
R	I	N	T	E	R	R	R	R	R	I	E
N	T	E	R	N	E	N	E	E	N	R	R
T	R	T	R	E	I	T	R	T	E	E	N
E	N	E	I	T	I	E	E	T	T	T	T
R	T	I	I	N	T	R	T	E	N	N	E
N	E	N	T	E	N	R	T	E	T	N	I
E	N	T	T	E	T	E	N	T	N	I	N
T	E	N	T	E	R	N	I	N	I	R	N

77 Busy canvas

The famous person is Toulouse Lautrec.

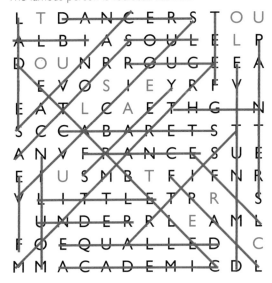

78 Pop picker

79 From A...

80 ...to Z

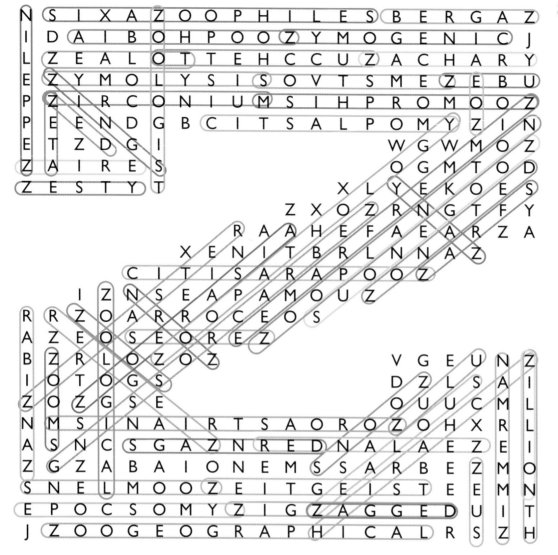

81 Square meal

The untouched food on the table is a pomegranate.

82 Everything must go

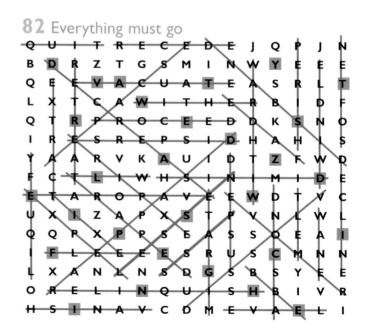

83 Carthorse

ACCORDION
BAGPIPES
BANJO
BASS DRUM
BASSOON
BIRDSCARER
CALLIOPE
CASTANETS
CELESTE
CELLO
CLARINET
CLAVICHORD
COR ANGLAIS

COWBELL
CYMBALS
DOUBLE BASS
DRUMS
EUPHONIUM
FIDDLE
FLUTE
FRENCH HORN
GITTERN
GUITAR
HANDBELL
HARMONICA
JEW'S HARP

KETTLE DRUM
MANDOLIN
MARACAS
OCARINA
ORGAN
PANPIPE
PIANOFORTE
PICCOLO
RECORDER
SAXOPHONE
SPINET
TAMBOURINE
TIMPANI

TIN WHISTLE
TRIANGLE
TROMBONE
TRUMPET
VIOLIN
VIRGINAL
WHISTLE
WOODBLOCK
WURLITZER
XYLOPHONE
ZITHER

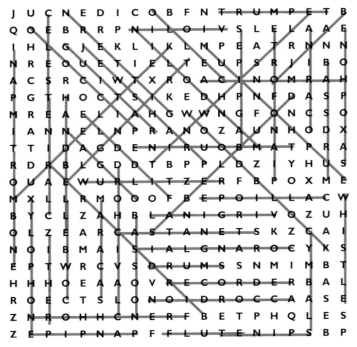

Scrabble solutions
84 Fourwise

The four anagrams are: ALLERGY, GALLERY, LARGELY and REGALLY. Only ALLERGY can be played on the board – at A2 across, scoring 87 points (37 plus 50 bonus points).

85 Target teaser 1

YOUTH at A4 across, also making THOSE, HE scores the target of 51 points. THORNY at J1 down, also making DIVERT, AN, BY scores 55 points. Playing UN to make UNDESIRED A8 across, also making UP, NO scores 47 points.

86 Re-creation 1

The plays to link the existing words are: KIWI at G5 down, also making BANK, ISLANDER. SEXY AT H8 down and RIVALRY at B11 across.

87 Triple tester

The eight triple-word plays possible are: H1 across MENSWEAR, O1 down ROWDIEST, A1 down MOLESTED, A8 down MENTALLY, A8 across DISTRUST & MISTRUST, A15 across YULETIDE(S), H15 across INDECENT.

88 Target teaser 2

The two scores of 45 points are: DISENTANGLED at A8 across and DIVERSE at D5 across, also making DEJECTION, IN. A higher score of 48 points is possible with OVERSEA at E5 across, also making ON, TA.

89 Target teaser 3

QUAINTER at B4 down, also making ALIKE, scores 30 points. OPAQUE at L5 down, also making ME, scores 31 points. EGGCUP at I14 across scores 32 points.

90 Re-creation 2

The words are all joined by forming: FONDUE at A1 down, EVACUEE at A6 across, BEAU at G5 down, SEIZURE at K8 down.

91 Spell wrecker?

PAINTERS
1 Ingres, 2 Raphael, 3 Monet, 4 Manet, 5 Giotto,
6 Rossetti, 7 Tissot, 8 Magritte, 9 Landseer,
10 Veronese.

COMPOSERS
1 Grieg, 2 Delius, 3 Strauss, 4 Holst, 5 Chopin,
6 Smetana, 7 Bruckner, 8 Vivaldi, 9 Bartok, 10 Poulenc.

NOVELISTS
1 Daniel Defoe, 2 George Eliot, 3 James Joyce,
4 Kingsley Amis, 5 Arthur Conan Doyle,
6 Emily Brontë, 7 Len Deighton, 8 Tobias Smollet,
9 Miguel Cervantes, 10 Edith Wharton.

ACTORS and ACTRESSES
1 Alec Guinness, 2 James Stewart, 3 Clint Eastwood,
4 Meryl Streep, 5 Boris Karloff, 6 Diane Cilento,
7 Lauren Bacall, 8 Barbra Streisand, 9 Elaine Stritch,
10 Burt Reynolds.

92 Confusibles
1 Eligible, 2 Deserts, 3 Principles,
4 Sleight, 5 Elicit, 6 Llamas,
7 Compliments, 8 Palette, 9 Silicon,
10 Affect.

93 Give me a brake

Oh dear! Spelling obviously isn't Jill's strong point. There are 19 mistakes in all, some of which involve missing or badly placed apostrophes. The postcard should read:

Dear friends

What a wonderful experience! Jack and I thoroughly recommend a visit to the States. People have welcomed us with their arms wide open. You've got to see it to believe it – the only disappointment has been the weather. Because we couldn't gauge what to expect we packed light clothing but New York is cold. Luckily Jack's aunt lent me a beautiful shawl. And the food! It's truly irresistible – especially the spaghetti. In other words, an idyllic holiday in an exciting and cosmopolitan city.

Wish you were here.
Jill

94 Writing wrongs

There are 16 mistakes in Martin's letter.

Dear Sir or Madam,

I am writing regarding the incessant noise coming from your premises. What is going on in there? Every night I am woken up around midnight – it sounds like a herd of elephants. What is worse, it sounds as if the elephants are drunk – but I bet you're not even licensed! Whatever is going on in there, if the practice isn't stopped soon I will be forced to take legal advice!

Yours in anger,
Martin Griffin

95 Spell well

This puzzle has no answers – the correct spellings are given in the question.

96 Square of knowledge

1 APOLLO
2 BRONZE
3 CHIANTI
4 EVEREST
5 HALLOWEEN
6 MADONNA
7 MIGRAINE
8 PACIFIC
9 SOUSA
10 WRIGHT

97 Try and try again

A ADO
B NEW YORK
C STATUE
D VANISH
E OFFEND
F TENTH
G OUTLAW
H THIN
I DAVID

I HAVEN'T FAILED, I'VE FOUND TEN THOUSAND WAYS THAT DON'T WORK.

98 Tiles

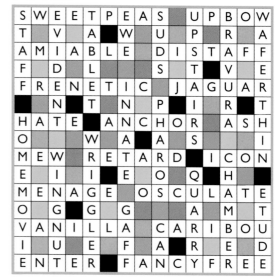

99 Quick crossword

100 Word pyramids

1 RE, IRE, SIRE, SPIRE, ASPIRE
2 AC, ACE, PACE, PLACE, PALACE
3 LE, LIE, LIVE, LIVER, SLIVER
4 ST, SET, SENT, SCENT, ASCENT
5 IT, SIT, SITE, SPITE, SPRITE
6 TI, TIN, TINE, TINGE, TINGLE
7 EN, TEN, TERN, STERN, ASTERN
8 PI, PIG, PRIG, SPRIG, SPRING, SPRINGE, SPRINGER

101 Letter change

1 CENT, DIME
2 BEECH, LARCH
3 DUTCH, GREEK
4 FELT, SILK
5 MILE, INCH
6 GOWN, ROBE
7 CARP, PIKE
8 DILL, MINT
9 FILE, PICK
10 CHAD, TOGO

102 Fore and aft

1 BA (rumba, basin)
2 EL (bowel, elbow)
3 TO (pinto, togas)
4 SO (torso, solid)
5 ID (cupid, idled)
6 PU (coypu, pushy)
7 AD (dryad, adapt)
8 TE (forte, tenet)
9 LI (styli, lilac)
10 EX (codex, exact)

103 Word ladders

1 MITE, MATE, MATS
2 NIL, NIP, NAP, GAP
3 POOL, POLL, PALL, PALE, PAGE
4 SEARS, STARS, STARE, STALE, STILE
5 CRASS, CRESS, TRESS, TREES, TREEN
6 ARMS, AIMS, DIMS, DAMS, DAME, NAME, NAVE
7 GLUE, GLUT, GOUT, POUT, PORT, PART, PANT, PINT

104 Word centres 1

1 diSHONEst
2 fiREPROof
3 atHEISTic
4 baTHROBes
5 apPETITes

105 Word centres 2

1 caTACOmb
2 soLOISts
3 seAQUAke
4 naMESAke
5 inDUSTry
6 siDEARms (or enDEARed)
7 inCUBAte
8 acCOLAde

106 Non-rhyming words

1 bOMB
2 cOMB
3 tOMB

107 Unusual words

ATE, making PRIMATE and ROSEATE.

108 Alphabetical order

FORTY.

109 Pronunciation puzzle

SCISSORS

110 Alphabet soup 1

1 HOUSEMAID
2 EQUATION
3 EUPHORIA
4 SEQUOIA

111 Alphabet soup 2

1 CAULIFLOWER
2 TAMBOURINE
3 TOURMALINE

112 Alphabet soup 3

AUCTIONED, CAUTIONED, EDUCATION

113 Kangaroo words

1 BLOOM
2 IDLE
3 UGLY
4 EATING
5 TUTOR
6 EVIL
7 LIES
8 ELATION
9 SUE
10 URGE

114 In a State

1 HAWAII, IOWA, OHIO, UTAH
2 neBRASka
3 North Dakota, North Carolina
4 New Hampshire, New Jersey, New Mexico, New York
5 Maine
6 Colorado, Idaho, New Mexico, Ohio
7 AR/KANSAS
8 Alabama, Arizona, Alaska, Ohio
9 VIRGINIA

115 Inflatable words

1 PASTIES
2 SATISFIED
3 PREVENTATIVE
4 AMICABLE
5 ORIENTATE
6 INSTANTANEOUSLY
7 CHARISMA
8 BOUNDARIES
9 NOURISHED
10 APPROPRIATE

116 Common property

LEMONADE: each word contains a girl's name at its centre.

117 Lost cities

1 PARIS, QUITO
2 OSLO
3 LENINGRAD
4 LONDON
5 KABUL
6 BERLIN
7 MOSCOW
8 TOKYO
9 REGINA, CONSTANTINE, SAN ANTONIO & SAMARKAND
10 LHASA, ESSEN, SALISBURY
11 BENDIGO, CARACAS, MOBILE, ACCRA
12 LIMA, PETRA, OLDHAM, CAMPINAS (PASADENA does not count because it's not hidden.)
13 BOLTON, MECCA, SPRINGS, CAIRO, ORLANDO
14 WARSAW, BELFAST, LIMA, DUBLIN, YORK
15 ELY, LYON, DUBLIN, BOGOTA, CARACAS, JODHPUR, GERONA

118 Algebraical words

1 hONEy
2 poTENtate
3 wEIGHTy
4 caNINE
5 neTWOrk
6 oPInion

119 What links?

All can have O added to the end to make another word.

120 Unusual clusters

rHUBArb, sovereiGNTy, bankruPTCy

121 Palindromes

1 pOSSESSOr
2 mONOTONOus

Back to fronts

122

DENNIS AND EDNA SINNED

123

MADAM, I'M ADAM!

124

RISE TO VOTE, SIR!

125

WARD NURSES RUN DRAW

126

WAS IT ELIOT'S TOILET I SAW?

127

A MAN, A PLAN, A CANAL — PANAMA!

You can solve logic puzzles 1–7 by transferring the information into the grids, then using the clues to deduce the rest of the information. Here we also supply descriptions of how to solve the first four puzzles.

1 Out to lunch

Nigel has tuna fish sandwiches (clue 1). Thus, the child with both ham sandwiches and chocolate cake cannot be Nigel and it isn't Mark (clue 2), so it must be Lucy. The child with fruit cake isn't Nigel (1), so it must be Mark. By a process of elimination, Nigel has Madeira cake and Mark has cheese sandwiches. Thus:

Lucy – ham sandwiches, chocolate cake;
Mark – cheese sandwiches, fruit cake;
Nigel – tuna sandwiches, Madeira cake.

2 On the shelf

Book B is red, Bob Willis wrote Book C and Book A is entitled *Long Days* (clue 1). Thus, the book by Claire Carter is B because it is to the right of a book (clue 2) and we know that Bob Willis wrote book C. Clue 2 also tells us that the green book is A. By a process of elimination we can work out that the blue book (2) is C. Dave Child thus wrote A, so (3) *Happy Hour* is B and *Magic Moments* is C. Thus:
Book A – *Long Days*, Dave Child, green;
Book B – *Happy Hour*, Claire Carter, red;
Book C – *Magic Moments*, Bob Willis, blue.

3 Wax works

Yellow candles were made on Thursday (clue 2), so (clue 3) knight-shaped candles were made on Monday, green candles on Tuesday and 500 orange candles on Wednesday. The knights are red (4). By elimination, white candles were made on Friday. Ivor made either 600 queens and 450 knights (4) or 750 queens and 600 knights. Thus, the batch of 600 were either queens or knights. So (2) 700 pawns and 600 yellow candles were made. Since knights are red (above), he made 450 knights and (4) 600 queens. Knights were made on Monday (above), so (1) 700 candles were made on Friday. By a process of elimination we can work out that 750 were made on Tuesday. Tuesday's batch wasn't bishops (1), so must have been rooks. Bishops were made on Wednesday. Thus:
Monday – 450, red, knights; Tuesday – 750, green, rooks;
Wednesday – 500, orange, bishops; Thursday – 600, yellow, queens;
Friday – 700, white, pawns.

4 Running commentary

None of the five boys in the puzzle finished fourth (intro and grid). Those who were third and/or sixth aren't Rupert (clue 1), Raymond (clue 2) or Richard (3), so must be Roderick and/or Rory; thus, (4) Rory was third and Roderick sixth. Raymond was second (2); so Richard (1) was first, Rupert was fifth and (3) Raymond's T-shirt is white with a grey stripe. Roderick's T-shirt isn't red (1), so (4) Rupert's T-shirt is red/brown. Richard wore a red/orange T-shirt (3). Rory's isn't cream/brown (2), so it must be cream/orange. By elimination, Roderick's T-shirt is cream/brown. The boy with green/yellow shorts isn't Rupert (1), Rory (2), Richard or Raymond (3), so it must be Roderick. Raymond and Richard wore blue shorts (2), so (3) Richard's are blue/purple and Raymond's are blue/yellow. Rory's are black/purple (2) and Rupert's are green/pink. Thus:

		SHORTS	T-SHIRT
First	Richard	blue/purple	red/orange
Second	Raymond	blue/yellow	white/grey
Third	Rory	black/purple	cream/orange
Fifth	Rupert	green/pink	red/brown
Sixth	Roderick	green/yellow	cream/brown

5 Driving question

A Ron, red;
B Millie, brown;
C George, black;
D Stephanie, blue;
E Julia, pink;
F Adam, green;
G Angela, grey.

6 Mixed fruit

Each bought the following (apples, bananas, pears):
Frank – 5, 11, 8;
Keith – 10, 7, 7;
Ruth – 7, 6, 12;
Jimmy – 11, 10, 10;
Norah – 6, 12, 13;
Sue – 9, 9, 9.

7 Healthy appetites

A Brian Willard – pineapple first, blueberry second;
B Ewan Potter – blackcurrant first, syrup second;
C David Symes – syrup first, pineapple second;
D Adam Lowe – strawberry first, banana second;
E Fred Robertson – banana first, lemon second;
F Graham Veness – blueberry first, strawberry second.

8 Card sharp

A = jack diamonds, B = 10 clubs, C = 4 hearts, D = 2 spades;
E = ace clubs, F = 3 hearts, G = 5 spades, H = 6 diamonds;
I = 7 hearts, J = king spades, K = 9 diamonds, L = 8 clubs.

9 Housey housey

1st F; 2nd A; 3rd D; 4th N; 5th G; 6th I; 7th H; 8th M; 9th O; 10th C; 11th B; 12th K; 13th L; 14th J; 15th E.

10 What the Dickens?

43=K, 45=D, 46=I, 37=D, 19=I, 40=K, 33=E, 12=D, 17=K, 10=E, 30=S, 16=E, 34=K, 20=S, 29=C, 15=N, 8=S, 21=D, 18=C, 14=N, 35=I, 11=K and 32=D. Thus:

11 Where the L?

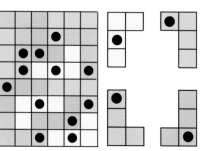

12 Target practice

Each person's score differs by a multiple of two from everyone else's. Therefore, each score must be made up of the same number of odd and even numbers.

Alison 37 (8 + 8 + 21)
Keith 35 (6 + 8 + 21)
Charles 33 (6 + 6 + 21)
Jill 31 (8 + 8 + 15)
Martin 29 (6 + 8 + 15)
Jonathan 27 (6 + 6 + 15)

13 Good arrows

Tabulate the possible scores so that each set equals 142. Only three ways are possible:

$$50 + 40 + 40 + 6 + 4 + 2 = 142$$
$$50 + 40 + 20 + 20 + 10 + 2 = 142$$
$$100 + 20 + 10 + 6 + 4 + 2 = 142$$

The first score must be Robin's, as this is the only row in which 44 can be scored in two shots. The third score is Marion's, as this includes a six and we have already established that the first score is Robin's. Therefore, Maid Marion hit the bullseye.

14 Draughtsmen on parade

The piece originally on square F6 jumps over and removes the pieces on E5, C5, C7, E7, G5, G3, E3 and C3 to finish on B2 (a slight variation, none the less plausible, is to reverse the order of the first four pieces, so you get E7, C7, C5, E5, then the rest in order).

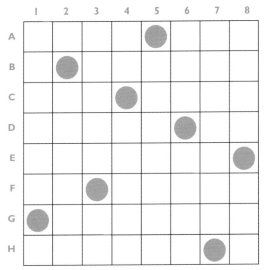

Notes: in the starting diagram the pieces A5, C4, D6, E8, G1 and H7 are the only ones in their respective rows or columns. So it is likely that we need to leave these pieces alone. Note also that there are no pieces in row B or column 2, so the final move must be to place a piece in B2. This final move must have started from D4. From here, you can work backwards to the starting position of F6. Though the rules of the puzzle allowed you to move horizontally and vertically, in fact only diagonal moves are required as in the real game of draughts.

15 Change sides

Piece 5 moves forward, then 4 over 5; 3 forward, 5 over 3, 6 over 4, 7 forward, 4 over 7, then over 8 and off the edge of the board; 3 over 6, then 7, then 8 and off; 2 over 5, then 6, then 7, then 8 and off; 1 forward, then over 5, then 6, then 7, then 8 and off.

16 One player only

The following numbers refer to the 16 squares and not to the 15 counters: 16 over 13 into 8 (thereby removing 13), then continue 4 to 13, 6 to 8, 9 to 7, 3 to 8, 12 to 5, 10 to 16, 15 to 6, 1 to 3, 3 to 8, 13 to 4, 6 to 8, 4 to 13 and, finally, 16 to 8.

17 At the last count

3 over 11, 9 over 10, 1 over 2, 7 over 15, 8 over 16, 8 over 7, 5 over 13, 1 over 4, 8 over 5, 6 over 14, 3 over 8, 6 over 3, 6 over 12, 1 over 6 and, finally, 1 over 9.

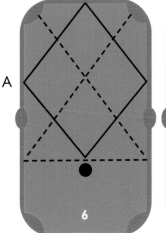

18 Back to black

Point A. The ball follows the path parallel to the dotted lines above.

19 Off the cushion

Five cushions. The ball will strike the black ball obliquely and clip it into the pocket as shown.

20 Cipherwords

You should have found BOUNTY and HUNTER.

Safe crackers

21 The combination is 54 (see diagram).

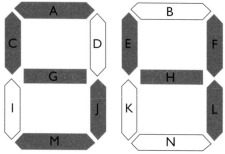

Explanations for false answers:

B A golden anniversary commemorates 50 years.
D Sagittarius is the sign of the archer.
I   Electrical voltage is measured in volts.
K A hypocaust is a system of under-floor heating.
N The first letter of the Greek alphabet is alpha.

22 The combination is 37 (see diagram).

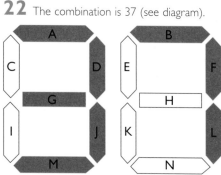

Explanations for false answers:

C Beethoven wrote the *Eroica Symphony*.
E The German flag is a tricolour of black, red and gold.
H The longest bone in the body is the femur.
I   P. G. Wodehouse wrote the *Jeeves and Wooster* stories.
K Tasmania is a state of Australia.
N The first regular colour television broadcasts in the UK began in 1967 (experiments from 1926).

23 The combination is 19 (see diagram).

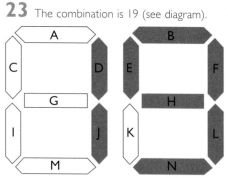

Explanations for false answers:

A Ethiopia was at one time called Abyssinia.
C The Dickens character Miss Havisham appears in *Great Expectations*.
G Louis Bleriot flew across the English Channel in July 1909.
I   Caligula was so insane he made his horse a consul.
K The Curtis Cup is a coveted trophy in women's golf.
M *Ruddigore* is a Gilbert and Sullivan operetta.

24 The Clambake Kid jail-breaks again

SETTING UP
Clambake used the silver dollar to dig a narrow slot in the wooden neck of the violin. He also polished his silver watchcase until he could see his face in it.

TO REACH THE KEYS
Clambake removed the strings from the violin. He used one to tie the flute to the neck of the violin, forming a makeshift pole. He tied the other three strings together into a long string and doubled it to form a loop. He tied one end round the mouthpiece of the flute, and ran the other end through the flute back to him, leaving the loop hanging out of the mouthpiece. He tied the rubber band across two bars to give himself an armrest. Then he picked up the 'pole' and reached through the bars until the loop lay over the keys. He pulled the string to close the loop, so trapping the keys. He then brought the keys back through the bars.

TO UNLOCK THE CELL DOOR
He couldn't reach round the metal plate, so he took the cell door key off the ring. He jammed the ring-end of the key firmly into the slot he'd dug in the neck of the violin. He passed the violin and key through the bars and used the reflective surface of his watchcase to help him guide the key into the lock. Then he passed the violin from hand to hand as a lever, so unlocking the cell door.

TO MOVE THE SLEEPING GUARD
The guard had to be moved very quickly. So Clambake poured the gun oil on the floor between the guard and the cell door. He passed the fire hose through the cell door, round the bars of the window, and back out again. He tied one end of the hose gently round the guard's legs. Then he pulled very hard, dragging the guard rapidly by his legs across the oiled floor into the cell. He slammed the door and locked it.

25 Builder's puzzle

26 Matchstick squares

27 Three to five

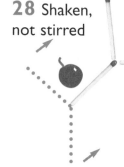

Four small triangles and one large triangle

28 Shaken, not stirred

29 Matchstick maths

π (Pi) = 22/7

30 'Here, boy!'

31 Triangles on demand

Construct a pyramid shape. The four triangles are the three sides plus the base.

32 Hidden intentions

1 'This is no time for making new enemies', Voltaire. (P = A etc.)
2 'A good book is the best of friends, the same today and for ever', Martin Tupper. (A = V, B = U, C = T, D = S etc.)
3 'We stand today on the edge of a new frontier', J. F. Kennedy. (Starting with the last set of words, each gives a clue as to what set comes next; so, WE STA, followed by ND TOD, then AY ONT...)
4 'This is a secret.' (Delete the word 'clue', which appears three times in alternate spaces.)
5 'Go to Paris on a plane to meet an Australian by the name of Ernie.' (Phonetic code – read it aloud!)
6 'We live our lives for ever taking leave.' (Fill in each gap with the letter of the alphabet that lies between the two either side, e.g., the first gap is a 'W' because 'W' lies between 'V' and 'X', the second gap must be an 'E' because 'E' lies between 'D' and 'F' etc.)
7 'Agent Smith steal enemy radar today.' (Put the words on top of each other, and read down the columns.)
8 It's phonetic. 'Humpty Dumpty sat on the wall, Humpty Dumpty had a great fall.'
9 The answer is 'Cryptic'. Take every word that sounds like a letter of the alphabet (sea = C, are = R, why = Y, pea = P, etc.)

33 Who's fooling who?

1 Take the first and third letter of each word and you get: 'Take left hand fork into town'.

2 'Hunger is the best sauce in the world' (Cervantes, *Don Quixote*). The 26 letters are laid out as follows:

So, starting at the number 1, we find that the first letter is an H, because the number 1 falls in the H segment of the target. The second letter is U, because the second letter falls in the U segment, and so on.

3 By laying the stencil on the grid in four different positions (including back to front), you get this quotation: 'One is not born a woman: one becomes one' (Simone de Beauvoir).

O	B	A	N	C	O	N	O
M	E	R	S	E	:	I	S
O	N	N	E	N	O	A	W
O	O	N	M	B	T	E	E

O	B	A	N	C	O	N	O
M	E	R	S	E	:	I	S
O	N	N	E	N	O	A	W
O	O	N	M	B	T	E	E

O	B	A	N	C	O	N	O
M	E	R	S	E	:	I	S
O	N	N	E	N	O	A	W
O	O	N	M	B	T	E	E

O	B	A	N	C	O	N	O
M	E	R	S	E	:	I	S
O	N	N	E	N	O	A	W
O	O	N	M	B	T	E	E

4 'Quiz Champion':
The number 1 above a letter means it turns clockwise by 90°
The number 2 means it turns clockwise by 180°
The number 3 means it turns clockwise 270°.

34 Rumbled

The message says:

THE STRIKE IS TOMORROW NIGHT – BE THERE BY NINE IN THE MORNING

The employer discovered the plot by typing the letter to the right of the letter in the code (so RGW becomes THE).

35 Password problem

The name commonly used for passwords was FRED, because it was so easy to type on the keyboard (a simple counter-clockwise circle of letters) and also easy to remember.

36 Shhhh!

The letter O. Each letter corresponds with the number that is above and to the left of it on the top row of numbers.

37 A sense of order

They are all 'calculator upside-down' words – i.e., type each number into a calculator, then turn the display upside down to show an English word. The (rather silly) phrase goes:

BIGGISH
BELLIES
GOBBLE
EGGS

38 Message received?

Each number represents one of the three numbers on the alphanumeric display of the telephone. So, for example, 438 translates to G, H or I followed by D, E or F, followed by T, U or V. The only possible word this can be is GET. Repeating this logic for the other words obtains the message:

THIS TELEPHONE IS OLD AND DOES NOT WORK – GET A NEW ONE.

39 Take a letter

The puzzle shows the lit segments of the calculator. By examining the unlit segments on the display, she realized that her manager wanted a black COFFEE.

40 Elementary?

The message says:

THE FIRST LETTER IS ADVANCED BY ONE POSITION, THE SECOND LETTER BY TWO POSITIONS, AND SO ON...

41 Check this

The word DIAGONAL can be formed. The red herrings were R and H.

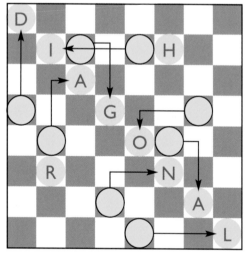

42 Spies are us

To solve the code, take the relevant letter from the name of each shape (i.e., the 4th letter from PENTAGON, the 3rd letter from TRIANGLE and so on). This gives the answer TIARAS.

43 Key code

The key to solving this is the question itself: '4 23 51' in the first word means 'take the 4th, 23rd and 51st letters of the question', which gives us THE. The whole message reads, appropriately enough,

THE CLUE IS IN THE QUESTION

44 Artful arrows

The green arrows should be interpreted as compass points (North, East, South, West). The blue arrows should be interpreted as directions (Up, Right, Down, Left). Taking the first letter of each direction (West, East, South, Up and so on) spells out: WE SURRENDER.

45 Code maze

Your route in Part One should spell the word PURPLE. The purple squares on your route in Part Two should spell STICK TO THE RED. The red squares in Part Three should contain, in order, the numbers 13, 9, 14, 15, 20, 1, 21 and 18. These letters of the alphabet spell out the word MINOTAUR, the mythical beast of the labyrinth in Ancient Greek mythology. The hero of that myth is THESEUS, which can be spelt out in Part Four to complete the maze

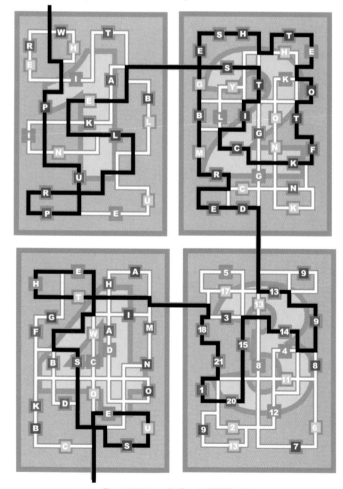

46 Chuck Diamond P. I.

Chuck tells us that The Bookworm stole the book by Tom Fox, and that The Bookworm suffers from vertigo, and so was not on the library roof, so Tom Fox's book was not on the roof either. He tells us that First Edition Frank had 20/20 vision – and we can see a pair of glasses on the roof from the crime scene photographs, so we know that the thief on the roof wasn't Frank either, which leaves us with Pages McLeaf as the thief on the roof. We also learn in this way that Pages McLeaf did not steal the Tom Fox book.

Chuck says that the noise of the glass case breaking would have been too loud to go unnoticed during the day, so the book in the case (the crime photo tells us it was *Corporal Clerk's Kazoo*) was not taken through the door, which was the only escape route used during the day.

The crime scene photographs also show us that *Memoirs of an Amnesiac* was written by Emily Austin. So we learn that Emily Austin's book was not stolen by The Bookworm and that *Memoirs of an Amnesiac* was not written by Tom Fox.

The crime scene photographs show that *The Beauty of Loneliness* was chained to a desk, and the piece of broken chain under the window informs us that this book was taken through the window, not the door or roof. So by a process of elimination we know that *Corporal Clerk's Kazoo* must have left via the roof, and must therefore have been stolen by Pages McLeaf and was not written by Tom Fox. We also learn that *Memoirs of an Amnesiac*, by Emily Austin, must have gone through the door.

If *Corporal Clerk's Kazoo* was not by Tom or Emily, it must have been by Barbara Taylor Broadfoot. So we know that *Corporal Clerk's Kazoo* by Barbara Taylor Broadfoot was stolen by Pages McLeaf through the roof. We know that The Bookworm stole Tom Fox's book, so First Edition Frank must have stolen Emily Austin's. If The Bookworm didn't steal *Corporal Clerk's Kazoo* or *Memoirs of an Amnesiac*, he must have stolen *The Beauty of Loneliness*, which must be by Tom Fox, and he must have taken it through the window. First Edition Frank must have stolen *Memoirs of an Amnesiac* by Emily Austin through the door. Case closed!

47 What's the dime?

1 12 onto 3
2 7 onto 4
3 10 onto 6
4 8 onto 1
5 11 onto 2
6 9 onto 5.

48 The thin blue line

Stand one coin on its edge on the line.

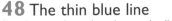

49 Tricky 19

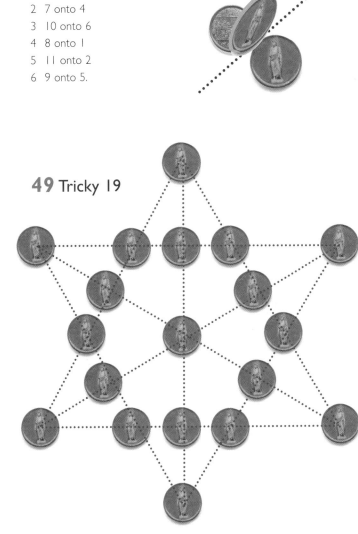

50 Corner challenge

Pick up any one of the four coins and place it on top of the coin diagonally opposite.

51 Penny dance

Surprisingly, the answer is twice, even though the circumference of the coins is the same. How can this be? One revolution comes from the coin revolving around itself, as it would do if the fixed coin wasn't there. However, in addition, the moving coin makes an orbit around the fixed coin, which counts as a second revolution.

52 Mirror image

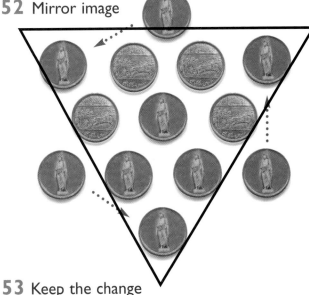

53 Keep the change

There is, of course, no extra pound. The way to think of it is this: the man paid £7 for his meal, the waiter took £2, and the man kept £1 in change: £7+£2+£1=£10. The puzzle is phrased so that the £2 tip appears to have been added to the £9 which the diner is out of pocket, when it fact it should be subtracted from it.

1 On target

Here is one possible solution for each target number.

1
341 = (75 × 3) + ((10 + 9) × 6) + 2   (17 ways)
832 = (75 − (9 + 2)) × (10 + 3)   (8 ways)
979 = (75 × (10 + 3) + 6 − 2)   (2 ways)

2
483 = (25 × (9 + 7 + 3)) + 8   (26 ways)
658 = ((9 × 3) − 1) × 25 + 8   (8 ways)
773 = (9 × (7 + 1) + 25) × 8 − 3   (3 ways)

3
173 = ((25 × 7) + 7) − 9   (16 ways)
854 = ((75 + 7) × 10) + 25 + 9   (6 ways)
337 = (75 × (10 − 7)) + ((25 − 9) × 7)   (3 ways)

4
623 = ((50 × 5 × 5) − 4) ÷ 2   (10 ways)
511 = (50 × 5 × 2) + 6 + 5   (8 ways)
917 = ((50 − 2) × ((6 × 4) − 5)) + 5   (3 ways)

5
361 = (8 × 7 × 6) + 25   (21 ways)
737 = (100 × 7) + 25 + 8 + 4   (8 ways)
995 = ((100 + 6) × 8) + ((25 − 4) × 7)   (2 ways)

6
243 = (((75 + 50) − 3) × 2) − 1   (10 ways)
345 = ((100 − 2) × 3) + 50 + 1   (7 ways)
321 = ((100 × 2) + 75 + 50 − 3 − 1)   (3 ways)

2 Testing times

1   1, 2 & 3.

2   21. You probably just guessed, which is fine, but you can also work it out algebraically. The two-digit number ab stands for $10a + b$, since the first digit represents 10s and the second represents units. If $10a + b = 7(a + b)$, then $10a + b = 7a + 7b$, and so $3a = 6b$, or, more simply, $a = 2b$. That is, the second digit must be twice the first. The smallest such number is 21.

3   18. $10a + b = 2(a + b)$, leading to $10a + b = 2a + 2b$, which equates to $8a = b$.

4   1⅓. Let x be the mystery number. Then the question translates into $2x = \frac{1}{2}x + 2$. Subtracting ½x from both sides, we get $(\frac{3}{2})x = 2$, so $x = \frac{4}{3}$, i.e., 1.333 or 1⅓.

5   3. $\frac{3}{2}x = x + \frac{3}{2}$. So ½x = ³⁄₂, and therefore x = 3.

6   Be careful: the question does not say the fish weighs 2 tons. It says it weighs more than 2 tons, i.e., 2 tons plus an unknown quantity.
$2 + \frac{1}{2}x = x$, so $2 = \frac{1}{2}x$ and hence $x = 4$ tons.

7   3 sheep, 2 goats, 1 horse. (Adding 3, 4 and 5 in this case gives twice the number of animals, so there must be 6 animals altogether.)

8   Let the four parts of 45 be called A, B, C and D, and the 'same number' for each operation be called x. From this we get:
A + 2 = x   B − 2 = x
2C = x, or C = ½x   ½D = x, or D = 2x
If we add all four equations together, we get:
A + 2 + B − 2 + C + D = x + x + ½x + 2x. So A + B + C + D = (⁹⁄₂)x.
But the total of A, B, C and D is 45. So 45 = ⁹⁄₂x, or 90 = 9x. So x is 10. Putting this back into the equation we readily obtain A = 8, B = 12, C = 5 and D = 20.

9   The elder is 17, the younger 7. Two years ago they were 15 and 5 respectively, and in 3 years' time they will be 20 and 10.

10   19, 9.

11   It's impossible. To raise his marks from 73 × 3 = 219 marks over three exams to 80 × 4 = 320 marks over four exams, he'd have to score 101% on his last exam.

12   Yes. What initially cost £1 now costs 96p because 100 − 20% = 80, and 80 + 20% = (80 + 16), which equals 96.

13   4411 = 401 × 11. Eleven people each spending £4.01.

14   Two dozen. If you increase both the number of hens and the amount of time available four-fold, the number of eggs increases 16 times. 16 × 1.5 = 24.

15   1 + 2 + 34 + 56 + 7 = 100. The key to this is noticing that the sum of the numbers in the tens places is 8 in the example given, and constructing an answer in which it is 8 again.

16   Pouring away half the mixture leaves the correct number of litres of black (2) and 1 litre of white. He then needs to add 3 litres of white to bring it back to the right shade.

17   A round trip is 13 miles (arrived at by adding all the distances and dividing by two − because you travel each road twice during the three journeys), so the direct routes from Bunstable to Unstable, from Unstable to Dunstable and from Bunstable to Dunstable are 5 miles, 6 miles and 2 miles respectively.

18   54321 × 99945 = 5429112345. The last digit of ***** must be 5 to give the final 5 of *****12345. So, 54321 × ****5 = *****12345. The digit before the 5 in ****5 has to be 4 to give *****12345. Proceeding in this way, digit by digit, we arrive at the five-digit number 99945.

19   324. 361 = 19 × 19; last year there were 18 × 18 = 324.

20   86.

21
1332	1	668
3	667	1331
666	1333	2

22   47.

23   631 × 542 = 342,002.

24   ⁴⁶³⁄₅12, which is just over ⁹⁄₁₀.

3 Round the bend

1   10. Opposite segments add up to 14.

2   19. Starting at 2 and moving clockwise three segments at a time gives the first eight prime numbers in sequence: 2, 3, 5, 7, 11, 13, 17, 19.

3   2454. Starting at the 6 and moving clockwise, double the number then reverse the digits. Hence:
6 × 2 = 12 (=21 when reversed)
21 × 2 = 42 (=24 when reversed)
24 × 2 = 48 (=84 when reversed)
84 × 2 = 168 (=861 when reversed)
861 × 2 = 1722 (=2271 when reversed)
2271 × 2 = 4542 (=2454 when reversed)
2454 × 2 = 4908 (=8094 when reversed).

4   12. The inner number is equal to twice the difference of the outer numbers in the same segment.

5   6. Each pair of numbers that straddles a spoke has the same sum as the opposite pair. That is:
9 + 7 = 8 + 8; 5 + 1 = 4 + 2;
9 + 6 = 7 + 8. Hence: 4 + 3 = 1 + 6.

6   15. Each inner number is equal to the product of the two outer numbers in the segment that appears one position clockwise. For example, 3 × 5 = 15, 8 × 3 = 24 and so on.

4 Number fun 1

4	+	1	×	11	−	1	=	54
−	10	+	20	×	30	×	■	
3	−	2	+	6	×	12	=	84
+	40	×	50	−	60	−	■	
17	+	18	−	24	×	18	=	198
×	70	−	80	+	90	+	■	
4	×	31	+	7	−	41	=	90
=		=		=		=		
72		23		49		35		

5 Number fun 2

4	×	11	−	29	+	8	= 23
×		×		+		×	
10	+	2	−	8	×	5	= 20
−				×		+	
22	+	3	×	2	−	22	= 28
+		+		−		−	
8	×	5	−	53	+	40	= 27
=		=		=		=	
26		24		21		22	

6 Number fun 3

15	−	11	×	17	+	11	= 79
+		−		+		×	
21	+	4	−	16	×	9	= 81
−		+		−			
16	×	3	−	11	+	21	= 58
×		×		×		+	
4	+	8	−	4	×	9	= 72
=		=		=		=	
80		80		88		87	

A = 9   B = 11   C = 4
D = 21   E = 16

7 Number fun 4

4	×	8	+	12	−	14	= 30
+		−		×		−	
9	−	10	+	2	×	11	= 11
−		+		−		+	
7	−	3	+	15	×	1	= 19
×		×		+		×	
6	+	13	−	16	×	5	= 15
=		=		=		=	
36		13		25		20	

8 Number crunch

```
9 1 7 3 5 2 8  ▮ 9 2 6 9 5 8 2
2 3 4 6 4 5 3  ▮ 5 4 3 1 7 4 7
6 8 1 5 8 2 8    6 7 3 9 3 6 8
9 8 7 9  ▮ 9 2 1 6  ▮ 9 5 2 9
2 3 6  ▮ 5 4 7 0 3 1 1 0 7 8 6
8 1 9 9 7  ▮ 2 3 9 3 0 7  ▮
4 5 1 0 2 8 4 6  ▮ 5 2 6 9 8 5
6 2 7 1 4 8 8   8 4 7 4 3 1 6
9 3 9 9 6 2  ▮ 7 5 0 1 6 0 1 4
▮ 1 2 3 8 3 0  ▮ 7 0 2 5 3
7 4 9 6 5 7 1 2 0 5 0  ▮ 6 0 1
2 8 1 0  ▮ 4 4 7 5  ▮ 9 4 0 4
6 2 5 5 1 4 0   8 0 1 7 3 4 8
9 6 1 7 0 0 6   2 0 6 8 1 5 7
4 0 0 3 7 6 5  ▮ 5 4 3 8 3 0 2
```

9 Double or nothing

£2. 50. Suppose he starts off with £x. Doubling it gives him £2x. Giving away £1 leaves £2x − 1. Trebling gives £6x − 3. Giving away £2 leaves £6x − 5. If this equals £4x, then £6x − 5 = £4x, so that £2x = 5. So x = £2.50.

10 Retail therapy

£13.50. After each transaction the shopper is left with a third of what she had before it. So what she had before a transaction is three times what she had after it. Working backwards, she must have started out with
3 × 3 × 3 × 50p = 27 × 50p = £13.50.

11 Heavy load

The sacks weigh 8, 14, 17 and 23kg.

12 Cambio

£32.67, which gives 76 plonks and 23 plinks.

13 Safe cracker

2672815164735843.

14 I blame this new money

The cheque was for £65.32. Miss Wittering mixed up 32 and 65 and expected £32.65. She received £65.32. If she spends 2p, she will have £65.30 – exactly double £32.65.

15 Three items or less

£13, £77, 9p.

16 Digital wizardry

Add 12534768 to give 24880446.

17 They call it 'math'

1 1930219265
2 6039021090
3 1616002296
4 1767177608
5 9991111997
6 5251504948
7 7477044077
8 1013911914
9 3441424344
10 2111221111

18 Guesstimations

1 8<u>3475</u>21698
2 23641<u>1439</u>9
3 <u>2902</u>999822
4 2<u>190</u>622223
5 80641<u>31069</u>
6 <u>1256</u>314131
7 1264<u>33</u>2929
8 1234<u>0665</u>43
9 12<u>132</u>15211
10 9981<u>612</u>099

19 Number challenge

1 Seconds in a day (86,400). There are 63,360 inches in a mile.

2 0.57, i.e., 1 divided by 1.76.

3
5	+ 10	− 2	+ 13	
13	+ 1	+ 12	− 17	+ 30
15	− 2	+ 13	+ 12 × 2	− 11
39	÷ 3	+ 6	+ 3	+ 4
13 × 1	+ 6	+ 7	+ 16	− 3

4 Let $x/(-6) = (-6) - x$
Then $x = 36 + 6x$
So $-5x = 36$, hence $x = -7.2$.

5 4050 square metres. 1 ha = 10,000 square metres = 2.47 acres. Therefore 1 acre = 10,000/2.47 = 4050 square metres.

6 Sundays in a millennium. There are 52,000 Sundays in 1000 years and 39,370 inches in a kilometre.

7 59°F (× 9 divided by 5 + 32).

8 76 × 15 ÷ 20 = 57.

9 South Australia. 380,070 square miles = 984,377 km².

10 $^8/_{18}$ = 0.44 ($^6/_{15}$ = 0.4).

11 Even = 110 (Odd = 100).

12 14.

13 188.52 cm ($2\pi r$).

14 5.

15 288 metres.

16 1461. One year was a Leap Year (366 days).

17 Neither – they are the same! (729).

18 9.

19 28.

20 1232 (the numbers in each of the others add up to 9).

21 40% is yellow, 60% is red.

22 6.

23 The cube root of 5 (1.71). The sq. root of 3 is 1.73.

24 £1120.

25 30 and 31.

26 220.

27 33 square cm (½ × base × height).

28 1.25 × 10 to the power of 21 (1.25 × 10²¹).

29 27 and 39.

30 85°.

31 139,000 (three)
140,000 (two)
100,000 (one).

32 £67.

33 11 × 12 × 13 = 1716.

34
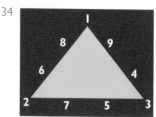

35 4 + 4 − ⁴⁄₄.

36 1968 (8961 upside down!).

37 Seven coins (50 + 9 + 9 + 9 + 5 + 2 + 1).

38 It divides into 5 triangles. Every triangle has a total of 180°.
5 × 180 = 900°.

39 27 seconds. If the 1st 'bong' to the start of the next one is 1 unit, then the start of the 2nd bong to the 3rd bong is a second unit – thinking this way, 5 o'clock constitutes 4 units. As the total time is 12 seconds, this means that each unit = 3 seconds (1¾). Working the same way, 10 o'clock = 9 units. 9 × 3 = 27 seconds.

40 15 hours and 56 minutes.

20 Digital conundrum

It's correct if you look at it in a mirror, giving the following calculation:

21 Knight moves

You can form the numbers 5034927618 and 5038167294. You can also form their reverses: 8167294305 and 4927618305. Hence four different numbers can be made. The key point is to realize that the number must start or end on the '5' key, followed/preceded by the '0' key, otherwise there is no way of using all ten keys during the route.

22 More or less?

In the LESS box. The word below each box relates to the number compared with the number of segments that make up the number. For example, the number 4 has 4 segments to it, so it goes in the EQUAL box. The number 7 is made up of 3 segments, and since 7 is more than 3 then it goes in the MORE box. Similarly, because the digit 0 is less than the number of its segments, it goes in the LESS box.

23 Oddly enough

67083416. The other numbers, when read upside-down, form English words. The words EGGSHELL, BESIEGES, ELIGIBLE, HELLHOLE and OBSESSES can be read.

24 Mobile mystery

First of all, it is straightforward to deduce that the middle-right number must be 0, since the product of row 2 and column 3 is 0.

Since Column 1 and Row 3 are both multiples of 7, the number 7 must appear in the button shared by these lines – i.e., the bottom-left button. We can deduce this because 7 is a prime number and there is no other way to split the number 7 up into smaller factors. If we did not place the 7 in that button, it would be impossible to make the 42 for this column and row.

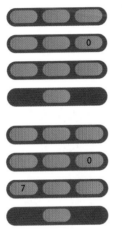

There are only two ways of making up the number 42 by multiplying three numbers together: $7 \times 6 \times 1$ and $7 \times 3 \times 2$.

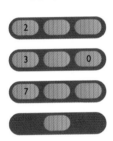

Suppose Column 1 contained the $7 \times 6 \times 1$ combination. Then either the '6' or '1' would appear in the top-left button. The '6' does not work because 6 does not divide into the product for Row 1 (80). '1' does not work either, because that would leave the buttons $1 \times ? \times ?$ on the top row to obtain 80, and there is no way of doing this unless we had a '10' button, which we don't have. Therefore, Column 1 must contain the $7 \times 3 \times 2$ combination.

By a similar argument, because 3 does not divide into 80, the 2 must be the top-left button and the 3 must be the middle-left button (right):

We can also notice that the product for Row 1 is a multiple of 5 but Column 2's product is not. This means that the 5 must appear in Row 1 but not Column 2 – hence '5' must appear in the top-right button. This leaves the '8' to appear in the top-middle button so that the top row is complete and has the required product of 80 (= $2 \times 8 \times 5$).

We know that Row 3 must be $7 \times 1 \times 6$ or $7 \times 6 \times 1$. Because 6 does not divide into 288 (the product for Column 2) then we know it must be $7 \times 1 \times 6$.

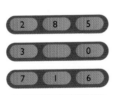

The remaining digits are the 4 and the 9. Since the bottom row is less than 8, it must contain the 4, so 9 must be the middle button.

25 Ali's wanderlust

The chance is 100%. The graph shows Ali's progress from Homesville to Big City (yellow line) and back (blue line). As long as she arrives in Big City on day one later than she sets off from Big City on day two, the lines must cross, indicating that the statement must hold true at some point during the journey.

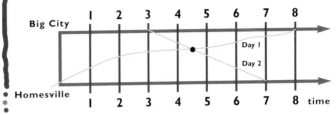

26 Funnel business

LEVEL 1 The balls should end up in something like the position shown (below). Only one ball is likely to fall into bins 1 and 7 because there is a 1 in 64 chance they end up there. This is because you need either six heads or six tails in a row, and the likelihood of this is $\frac{1}{2} \times \frac{1}{2} \times \frac{1}{2} \times \frac{1}{2} \times \frac{1}{2} \times \frac{1}{2} = \frac{1}{64}$. Since there are 64 balls in total, on average one ball should fall into bin 1 or bin 7.

LEVEL 2 The most balls fall into bin 4 because this requires three tails and three heads, but in any order. As such, there are 20 routes into this bin.

LEVEL 3 You may have noticed that the graph represents a bell curve (as shown by the black line). If you were to perform this experiment for real, it is highly unlikely that you would obtain exactly the picture shown. This is because probability describes what would happen over an infinite number of repetitions, and flukes (such as seven balls going into the '1' bin) can occur in the short term. What is true is that the rough shape of the curve should hold, particularly if you perform the experiment a number of times and then average out the results.

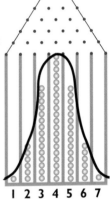

27 Curve ball

LEVEL 1 The simplest explanation is that the scientist threw the ball up in the air.

LEVEL 2 The blue line is the 'height above ground' – this is the natural shape that projectiles make (unless there is significant wind resistance). The red line is the speed – this slows down to zero when the ball reaches its peak. The acceleration line is green – it is constant because the gravitational force is effectively constant (unless the ball is fired high up into the atmosphere, at which point the Earth's gravitational pull becomes weaker).

LEVEL 3 The shape of the 'height above ground' graph is called a parabola.

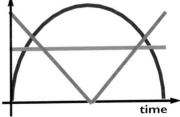

28 Ages apart

32. The key to the puzzle is to realize that, in the circumstances given, the age difference must be equal to the time elapsed. Sixteen years ago, we can see that the difference between Peter and Gail's age was 16 years. Obviously, this never changes. But now Peter is 48 the difference only accounts for one-third of his age rather than half.

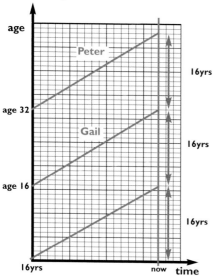

29 Fishing for numbers

Take a net and catch, say, a hundred fish from the pond. Dab each of them with a spot of paint that will not dissolve in water, and return them to different parts of the pond.

Wait until they disperse and then net another hundred. Some from the second catch will be marked with the spot. Let's say that six fish from the second batch are marked. It is reasonable to assume that the first catch represented 6% of the total fish population, which makes the total just short of 1700 (if 100 = 6% of the total = $100 \times \frac{100}{6}\% = 1666.66$), proving that your friend's estimate was not badly off the mark. If you repeat the exercise once or twice your result will become more accurate.

30 Austrian blonde

The minimum percentage is 10%. Sixty per cent of the population is female, so 40% is male. Of the 70% with blue eyes, 40% could be male, so a minimum of 30% must be females with blue eyes. If 70% of the population has blue eyes, 30% must have eyes of another colour. Of the 80% with blonde hair, 40% could be male, and 30% could be females with eyes of another colour, leaving a minimum 10% of the population certain to be female and to have both blue eyes and blond hair. The answer is immediately available using

the following formula: add all percentages (60 + 70 + 80 = 210), then deduct the product of 2 (one less than the features – female, blue eyes, blond hair) and 100%. 210 – 200 = 10%.

31 The three coin fallacy

It is a mistake to assume that the third coin can have only two positions, i.e., heads or tails. This would apply only if the third coin were always the same. In fact three coins can give rise to the following permutations:

This proves that the probability that all coins come out alike, i.e., H H H or T T T, is indeed 2 in 8, or ¼.

32 Double the trouble

There are four possible combinations with two children as far as their sex is concerned: boy-boy, boy-girl, girl-boy, girl-girl. It is important to realize that boy-girl and girl-boy are two different events.

Fred. As girl-girl is ruled out by the premise, the probability that both are boys is ⅓.

Steve. Let us now consider the same four combinations in the order of older first and younger second. Boy-boy and boy-girl are ruled out, making the probability of girl-girl ½.

33 It's lovely – what is it?

A 60%. Let us call the presents A, B and C, belonging to M, J and S respectively. There are six possibilities for distributing them among the shoppers:

	1	2	3	4	5	6
M	A	A	B	B	C	C
J	B	C	A	C	A	B
S	C	B	C	A	B	A

Only in cases 4 and 5 does no one receive the correct present, leaving four cases, i.e., two-thirds, in which at least one present goes to the right owner.

B The probability is zero. One shopper alone cannot receive the wrong present. If one shopper has the correct present, the other two must have the correct presents or the wrong ones. A minimum of two shoppers must have the wrong present.

34 Number maze 1

35 Number maze 2

36 Game, set and lunch

Catherine has won both her matches. However, she has only won two sets. Therefore, she must have won both matches by one set to love. The three sets that Suzanne won cannot have been during her match with Catherine, so must have been during her match with Helen. But this was a draw, so Helen must also have won three sets in that match.
The final table looks like this:

The three matches were:
Catherine beat Suzanne 1–0
Suzanne lost to Catherine 0–1
Suzanne drew with Helen 3–3.

	Played	Matches won	Matches lost	Matches drawn	Sets won	Sets lost
Catherine	2	2	0	0	2	0
Helen	2	0	1	1	3	3
Suzanne	2	0	1	1	3	3

37 Duel on the green

Chris hasn't lost a single hole so far. Neither has he drawn any matches. Therefore, he must have played only one match, which he won by 5 holes to 0. Notice that Archie has lost only three holes so far. This means that Chris has not played Archie yet, hence Chris's 5–0 game must have been against Bernard. The only remaining possible match is Bernard against Archie. The three holes lost by Archie must have been holes won by Bernard in their match. Of the six holes lost by Bernard, five have already been accounted for in his match with Chris. Therefore, Archie must have won one hole in the match with Bernard.
Final table:

The two matches were:
Bernard beat Archie by 3 holes to 1
Chris beat Bernard by 5 holes to 0.

	Played	Matches won	Matches lost	Matches drawn	Holes won	Holes lost
Archie	1	0	1	0	1	3
Bernard	2	1	1	0	3	6
Chris	1	1	0	0	5	0

38 Football mad

Galway have played two matches. One of these is already accounted for as a defeat. The other must be a victory, because they have scored more goals than they have conceded. Lingmouth cannot have drawn a match, because there is no team left to draw with. We can work out Lingmouth's goals scored by noting that the total of the two columns 'Goals for' and 'Goals against' must be the same. In this way we can work out that Lingmouth's 'Goals for' total must be 0. If Lingmouth have not scored any goals but have conceded five, we know that their only game was a 5–0 defeat.
The situation is now as follows:

	Played	Won	Lost	Drawn	Goals for	Goals against
Brockington	2	2		0	5	2
Galway	2	1	1	0	7	4
Lingmouth	1	0	1	0	0	5
Shrubville	1		1	0	1	2
South Keel	2	1		0	2	2

Who could have beaten Lingmouth 5–0? The only possibilities are Galway and Brockington. It can't be Brockington because then they would have no goals left for their second win. So it must have been Galway. If Galway scored five goals in that match without reply, then their other match must have been a 4–2 defeat. This must have been against Brockington, the only other team left who could have scored four goals. This means Brockington must have won their other match 1–0.
It is clear from the table that South Keel must have lost at least one match. Because Lingmouth played only against Galway, and Galway's two matches were against Lingmouth and Brockington, South Keel must have played Shrubville and Brockington – otherwise there is no one left to play with; one of these was a defeat and the other a win. We have already established that Brockington's other match was a 1–0 affair, so South Keel must have lost that match and won the match with Shrubville instead. The South Keel versus Shrubville match must have had a score of 2–1 for all the scores to tie up. Therefore, Shrubville and Brockington have not yet played each other.

To summarize:

Brockington beat Galway   4–2   Brockington beat South Keel   1–0
Galway beat Lingmouth   5–0   South Keel beat Shrubville   2–1.

	Played	Won	Lost	Drawn	Goals for	Goals against
Brockington	2	2	0	0	5	2
Galway	2	1	1	0	7	4
Lingmouth	1	0	1	0	0	5
Shrubville	1	0	1	0	1	2
South Keel	2	1	1	0	2	2

39 Mr Punch

First we note that 50 points are awarded for each bout, or 150 in total for all three bouts. The best Garish Gary could have done is 25 points for one draw. The best Brian Brawny could have done is 50 points for two draws – his 75 points cannot be for three draws because we know he must have some points from knockdowns, and it cannot be 50 points for a win and a loss because we are told that Brian Brawny was undefeated in all bouts. This leaves 150 – 25 – 50 = 75 points for Steve Supreme to have won from wins and draws. If Brian Brawny had two draws, then Steve Supreme must have beaten Garish Gary. So far we have:

	Points (total)	Points (wins /draws)	Points (knockdowns)
Garish Gary	40	25	15 (= 3 knockdowns)
Brian Brawny	75	50	25 (= 5 knockdowns)
Steve Supreme	110	75	35 (= 7 knockdowns)

Garish Gary had 3 knockdowns over the course of his two bouts. So this must have been 1 knockdown in one bout, and 2 in another. Let's suppose the single knockdown was in his bout with Brian Brawny, which was a draw – hence Brian Brawny knocked down Garish Gary once. Since Brian Brawny gained 5 knockdowns over two bouts, in the Brian Brawny *versus* Steve Supreme bout (another draw) there must have been 4 knockdowns on each side. However, we were told in the question that there were never 8 knockdowns in a single bout. Therefore, our assumption was wrong and Garish Gary's single knockdown was in the Steve Supreme bout. We can also conclude that Brian Brawny *versus* Garish Gary was a 2–2 draw, and Brian Brawny *versus* Steve Supreme was a 3–3 draw. Of Steve Supreme's original 7 knockdowns, there are 4 left for his match with Garish Gary who, as we've just deduced, had only 1 knockdown in this fight. Therefore, Steve Supreme beat Garish Gary by 4 knockdowns to 1. The final results are therefore:
Steve Supreme drew with Brian Brawny (3 knockdowns each)
Steve Supreme beat Garish Gary (4 knockdowns to 1)
Brian Brawny drew with Garish Gary (2 knockdowns each).

•••

40 What's the time 1?

The little hand should be pointing to 12. Taking the clock faces in order, the totals produced by adding the numbers to which the two hands point progress as follows: 6, 12, 18, 24.

41 Number square 1

X = 3. Looking across each row, the numbers progress: +3, -4, +3. Looking down each row, the numbers progress: +4, -3, +4.

42 Number targets 1

X = 16. Reading down target 1, the numbers increase by 9 in each square. In target 2 they increase by 6 in each square and in target 3 by 3 in each square.

43 Mathematical badges

X = 7. Take the number formed reading clockwise in each circular badge to form the following left-to-right sequence: 199, 217, 219, 221, 225. Each total increases by twice the value of the top digit on each badge: 199 + 18 (2 × 9) = 217. 217 + 2 (2 × 1) = 219 and so on.

44 Pizza poser

X = 13. Our student started with (3) and travelled clockwise, jumping one segment at a time and adding 1, then 2, then 3. The sequence she created was 3, 4, 6, 9, 13.

45 Number square 2

X = 4. Looking both across and down, the sum of each pair of numbers is one greater than that of the previous pair. For example, looking across row 1 we find 2 + 3 (=5) and 4 + 2 (=6), while looking down row 1 we find 2 + 7 (=9) and 5 + 5 (=10).

46 Umbrella trouble 1
X = 31. Start at the lowest number (6) and work clockwise, adding progressive odd numbers each time and jumping two segments at a time to unravel the sequence: 6 (+ 1) 7 (+ 3) 10 (+ 5) 15 (+ 7) 22 (+ 9) 31 (+ 11) 42.

47 What's the time 2?
At each stage the big hand moves +2, +3 and +4 and the little hand moves -1, -2 and -3. On the third clock face, therefore, the little hand should point to 5 (alongside the big hand) and on the fourth clock face the big hand should indicate 9.

48 Stepping stones 1
X = 8. The totals on each stepping stone left to right should be: 5, 6, 7 and 8.

49 Amazing number maze
Follow the route shown below to unravel the sequence 4, 8, 12, 16, 20, 24, 28, 32, 36.

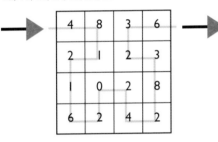

50 Number square 3
X = 20. Start at the top right-hand corner and work along the top line, then back along the second line and so on. The numbers progress as follows: +3, -2, +1. Finish at the bottom left-hand corner square with 20.

51 Number targets 2
The top number on each target is formed by multiplying the numbers in the previous set. The bottom number on each target is formed by adding together the previous two numbers.

30
11

52 Number targets 3
X = 48. Working down the first target, multiply by 3 and add 1 each time. Going down target 2, multiply by 3 and add 2 each time and going down target 3, multiply by 3 and add 3 each time.

53 Number towers
X = 67½. Working down from the top of tower A, each box adds 7½ to the previous number.

54 Number in the hole
X = 37.
A (10 + 11 + 18 + 19) ÷ 2 = 29
B (12 + 13 + 20 + 21) ÷ 2 = 33
C (14 + 15 + 22 + 23) ÷ 2 = 37
D (16 + 17 + 24 + 25) ÷ 2 = 41

55 Number roulette
X = 64.
17 − 3 + 6 = 20, 81 − 6 + 8 = 83, 116 − 6 + 10 = 120, 64 − 10 + 1 = 5.

56 Identity parade
X = 127. The difference between each number in the sequence is an accumulation of squared numbers. So, 17 − 1 = 16 (4²), 42 − 17 = 25 (5²), 78 − 42 = 36 (6²) and so on. X must equal 78 + (7²) = 127.

57 Triangle teaser
X = 27.
A (16 + 17 + 18) − (7 + 8 + 9) = 27
B (13 + 14 + 15) − (4 + 5 + 6) = 27
C (10 + 11 + 12) − (1 + 2 + 3) = 27

58 Umbrella trouble 2
X = 24. Start at the 1 in the top right position and, working clockwise, jump to alternate segments, multiplying by 1, 2, 3, 4, 5, 6 in turn to unravel the sequence 1, 1, 2, 6, 24, 120, 720.

59 Line 'em up!
X = 324. To obtain each number, multiply the previous number by 6.

60 Slice of pie
Starting at 16, jump over 2 segments and add 17 = 33. The sequence is: 16, 33, 50, 67, 84, 101, 118, 135. Therefore X is 84.

61 Orange segments
The identically placed segments in the three slices A, B and C always add up to 28 (e.g., 11 + 2 + 15 = 28). Therefore X = 10.

62 Number sequence 1
There are two sequences following alternately:
(+6) 62, 68, 74, 80, 86 and (-5) 57, 52, 47, 42
Therefore X is 42 and Y is 86.

63 Hexagonal place mats

A (4 × 5) – 8 = 12
B (6 × 7) – 9 = 33
C (8 × 9) – 10 = 62
D (10 × 11) – 11 = 99
Therefore X = 99.

64 Number queue 1

X = 34½. Add 9¼ to the first number to obtain the second number; subtract 3½ from the second number to obtain the third; proceed alternately adding 9¼, then subtracting 3½.

65 Complete the circle

X = 180. In each case the trick is to deduce which number, when multiplied by three of the numbers, will give the three numbers opposite those.

A	B	C
4	7	9
4 × 19 = 76	7 × 16 = 112	9 × 19 = 171
4 × 4 = 16	7 × 14 = 98	9 × 21 = 189
4 × 9 = 36	7 × 19 = 133	9 × 20 = 180

66 Number queue 2

Add 11⅞ to each number to obtain the next number. X is therefore 51¾.

67 Time watch

SINGAPORE
TUESDAY 11.10AM

MEXICO CITY
MONDAY 10.10PM

68 Round trip

Thursday 5am.
8hr + 3hr + 10hr + 1hr + 7hr + 1 week + 16hr = 8 days and 21 hours later. (The time difference doesn't matter as she ends up where she started.)

69 Hello L.A.!

10.30pm.

70 Passing the time

1:30am on Saturday, February 1. By international agreement travellers change dates at the moment they cross the international date line, which is an imaginary line at 180° longitude. If you cross the line heading west you add a day; if you cross the line heading east, you subtract a day. Bob sailed past midnight, making a time of 1.30am on Friday, January 31. But he had also sailed across the date line heading west, so he also added one full day to the date, making it 1.30am on Saturday, February 1.

Out of this world
71

Planet B does one full orbit in six years. This means that in one year it travels 60 degrees around the circle, because 360 degrees divided by six = 60 degrees. By the same token, planet A only travels 360 ÷ 24 = 15 degrees a year. Therefore planet B will be ahead of planet A by 60 – 15 = 45 degrees every year. Therefore they will meet up again when this lead has built up into 360 degrees, which will happen in 360 ÷ 45 = 8 years' time. A way of seeing this in table form is as follows:

Period (years)	6	24	
degrees/year	60	15	
Year	B	A	B minus A
	(degrees travelled)		
0	0	0	0
1	60	15	45
2	120	30	90
3	180	45	135
4	240	60	180
5	300	75	225
6	360	90	270
7	420	105	315
8	480	120	360
9	540	135	405
10	600	150	450
11	660	165	495
12	720	180	540

72

Note that planet B is slightly faster than planet A. Therefore the next time they will be in a straight line will be when B is 180 degrees ahead of planet A. Since B is already 45 degrees ahead of A, there is only 135 degrees left to make up.
Planet A travels at 15 degrees a year, as in the previous puzzle.
Planet B travels at 360 ÷ 20 = 18 degrees a year. Therefore planet B gains on planet A by 3 degrees a year. As we already know there are 135 degrees to make up, the planets and the Sun will be in the same straight line in 135 ÷ 3 = 45 years' time. This corresponds to planet A travelling 1.875 rotations and planet B moving through 2.25 orbits. The resulting situation at that time would look like this (right):

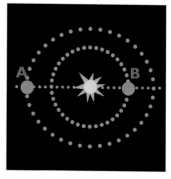

73

The key thing to realize here is that because the two orbits are in different geometric planes, there is a very limited number of places where the planets can be if both planets and the Sun are to be in the same straight line. In the diagram shown below, planet A must be on the red or blue spot (which happens every 12 years), and planet B must be on the yellow or green spot (which happens every seven years).

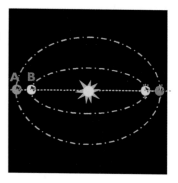

If two events happen at intervals of seven and 12 years, to find the next time they will happen simultaneously is to find the lowest common multiple – that is, the smallest number that can be divided by both seven and 12 without leaving a remainder. This is 84, so the planets and the Sun will be in a straight line again in 84 years' time. During this time, A will have orbited 3.5 times and B will have orbited six times, so in fact they will end up on opposite sides of the Sun.

74

The number of orbits B will have made at the required solution will be $(x + \frac{1}{12})$, where x is the number of whole orbits and $\frac{1}{12}$ is the extra $\frac{1}{12}$ of an orbit (30 degrees) it needs to make up to arrive at the intersection point.

The number of years to intersection is equal to the number of orbits multiplied by the time taken for each orbit. This is $(x + \frac{1}{12}) \times 24$, or in simpler terms $24x + 2$.

Clearly the answer must be a multiple of seven years, otherwise planet A will not be at the intersection point. Hence $(24x + 2)$ must be divisible by seven.

Trying values for $x = 1, 2, 3...$ we get:
$(24 \times 1) + 2 = 26$ (not a multiple of 7)
$(24 \times 2) + 2 = 50$ (not a multiple of 7)
$(24 \times 3) + 2 = 74$ (not a multiple of 7)
$(24 \times 4) + 2 = 98$ (a multiple of 7).

Hence the answer is that they will collide in 98 years' time. During this time, A will have made $\frac{98}{7}$ = 14 orbits and B will have made $98 \div 24 = \frac{41}{12}$ = 3.42 orbits.

75 Magic 34 square

7	13	4	10
2	12	5	15
9	3	14	8
16	6	11	1

76 Magic prime square

103	79	37
7	73	139
109	67	43

77 Anti-magic square

4	(14)	15	1
9	7	(6)	12
(5)	11	10	8
16	2	3	(13)

78 Magic 264 square

It remains a magic square when turned upside down – i.e., 18 + 99 + 86 + 61 = 264 as does 19 + 98 + 66 + 81. The numbers still form a magic square when read back-to-front – i.e., 18 + 99 + 86 + 61 = 264, as does 16 + 68 + 99 + 81.

79 Magic 65 square

14	20	21	2	8
10	11	17	23	4
1	7	13	19	25
22	3	9	15	16
18	24	5	6	12

80 DIY magic 111 square

35	1	6	26	19	24
3	32	7	21	23	25
31	9	2	22	27	20
8	28	33	17	10	15
30	5	34	12	14	16
4	36	29	13	18	11

81

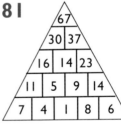

82

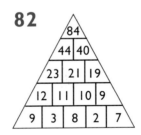

The first two pyramids are relatively easy. The trick is to start by working out which number we can know for sure; that number will be the key to the next and so on.

83

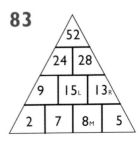

We need to find the missing number from the bottom line, M. The 28 in the second row is equal to the left and right numbers below it, here called L and R. We can work out that L = 7 + M. Also that R = M + 5. Putting this together: 28 = L + R = (7 + M) + (M + 5) = 2M + 12. Hence, M = 8. From here it's easy to work out that the number at the top of the pyramid is 52.

84

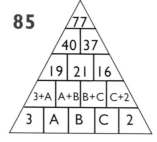

You may have found that it was difficult to get the numbers in the left-hand side of the pyramid. The key block is the one that lies between the 4 and the 7. One perfectly legitimate approach is to keep trying different numbers until you get the right one! However, it can be calculated as follows. Let this block equal an unknown number (let's call this x). Then the block above the 4 and the x must be 4 + x and the block above the x and the 7 must be x + 7.

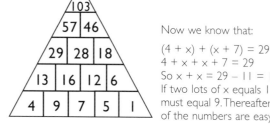

Now we know that:

$(4 + x) + (x + 7) = 29$
$4 + x + x + 7 = 29$
So $x + x = 29 - 11 = 18$
If two lots of x equals 18, then x must equal 9. Thereafter, the rest of the numbers are easy to find.

85

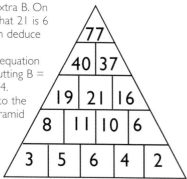

In this pyramid, the top bricks are easy to fill in but the bottom ones are somewhat harder. Let's label the blank bricks on the bottom row A, B and C. Following the same method as the previous puzzle, we get the partial solution shown (left).

We obtain these three equations:
Equation 1: $19 = (3 + A) + (A + B)$
Simplified: $16 = (2 \times A) + B$
Equation 2: $21 = (A + B) + (B + C)$
Simplified: $21 = A + (2 \times B) + C$
Equation 3: $16 = (B + C) + (C + 2)$
Simplified: $14 = B + (2 \times C)$
If we add together equations 1 and 3, we get:
$16 + 14 = (2 \times A) + B + B + (2 \times C)$
$30 = (2 \times A) + (2 \times B) + (2 \times C)$
So the sum of A, B and C must be 15. Now look again at equation 2 – on the right-hand side this also has an A, B and C, but it also has an extra B. On the left-hand side, we note that 21 is 6 more than 15. Hence we can deduce that B = 6.
By plugging B = 6 back into equation 1, we see that A = 5. And putting B = 6 into equation 3 gives C = 4. The results can be placed into the appropriate blocks in the pyramid (shown right).

86 Spell it out

1. EIGHT
2. EIGHTEEN
3. TWELVE
4. ELEVEN
5. THIRTEEN
6. THIRTY
7. FIFTY-SEVEN
8. SIXTY-SIX
9. FORTY-FIVE
10. NINE
11. TWENTY-FIVE
12. THREE
13. FIFTY-TWO
14. FOUR
15. SIX
16. FIVE

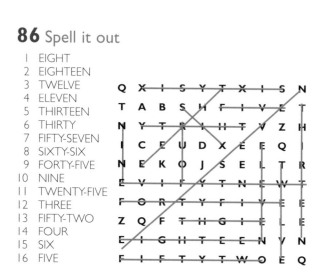

87 Total confusion

1. 1001
2. 1221
3. 5929
4. 600,000
5. 125,000
6. 22,299
7. 1024
8. 40,404
9. 2520

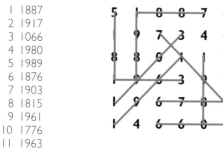

88 When ... and where?

1. 1887
2. 1917
3. 1066
4. 1980
5. 1989
6. 1876
7. 1903
8. 1815
9. 1961
10. 1776
11. 1963

The remaining unused digits are 4s.

89 Tile and tile again 1

90 Tile and tile again 2

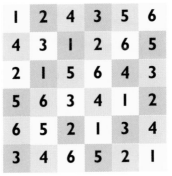

1	2	4	3	5	6
4	3	1	2	6	5
2	1	5	6	4	3
5	6	3	4	1	2
6	5	2	1	3	4
3	4	6	5	2	1

91 A pouring problem

There are only two ways in which you can begin decanting: you can either pour water into jug B until jug B is full or pour water into jug C until jug C is full. During the operations you must avoid a situation in which both B and C are entirely full because then the only way to proceed would be to pour the contents of B and C entirely into A – in other words go back to the beginning and start again.
The two possibilities are:

JUG	A	B	C	A	B	C
Commence (litres)	8	0	0	8	0	0
Operation 1	3	5	0	5	0	3
Operation 2	3	2	3	5	3	0
Operation 3	6	2	0	2	3	3
Operation 4	6	0	2	2	5	1
Operation 5	1	5	2	7	0	1
Operation 6	1	4	3	7	1	0
Operation 7	4	4	0	4	1	3
Operation 8				4	4	0

To start by pouring into jug B until it is full produces the solution with the least number of decantings, which is seven.

92 Heavy duty drink

750g. Remove a bottle of wine from the left pan, and the only bottle from the right pan. The scale will still balance, making the weight of one bottle equal to half of 3 x 500g. The number of carats in the bars is irrelevant.

93 Dollar dilemma

Only a single weighing is necessary to identify the counterfeit stack. Let x be the weight of a genuine silver dollar. Take one coin from stack no. 1, two from stack no. 2, three from stack no. 3, and so on up to stack no. 10, from which you should take all ten coins. Weigh the whole sample. The sample should weigh 55x. The number of grams that the sample weighs over or under 55x corresponds to the number of the stack containing the counterfeit coins. For instance, if the sample weighs 7g more than it should (or 7g less), then the stack containing the counterfeit coins is no. 7.

94 A lightweight intruder

Two weighings will do it. Put three coins on each of the pans. If they don't balance, take two of the coins from the lighter side and weigh them. The lighter coin is the fake. But if they balance, it is the third coin. Now let us assume that the three coins on each side balance. Then you proceed with the remaining three as described above.

95 The manuscript

No. He could only achieve the daily average of 4000 words if he were to complete the second half of his manuscript in no time. If you don't believe me, think again.

96 Piggybank puzzle

97 In the pink

98 Novice nonogram

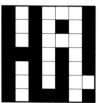

99 Calm your thoughts

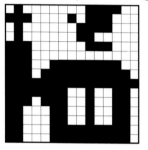

100 Big test

101 Saturation point

½kg. Originally 1% of the total weight is sponge (i.e., 10g of the total 1000g). After squeezing, 2% of the total weight is sponge. The sponge itself still only weighs 10g, so the weight of the wet sponge must be 500g (since 2% of 500g equals 10g).

102 Card magic

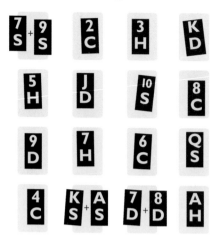

103 It's a frame up!

Lay the 8 of Clubs over the 7 of Hearts and the 6 of Clubs over the 5 of Diamonds, and all the sides will add up to 23. (Did you realize you can't use two 5s because there are already three in the frame?)

104 Cards at the table

105 Mismatched cards

106 Three blind dice

36. (Each dice has a total of 21 spots – opposite sides always total 7 – since we can see 27 spots, there must be 63 – 27 = 36 hidden from view.)

107 Flat out

A and C.

108 Roll over

Take the first dice, the 6, as an example. Because opposite faces always add up to 7, you know that 1 is on the opposite face. Therefore, the four numbers that are a quarter-turn away from the 6 are 2, 3, 4 and 5. Similarly for the other two dice. Therefore the options are:
(2, 3, 4 or 5) × (1, 2, 5 or 6) – (1, 3, 4 or 6) = 11
By considering each combination in turn, we find that there are two solutions as follows:

109 Seeing spots

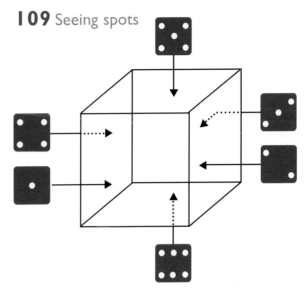

110 Picture this

One way you could have started to solve this was to notice that the blank of 6-blank has to be in the same row as the 5-4 piece, the only piece that adds up to 9 by itself.

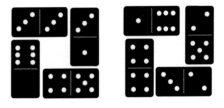

111 Domino-henge

Note that the 6-3 and the 5-4 pieces could be interchanged.

112 Wall of dominoes

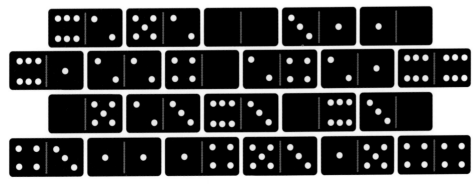

1 Think about it

1 It must be Derek, because George, Robin, Chris and Sam can be girls' names, whereas Derek cannot.

2 If the machine really did return him to the exact same point in space, when he returned he would find that he was completely off the planet Earth, because in an hour it will have moved approximately 72,000 km (45,000 miles) along its orbit around the Sun.

3 The rule does work, depending on the days you are describing. The rule makes use of the fact that New Year's Day falls seven days after Christmas Day, and hence is the same day of the week. However, the day seven days after Christmas Day in the year 2000 is New Year's Day, 2001. There is no significance in the choice of the year 2000 – Christmas Day and New Year's Day in the same year always fall on different days of the week.

4 She was a female priest/vicar.

5 It was the same person. Winston Churchill was prime minister between 1940 and 1945 and again between 1951 and 1955.

6 The planet Venus. The rotation of this planet is so slow that its day is longer than its year – in other words, the time taken for the planet to revolve around its own axis is longer than the time it takes to do a complete orbit around the Sun. Therefore, if you are to have a birthday every year it must take place every day.

7 He drove in reverse. Technically, it is also possible to do this by starting your car just short of the North Pole, but we challenge you to find a tarmac road in the Arctic.

8 He is my father's identical twin.

9 She may live in Texas, but she started her journey north of New York.

10 October, because it has 31 days plus an extra hour gained when the clocks go back.

2 Weird words

1 'Have I rolled a "YES"?'.

2 The word 'therein' (the, there, he, her, here, ere, rein and in).

3 Queue (sounds like 'q').

4 Arrowroot, which uses the A, W and T once, and the R and O three times each.

5 Turn the 'd' and 'u' letters upside-down to give 'p' and 'n'. You can now form the word 'elephant'.

3 A number of puzzles

1 Only four are required. At worst, she can pick out one glove of each colour. The fourth glove must match with one of the previous colours. It does not matter if she picks out two left-hand or right-hand gloves, because she can turn a left-handed glove inside-out to make it right-handed and vice versa.

2 All of them – into two parts of 20.5, 28, 41.5, 55.5 and 82 respectively.

3 No – my friend will simply say 'the score will be 0-0, before the match starts'.

4 Add a single (albeit curvy) line at the beginning to make it 'SIX'.

5 None, because steel floats in mercury.

6 73 and 03 (the sequence increases in blocks of three, though the commas are in the wrong places: 3, 6, 9, 12, 15, etc. The next multiples of 3 would be 27, 30, and 33).

7 The time is 12.34 and 56 seconds, so if this were read on a digital clock it would be: 1234567890 (12:34:56 7/8/90).

4 Children's miscellany

1 Once – after the first subtraction you are taking 3 from 93 and so on.

2 The outside.

3 Wait until the peacock flies away.

4 Your answers should have been Snow White, cream/white, and water. Did you say 'milk' to question iii?

5 I undid the knot and threaded one doughnut back off the rope.

6 He hung the hat over the barrel of his gun.

7 The other end of the rope is not tied to anything.

8 Your breath.

9 You would rather the rhinoceros attacked the elephant.

10 It is a ghost train at a fairground.

Lateral know-how

5 Pull the comb through your hair several times. This will create static electricity on the comb. Then drag the comb across the salt and pepper, just high enough so that the comb does not actually touch it. The pepper particles will seemingly jump up and land on the comb, while the salt will stay where it is.

6 Bend the straw then place it into the bottle, as shown right. You will now be able to lift the bottle using the straw.

7 Clock it

Draw a line over the second '1' so that it now reads 10 TO 10.

8 Hold on

Your right elbow, hand or forearm.

9 This way to exit . . .

The doors opened inwards. The people panicked and pressed against the doors so that they effectively prevented themselves from opening them. Regulations nowadays specify that doors in public venues must open outwards to prevent this sort of thing from happening.

10 Sibling rivalry

The sheet of newspaper is slid under a door and the twins stand on the paper, one on either side of the door. They can see each other through the keyhole.

11 The long and short of it

They did it like this because Alf had longer arms than Bert and so could reach higher when standing on his short brother's shoulders than the short-armed brother could have reached if he were to stand on the taller brother's shoulders.

12 Judge a book

It was a volume of an encyclopedia (containing articles with titles from How to Jog).

13 Auto rewind

The tape that had just been played felt warm.

14 Fast work

It was a sand-filled egg-timer, which it was Fred's job to make.

15 Heave-ho...ping!

They tie one end of the rope to railings, a tree or some other solid thing. Having that at one end and 12 men pulling at the free end is equivalent to having 12 men at each end – and the rope will snap.

16 Losing your head

He was a breakdancer, whose head moved around the floor in a larger circle than his feet. There is theoretically no limit to how far your head can move farther than your feet. There would be a problem of course if it did so in the same straight line!

17 Junk and disorderly

He was seeing it upside down. So 1661 would have read 1991.

18 Food for thought?

It was the restaurant on a ferry in stormy weather.

19 Spoken impish 1

Impolite (imp & alight).

20 Cube it

Add two vertical matches and one horizontal match so that a digital number '8' is formed. Eight is the cube of 2 ($2^3 = 8$).

21 Nouvelle cuisine

In one fairly sharp motion, spin the dish on the table. The centrifugal force will cause the olives to move to the outside, as shown.

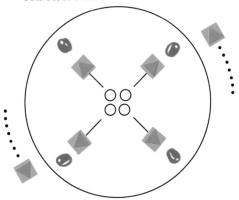

22 The pyramid game

Add together the centre two cards, multiply by 3, then add the outer two cards. If this result is a 2-digit number, add the digits together and repeat until you get a single digit. You will find that this is the number of the top card.

Using the example given in the question, we get $(2 + 3) \times 3 + 5 + 9 = 29$. Now $2 + 9 = 11$, hence $1 + 1 = 2$, which is correct.

This works because there are three routes from the centre cards to the top of the pyramid, and hence they get triple-counted in comparison with the outer cards. You can extend this game further – for example, for a five-layer pyramid the multiplying factors for each card would be 1 4 6 4 1 instead of 1 3 3 1.

23 Cornered

The player must slide the coin two spaces to the right, so that it rests on the diagonal between S and F. In fact, any of the spaces on the diagonal are 'safe' positions because from here it is impossible for the next player to slide the coin to F in just one turn. The winning strategy is therefore always to keep the coin on this key diagonal.

24 The last coin

Ensure that you go second. Whatever coin(s) your opponent takes, take the coin(s) diametrically opposite. This way you maintain the symmetry of the situation and, since taking the final coin or pair of coins is an unsymmetrical situation, your opponent can never win.

25 X marks the spot

The colouring of the board was a clue. You might have noticed that the existing three coins are on differently coloured spaces. The next coin must go on any space of the only remaining colour, marked here with Os.

If you take any two spaces of the same colour, you'll notice that there is always a space halfway between them. (The reason behind this is a property of odd and even numbers.) Therefore, you can only ever play one coin on each of the four colours.

Thus, whoever plays the fifth coin must lose. So the winning strategy is always to go second. It is not a very good game, considering that the longest it can possibly last is four moves before someone must win on the next move.

26 The conjuring trick

The chance that player 2 will pick the correct tumbler from the outset is 1 in 3. Therefore, if player 2 does not choose to switch, he or she will win 10 games out of every 30, on average.

However, it is twice as likely that the coin is in the tumbler that is not picked. Therefore, if player 2 always chooses to switch, he or she will win 20 games out of every 30, on average. It looks like the chance is 50-50, because there are two tumblers, one of which contains the coin. However, the specific sequence of events in the puzzle means that this conclusion is not valid.

Where on earth am I?

27 China (chin + A).

28 Turkey.

29 Finland (F in Land).

30 Uganda (ewe + gander).

31 Antarctica (ant + ark + ticker).

32 New Zealand (news + eel + and).

Cinema greats

33 Jack Lemmon (jack + lemon).

34 Beau Bridges (bow + bridges).

35 Orson Welles (oars + and + wells).

36 Roman Polanski (row + man + pole + and + ski).

37 The riddle of the Sphinx

Man. Babies go about on all fours, people on two feet, old people use a walking stick.

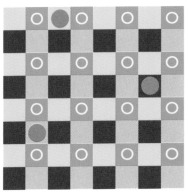

38 A fishy tale
Fleas or lice.

39 A Biblical poser
The answer given was a dead lion in which wild bees were making honey.

40 A weighty problem
The word 'ton'.

41 Most curious beast
A falconer on his horse with a falcon on his wrist.

42 Creepy crawlie
A dining table and four chairs.

43 New for old
The second hand on a watch.

44 Call me Quin
A spare tyre.

45 All tied up
A pair of shoes.

46 Precious metal
A drawing pin stuck in a shoe.

47 All things to all men
HE, HER, HERO, HEROINE.

48 Striptease
AITCH.

49 Less is…no less
A postman.

50 Spoken Impish II
Impact (imp + act).

51 Children's test
A Very big hands.
B It can fall on any day of the week.
C No, but April May.
D It makes oil boil.

52 To catch a thief
The man used a telephone to send a message to the pager, along the lines of 'You've won the office sweepstake. Come to this address at 3pm tomorrow to collect your winnings.' The address sent was the man's home address. The person that currently had the pager would almost certainly be the thief. When the thief duly arrived to collect his 'winnings' the police (who had previously been tipped off by the victim) were ready to arrest the man.

53 Spoken Impish III
Impart (imp + art).

Fur balls
54 Catacomb. 55 Catatonic.

56 Colloquial Impish
Implore (imp + law)

57 Wood you believe it
If you look carefully, you will see that there are actually two planks underneath the other five.

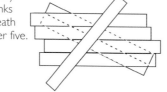

58 Crystal
Zero. The sum of the lengths of two of the sides of each triangular end is equal to the length of the third side, therefore each end must actually be a straight line and the figure must have no volume because it exists in only two dimensions.

59 Whatever next?
12,215,308,523,345,917 (just add one to the, rather large, whole number).

60 Is that Danish?
TBERNTTBE

The letter 'O' has been omitted from the phrase 'To be or not to be' (from *Hamlet* by William Shakespeare).

61 The odd couple
SA ER FI ES

A and F. If you remove this pair of letters you are left with the word series.

62 Polyominoes
The lines inside each polyomino form one of the letters in the word CURIOUS.

63 Missing card
The phrase 'KING OF HEARTS' can be formed by rearranging the 12 letters of the alphabet missing from the arrangement of cards.

64 Letter grid
Place Z in the third row of the grid as shown below so that the empty squares form the other omitted letter, which is T.

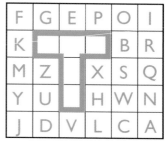

F	G	E	P	O	I
K				B	R
M	Z		X	S	Q
Y	U		H	W	N
J	D	V	L	C	A

65 Missing square
Read down each column of letters to find islands, tumbler, calcify. The missing square contains an L.

66 Tower
PARIS. View the diagram at an angle from below to see Eiffel.

67 Think globally
The row of circles at the top of the grid represents the nine planets in the solar system and beneath are their respective names.

o	o	o	o	O	O	O	O	o
M	V	E	m	J	S	U	N	P
E	E	A	a	U	A	R	E	L
R	N	R	r	P	T	A	P	U
C	U	T	s	I	U	N	T	T
U	S	H		T	R	U	U	O
R				E	N	S	N	
Y				R			R	E

68 Password
ANGLE. The sentence next to the buttons should be interpreted as follows: To open the door try angle (Triangle).

69 Briefcase
Upper. The words TOP SECRET are in upper-case letters.

70 Old Impish
Impale (imp + ale)

71 On the make
A Toyota. A to Y ot (back to) A.

The key to solving puzzles 1–14 is to work out which elements are repeated in each row and then work out what's missing in the gap. In puzzle 1, for example, each row contains four elements:

letters   A, B and C
asterisks   one on the right, one without and one on the left
circle   only one letter appears in a circle
colour   two red letters and one blue letter.

From this it should be easy to work out that row three is missing a red letter A in a circle without an asterisk. The same principle should be used to solve the other puzzles.

14 Fly away Peter

The answer is C but the logic changes from one row to the next. In the first row, you add the dots on the first two ladybirds to get the third; in the second row, you subtract the dots on the second ladybird from the first to get the third; in the third row, you multiply the dots on the first two ladybirds to get the third.

15 Canny thinking

Some potential alternative uses include:
A tiny 'kick stand' for the can.
A miniature catapult.
An ice scraper if you have lots of time to clean off your windscreen!
Collect a few for emergency false fingernails.
A tiny ring for your little finger.

16 Mona Lisa teaser

Here are some answers we prepared earlier:
The grin was because she had done the old 'exploding paintbrush' trick and was just waiting for it to go off.
'My foot's gone to sleep.'
'If he tells me to "cheer up" once more...'
'I can see right up Leonardo's nose.'
'I can't wait for the photo booth to be invented – five days of sitting around, just for a passport photo…'

17 A hole lotta trouble

Did you get out of the hole on this one? Some suggested answers:
Because the holes they fit are round.
So they can be used as a tray to carry cups of tea above ground.
Someone at the factory lost their ruler and there were only compasses left.
For the same reason that plugholes are round – whatever that may be.

18 Compu-less

Our favourite responses:
People would use real coasters for their coffee cups instead of free CDs.
Wilma Flintstone would retain her status as top pin-up (since Lara Croft would never have existed).
Upon hearing the word 'keyboard', people would think of a piano.
'Reboot' would mean 'put your shoes back on'.
The @ symbol would have remained in well-deserved obscurity.
A printer would be a person, not a machine.

Words and meaning

19 MAUNDER, RAMBLE.

20 d: OF THE GUMS.

21 TOFFEE: (all can be followed by APPLE).

22 a: FREQUENCY.

23 IGNORANT.

24 LAUDABLE.

25 VULNERABLE.

26 c: ANXIETY.

27 b: HARASSMENT.

28 UPSET, COMPOSED.

29 c: KINESO.

1 Easy as ABC
D is the missing figure.

2 Poly-gone
C is the missing figure.

3 Star sign
A is the missing figure.

4 Jumping for joy?
D is the missing figure.

5 Find the flag
C is the missing figure.

6 Square off
C is the missing figure.

7 Where are you @?
C is the missing figure.

8 Sun spot
D is the missing figure.

9 I say
C is the missing figure.

10 Crack this
D is the missing figure.

11 Geometric gap
B is the missing figure.

12 On target
C is the missing figure.

13 Joust about
A is the missing figure.

Letters and sequences

30 CLOUD BREAK.

31 BY THE WAY.

32 Chisel: LOCH/CHIN; THIS/ISLE; FUEL/ELSE.

33 What's in a name? that which we call a rose by any other name would smell as sweet (From *Romeo and Juliet* by William Shakespeare).

34 OFFSCREEN, ROUGHHEWN, MOUSSAKA.

35 ALTNS = SLANT.

36 RID: PUTRID & RIDDEN.

37 LIFE.

38 JENNET (a female donkey).

39 MOREOVER.

40 SOLOMON, SUMATRA, MADEIRA.

41 Turn again
CHRONICLE.

42 Lost beauty
ELIZABETH, to give:
TIE, PAL, SKI, FEZ, PEA, NIB, RUE, SAT and ASH.

43 SIX (two legs per vowel).

44 40

Innings	Runs	Average
10	220	22
20	800	40
30	1020	34

Let Y equal the number of runs scored in the last 20 innings. The average over 30 innings is:
$((22 \times 10) + (Y \times 20))/30 = 34$, thus $220 + 20Y = 1020$, therefore $20Y = 800$, so $Y = 40$.

45 $33 \times 11 \div 3 - 6 = 115$.

46 The total is 0. Because 0 is part of the chain it follows that no matter how many numbers you multiply together the answer has to be 0.

47 1568. Concentrate on the women first. There are 8 women to choose from first, then 7, then 6 then 5, leaving one choice from 4 for the final female team member. Multiplying together 8, 7, 6, 5 and 4 gives the theoretical number of ways of choosing 5 women from 8 but in a given order. But a team consisting of Alice, Betty, Claire, Donna and Erica is just the same no matter the order in which you picked them. So we need to divide this figure by the number of ways in which it is possible to arrange five people. This is equal to $5 \times 4 \times 3 \times 2 \times 1$.

$$\frac{8 \times 7 \times 6 \times 5 \times 4}{5 \times 4 \times 3 \times 2 \times 1} = 56$$

The same logic goes for the men, except that there are six men:

$$\frac{8 \times 7 \times 6 \times 5 \times 4 \times 3}{6 \times 5 \times 4 \times 3 \times 2 \times 1} = 28$$

Multiply the two together to get 1568 possible selections.

48 4585. In all the others you can multiply the last two digits together to obtain the first two digits e.g., 2464 ($6 \times 4 = 24$).

49 $$\frac{6 - 9 \times 7}{6 + 4 \times 3} \times \frac{-57}{18} = -3\tfrac{1}{6}$$

(The standard order of operations states that the multiplication must be done first.)

50 $\tfrac{7}{22} \div \tfrac{14}{44} = \tfrac{7}{22} \times \tfrac{44}{14} = \tfrac{2}{2} = 1$.

(To divide one fraction by another, invert one fraction then multiply the fractions together.)

51 9523164. This is a number movement puzzle. You can work out the answer by looking at the positions of the digits and numbering them accordingly:

(1234567)	(4673251)
7598123 is to	8239517

as

(1234567)	(4673251)
4139652 is to	9523164.

52 96

$32 \times 50p = £16.00$
$32 \times 20p = £6.40$
$32 \times 10p = £3.20$
$£25.60$

53 Banana = 9p, Apple = 6p.

Let A = apple and B = banana.
Let $6A + 9B = 117$ [1] and $5A + 11B = 129$ [2]
Multiplying [1] by 5 and [2] by 6 gives:
$30A + 45B = 585$ [3] $30A + 66B = 774$ [4]
Subtracting [3] from [4] gives:
$66B - 45B = 774 - 585$, thus $21B = 189$, so $B = 189/21 = 9$, so a banana = 9p.
(Substituting this back into an earlier equation reveals that an apple is 6p.)

54 10,116. Let us suppose that the winner received V votes. Then the total number of votes cast will be V + (V − 696) + (V − 2968) + (V − 7158). We know that 29,642 votes were cast in total, so:

4V − 10,822 = 29,642

4V = 29,642 + 10,822 = 40,464

Hence V = 40,464 ÷ 4 = 10,116.0.

55 36 minutes: $\dfrac{45 \times 8}{10}$

56 4. In each case the figure on the right is multiplied by the figure at the bottom. The figure on the left is then subtracted to give the central figure. Since 5 × 4 = 20, it follows that '?' must equal 4 because 4 from 20 gives 16.

57 0. Looking across each line and down each column, the sum of alternate digits is equal. So, for example, in the last row 3 + 1 = 4, so '?' must equal 0 (likewise in the last column 5 + 3 = 8).

58 1. The sequence is subtract 4, divide by 2, subtract 4, divide by 2...

59 27. In each case multiply the first two digits then add on the third digit on the left to give the number on the right. Since 6 × 4 + 3 = 27, that is the answer.

60 1413. The sequence is to add the second number of the first shape to the first number of the second shape, then add the first number of the first shape to the second number of the second shape, hence 9 + 5 = 14 and 7 + 6 = 13 (1413).

61 8. In each case multiply the box on the left by the middle number, then subtract the box on the right. The answer is the two-digit number in the middle column. Hence, 5 × 8 = 40 − 2 = 38.

62 31. The trick here is to find the relationship between the numbers in each vertical column.
1st column even numbers
2nd column odd numbers
3rd column prime numbers
4th column square numbers
The next prime number in the sequence is 31.

63 32. The number in the sequence are all consecutive non-prime numbers.

64 68. In each case the number at the top is subtracted from the number on the right. The answer is divided by four to give the number on the left. So, 68 − 24 (÷ 4) = 11.

65 The sequence that you need to work out to find the missing answers is:

B + C = A and A + C = D

(C + D) − (A + B) = E

Hence B = 2; D = 10; E = 6.

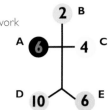

66 Lock in place

67 Patchwork
B

68 Wedges
A, C, D, E

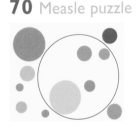

69 Flat dice
D

70 Measle puzzle

71 Triangle wrangle
24. Triangles are formed by the following segments:
1, 2, 3, 6, 7, 8, 9, 10,
1+4, 2+5, 3+4,
5+6, 7+8, 8+9,
9+10, 1+4+8,
2+5+9, 7+8+9,
8+9+10, 1+2+4+5,
3+4+5+6,
7+8+9+10,
3+4+7+8,
5+6+9+10

72 Vision only

73 Round and round
12

74 Went to mow
1 hour 20 minutes.
The rate of mowing = Area cut ÷ time taken, so:
  Rate (man 1) = p/3
  Rate (man 2) = p/4
  Rate (man 3) = p/6
(where p = pitch)
If all three men work together, we need to add their speeds together to get:
(p/3) + (p/4) + (p/6) = p/t
where t is time. Notice that all the ps cancel out (i.e., the size of the pitch doesn't affect the answer.)
So we're left with:
1/3 + 1/4 + 1/6 = 1/t
Putting the left-hand side over a common denominator:
(4 + 3 + 2)/12 = 1/t, therefore 9/12 = 1/t
Taking the reciprocals (i.e., inverting both fractions):
t = 12/9, or 1.333 hours, or 1 hour 20 minutes.

75 Points north
11.
NW by W
N by E
NW
NNE
NW by N
NE by N
NNW
NE
N by W
NE by E
N

76 Designer flag
D. The black dot moves one side clockwise at each stage and alternates outside and inside the rectangle. The star moves in exactly the same way. The eclipse alternates between two sides, first inside, then outside the rectangle.

77 Cool eggs
B. At each stage the small blue and pink circles in the eclipse change places. The larger blue circle moves one place to the right at each stage, so it ends up to the right of the eclipse.

78 Star-crossed
B. The contents of each hexagon are determined by the contents of the two hexagons directly below it. Stars are only carried forward when they appear once in a position. When they appear twice in the same position they are not carried forward.

79 Whorls
C. It spirals anticlockwise. The other figures all spiral clockwise.

80 Computer talk
3510. Start at the right and double the figure each time, then add together the numbers represented by a 1.

2048	1024	512	256	128	64	32	16	8	4	2	1
1	1	0	1	1	0	1	1	0	1	1	0

2048 + 1024 + 256 + 128 + 32 + 16 + 4 + 2 = 3510.

81 Spot the amoeba
D. The figure is exactly the same shape except that large circles become small and vice versa.

82 Beach souvenir
78.75kg. Let y = weight of sand
17.5kg + ⅛ y = y,
therefore 17.5kg must equal ⅞ y
So ⅛ y must equal 8.75kg,
so 8.75kg × 9 = y
Answer 78.75kg

83 Easy reading
28. There are four ways of reaching the Ys in the corner of the diamond, and three ways each of reaching any of the eight Ys along the sides of the diamond. Hence: (1 × 4) + (3 × 8) = 28.

84 Fruit corner
Apple = 4½p, Banana = 5½p.

The trick is to multiply each equation by a number so that's it's possible to eliminate one of the variables:

	6A + 3B	= 43½p	Multiply × 5
	5A + 7B	= 61p	Multiply × 6
1 =	30A + 15B	= 217½p	
2 =	30A + 42B	= 366p	Subtract 1 from 2
	27B	= 148½	
	one B	= 5½p	
	one A	= 4½p	

85 Dice tower
19. Since the opposite faces of a dice always add up to 7, the total must be (4 × 7) − 6 − 3 = 19.

86 Unfinished work
50. As there are four blocks along the top, the smallest cube that can be constructed is 4 × 4 × 4 = 64 blocks. As there are 14 blocks in position already, a further 50 blocks are required to construct a solid cube.

87 A question of balance
6kg   8 × 9 = 72, 12 × 6 = 72

88 One into two

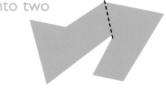

89 Downward attraction
C. It's a boomerang, which spins round its centre of gravity in flight.

90 Uphill struggle
D (because gravity is a downward force).

91 Under pressure

Place a tick in this box ✓ if E is the last letter of this sentence. If the reverse sides of the dice in figure A would total 10, write ZEBRA in this space **ZEBRA**. If the plural of mouse is mice, write MICE in this space **MICE**, if it isn't, write NICE. How many of the words in this sentence have not been spelt innkorrektly? **12**. Tick this box if you can spell the word ~~iguana~~ from the letters in figure B ✓. If the circle in figure C has a greater area than the triangle, cross out the word in the previous sentence that contains the most vowels. If the triangle has a greater area, cross out the word lobster here. If Bill Clinton's middle name is the same as the last name of a former US president, write IT IS here **NO**, unless Ronald Reagan's middle name is the same as a former British Prime Minister's, in which case write NO instead. If the flags of three European countries are contained in figure D, write SUPER under this line **Super**. If Norway is one of them, write DUPER above the line, unless the name of a South American country can be found in the previous sentence, in which case write SUPER. Circle the word in this puzzle that contains the most letters, unless it is spelt ⟨incorrectly⟩ in which case circle the word that contains the second largest number of letters.

E is the last letter of the first sentence. The reverse sides of a dice always add up to 7, so the reverse sides of the shown dice – 4, 5 and 2 – would be 3, 2 and 5, and do indeed total 10. The plural of mouse is mice. All the words in the sentence have not been spelt incorrectly except innkorrektly. The word iguana can indeed be spelt from the letters in figure B, even though there is a spare U. Iguana is the word in the sentence that contains the most vowels. A circle with the same width and height as a triangle has a greater area. Bill Clinton's middle name is Jefferson, a former US president. Ronald Reagan's middle name is Wilson, a former British Prime Minister. The flags are of Sweden, Denmark and Finland. The word PERU appears in the previous sentence. The word incorrectly is the longest word and has been spelt correctly, so INCORRECTLY should be circled.

92 Just say yes or no
1 No, pink is before red
2 No, Snoozy isn't
3 Yes
4 Yes
5 Yes
6 No, 1930 wasn't
7 Yes
8 Yes, Hygiene and Phial

93 Lost property office
1 4
2 A book
3 3
4 3
5 An eagle
6 13 (7 keys and 6 balls)
7 The spear (top left)
8 Red
9 2
10 2 (top left)

94 After the storm
1 A
2 Red
3 B
4 6 (purple)
5 N
6 Yellow
7 2 (R and W)
8 Pink
9 A
10 I
11 3 (A, I and O)
12 N
13 B
14 Pink
15 3 (I, N and O)

95 Touch-tone test
1 6
2 #
3 7
4 0
5 8
6 24 (7 + 8 + 9)
7 5
8 15 (2 + 5 + 8 + 0)
9 8
10 4 (2, 3, 5, 7)
11 9
12 8
13 3
14 5 (letters in SEVEN)
15 4

96 Count your cards
1 5 of Clubs
2 6 of Clubs
3 Diamonds
4 Clubs
5 Hearts
6 Queen
7 9
8 Spades
9 9 (2, 4, 7, 8, 9, 10, J, Q, K)
10 Diamonds
11 7
12 23 (4 + 9 + 10)
13 5 of Clubs
14 42 (3 + 5 + 6 + 8 + J(10) + K(10))
15 44 (6 + 7 + 8 + 9 + 4 + Q(10))

97 Image-conscious
1 Padlock
2 Spider
3 Four (letters in 'Star')
4 5
5 3
6 8 (Heart)
7 3 (eye sounds like 'I')
8 Clock
9 Key
10 11 (eye (3) plus heart (8))
11 12 (4 + 8)
12 14 (2 × 7)
13 75 (3 × 5 × 5)
14 3 (6 – 3)
15 27 (3 + 8 + 7 + 4 + 5)

98 Colourful memories
1 Nail varnish bottle
2 Gift bow
3 Zip
4 Pen
5 Screwdriver
6 Trumpet
7 Feathers
8 Small bowl
9 Fire engine
10 Peg
11 Purse
12 Watch
13 Teddy bear
14 Brass ring
15 Button

99 The corners of your mind
1 Plug and chain
2 Scissors
3 Vase
4 Screw
5 Half-moon
6 Sweet
7 Padlock
8 Heart
9 Rings
10 Fish
11 Keys
12 Shells
13 Safety pin
14 Marble
15 Hairband
16 Dice
17 Reel of thread
18 Spectacles
19 Lightbulb
20 Egg
21 Aeroplane keyring
22 Spanner
23 Lipstick
24 Candles
25 Beaded necklace

100 Jack Brady, Private Investigator
1 Red 1957 Plymouth
2 Blue
3 Bottom left-hand
4 Brady is incorrectly spelt
5 Oak
6 31st and Main
7 Blonde
8 Four years
9 Drained her glass
10 Chinos

101 The old man and the whale
1 Iztacalco
2 Tuxpan
3 Pedro
4 The Tula
5 10 feet across
6 Right (starboard)
7 Snapper
8 Like summer thunder
9 The Pole star
10 A tsunami

102 The race
1 Gamegirl
2 Sean Casey
3 Banana Skin
4 4 to 1
5 Pete Broad
6 First Gear or Lazy Bones
7 Mike Stack (on Last Straw)
8 Blue and white
9 Idle One, Dozy Lad, Sleepwalk
10 Yellow

103 The mission
1 Black
2 Gregorovich
3 Freya Berga, Mathilde Masseuse, Tracy Boggins
4 White
5 In Washington Park
6 Six of Clubs
7 The Kool Kat Klub
8 His right hand
9 'Quicker than that, I think.'
10 The voice said 'Good luck', not 'Good luck, Jon'

104 Identity parade
1 3, 6 and 7
2 2
3 5
4 6
5 3
6 Brown
7 9
8 7
9 Yellow
10 4
11 The right
12 Triangular

1 Brought to book

Aslan	Napoleon
Bilbo Baggins	Oompa Loompas
Christian	Passepartout
Doolittle	Queeg
Esmeralda	Rosinante
Fiver	Shere Khan
George	Timmy
Humbert Humbert	Ursus
Ishmael	Valjean
Jim Hawkins	White Rabbit
Karla	Xavier
Little Nell	Yossarian
Morgana	Zillah

2 The wild alphabet

Acorn	Juniper	Sardine
Basenji	Kangaroo[2]	Tarantula
Canary	Ladybird[3]	Ungulate
Dill	Mongoose	Vanilla
Echidna	Narcissus	Wolfsbane
Flax	Ostrich	Xylem
Gopher[1]	Pawpaw	Yak
Horseradish	Quagga	Zebu
Iguanodon	Roadrunner	

[1] From the French gauffre.
[2] The legend goes that an explorer pointed towards one and asked an Aborigine what it was, to which the reply was 'Kangaroo' – 'I don't understand'.
[3] In the Middle Ages, farmers believed that the help given by ladybirds in eating crop pests was a manifestation of the Virgin Mary herself.

3 Name the author

Adams, Douglas (author, book: *The Hitch-Hiker's Guide to the Galaxy*)
Barnum, Phineas T. (showman)
Chaplin, Charlie (actor and filmmaker)
Descartes, René (philosopher and mathematician. It means: 'I think therefore I am')
Einstein, Albert (physicist)
Fleming, Ian (author, book: *Dr No*)
Goldwyn, Sam (film producer)
Hendrix, Jimi (rock musician, song: 'Purple Haze')
Ibsen, Henrik (playwright, play: *The Master Builder*)
Jackson, Andrew (seventh President of the USA)
Kipling, Rudyard (author and poet, book: *The Just So Stories*)
Liberace, Wladziu (performer)
Mitchell, Margaret (author, book: *Gone with the Wind*)
Nixon, Richard (37th President of the USA)
Orwell, George (author, book: *Animal Farm*)
Parker, Dorothy (writer and critic)
Quiller-Couch, Sir Arthur (writer, also known as 'Q', work: *A Lady Jane, Sapphics*)
Ritz, César (Swiss hotelier)
Stanley, Sir Henry (explorer)
Tolkien, J. R. R. (author, book: *The Lord of the Rings*)
Ustinov, Peter (actor, director, writer, book: *Dear Me*)
Virgil, Publius (Roman poet, book: *Aeneid*)
West, Mae (actress, film: *Klondike Annie*)
Xenophon (Greek historian, book: *Anabasis*)
Yeats, W. B. (poet, poem: 'The Ghost of Roger Casement')
Zappa, Frank (rock musician and songwriter)

4 Wish you were here?

1 The Chrysler Building, New York, USA
2 Angkor Wat, Angkor, Cambodia
3 The Colosseum, Rome, Italy
4 The Duomo, Florence, Italy
5 Edinburgh Castle, Edinburgh, Scotland
6 Bodnath Temple, Kathmandu, Nepal
7 Sagrada Familia, Barcelona, Spain
8 Schönbrunn Castle, Vienna, Austria
9 St Basil's Cathedral, Moscow, Russia
10 Pyramid of the Moon, Teotihuacán, Mexico
11 Taj Mahal, Agra, India
12 Stonehenge, Salisbury Plain, England

5 Completely barking

1 Bulldog
2 Boston Terrier
3 Boxer
4 Beagle
5 Doberman Pinscher
6 Golden Retriever
7 Dalmatian
8 Chihuahua
9 Basset Hound
10 Pomeranian
11 Cocker Spaniel
12 Greyhound

6 Science

1 Albert Einstein
2 The Manhattan Project
3 Alexander Fleming
4 Transistor
5 The Hubble Space Telescope (named after Edwin P. Hubble)
6 Alchemy
7 Charles Wheatstone
8 Charles Babbage
9 Gunpowder
10 Nylon

7 Literature

1 Louisa M. Alcott
2 Mowgli
3 Merlin
4 The US Civil War
5 Nikolai Gogol
6 Peter Pan
7 Henry Fielding
8 (Nick) Bottom
9 J. D. Salinger
10 T. S. Eliot

8 Record breakers

1 Reticulated python at 9m (30ft)
2 Mt Everest at 8848m (29,028ft)
3 The blue whale
4 Jupiter
5 The giant squid
6 Brazil
7 The Yangtze, China (5470km/3400 miles)
8 A temperature of 58°C (136°F) in the shade has been recorded in Libya
9 The Archers
10 The bee hummingbird at 35g (1¼oz)

9 The Olympics

1 Ben Johnson
2 Theodosius I
3 Amsterdam
4 Cross-country skiing and target shooting
5 Steve Ovett
6 London, England
7 Donovan Bailey
8 Athens, Greece
9 Marathon
10 Jesse Owens

10 Empires

1 The Roman Empire
2 The Byzantine Empire
3 The Egyptian Empire
4 The Trojan horse
5 The British Empire
6 The Spanish conquistadores
7 Darth Vader
8 The Mongol Empire
9 The Turkish Republic
10 India

11 Hollywood

1 *The Birds*
2 Zsa Zsa Gabor
3 George Raft
4 Steven Spielberg
5 Charlie Chaplin
6 Ingrid Bergman
7 Mack Sennett
8 Richard Burton
9 Rudolph Valentino
10 John Wayne

12 Music

1 Ludwig van Beethoven
2 John Lennon
3 Wolfgang Amadeus Mozart
4 Ragtime
5 Trumpet
6 Phil Spector
7 Gilbert and Sullivan – Sir William Schwenck Gilbert and Sir Arthur Seymour Sullivan
8 *The Sound of Music*
9 Elvis Presley
10 Grunge

13 Animal world

1 Duck-billed platypus
2 Cheetah
3 They cool the elephant's blood
4 Porcupine
5 Mammal
6 No
7 Ostrich
8 Coelacanth
9 Hibernation
10 Owl

14 Game facts

1 Nadia Comaneci in Montreal, 1976
2 17 years (227 days)
3 3m (10ft)
4 Javelin, hammer, discus, shot, triple jump
5 Skiing
6 1994
7 Basketball, the highest international score ever
8 Brazil
9 Jack Nicklaus
10 Because it is a 500 mile long motor race

15 Sporting chance

1 American Football   (USA)
2 Snooker   (UK)
3 Cricket   (Antigua)
4 Golf   (USA)
5 Cricket   (Sydney Cricket Ground, Australia)
6 Horse-racing   (USA)
7 Tennis   (USA)
8 Motor-racing   (Belgium)
9 Rugby   (Scotland)
10 Football   (Spain)

16 Motor mania

1 53
2 Bananas – as in the film *Herbie Goes Bananas*
3 It was the first land vehicle to break the sound barrier
4 Volvo
5 Aston Martin DB5
6 Dave Starsky (of 'Starsky and Hutch')
7 The Model T Ford
8 Karl
9 A Delorean
10 Alec Issigonis

17 Hobby horse

1 The zenith
2 The decorative shaping of hedges, plants and trees
3 A numismatist
4 Ten pin bowling. It's a ball
5 A photographer, to connect a flash to a camera
6 Knitting, it's a trellis or basket weave of knitted strips
7 Prestidigitation
8 Chess
9 Hawaii
10 Origami

18 Then add a pinch of...

1 Types of herbs
2 Types of tea
3 Types of pasta
4 They are bean-based or products of beans
5 Chillies
6 Fungi
7 Potatoes
8 i   Scones
   ii Grill
   iii Black treacle
   iv Crisps
   v   Prawns
   vi Coriander
   vii Aubergine
   viii Water biscuits
   ix   Spring onion
   x   Cos lettuce
   xi   Icing sugar
9 The dried stigmas of the saffron crocus.
10 All are salmon at various stages of its development (from newly hatched eggs to the few mature spent salmon that survive after spawning).

19 Eat locally

1 i   France (thin pancakes flavoured with orange and flamed in curaçao)
  ii   South Africa (lightly curried minced beef, topped with a custard and baked)
  iii United States (cooked fruit topped with blobs of batter or raw biscuit/scone dough and baked)
  iv   Japan (pieces of vegetable or seafood deep-fried in a light batter)
  v   Greece (layered meat and aubergine or potato, flavoured with tomato, topped with an enriched white sauce and baked)
  vi   Thailand (fermented-fish sauce)
  vii India (rich cream sweet flavoured with saffron and cardamom)
  viii Italy (rich cream dessert, lightly set with gelatine, served with fruit or a vividly flavoured sauce)
  ix   Scotland (mashed potato and cooked cabbage, mixed with butter-fried onion and chives, covered with grated cheese and grilled or baked)
  x   Australia (a type of semi-aquatic crayfish found in much of that country)
  xi   Alsace (a cross between quiche and a pizza, with a very thin yeast-dough base, topped with a creamy onion mixture with crisp bacon)
  xii Spain (casseroled chicken and rice, usually flavoured with saffron and tomatoes)
  xiii Russia (strudel-shaped baked pie, using either bread dough or flaky pastry, rolled round a layered filling of salmon or firm white fish, hard-boiled eggs, rice or buckwheat, enriched with butter)
  xiv Switzerland (melted Emmental and Gruyère cheese, white wine and kirsch, kept hot in a chafing-dish/fondue pan, into which cubes of bread are dipped on long forks)
  xv   Morocco (soup eaten at the end of the day's fasting during Ramadan: vegetables, lentils, beans and other pulses are cooked in water or stock, sometimes enriched with meat, and seasoned with spices and herbs)
  xvi England (a sort of spiced Yorkshire scone/biscuit containing currants)

2 i   Spinach
  ii   Blood-orange juice
  iii Tomato
  iv   Onion
  v   Mushroom
  vi   Carrot
  vii Apple
  viii Cream
  ix   Truffle

3   Cake

20 Mainly wine

1 Port
2 Soave (a dry white wine from the Veneto region of north-east Italy)
3 Barrels
4 i   Pinot Blanc/Weissburgunder/Clevner
  ii Syrah/Marsanne Noir
  iii Malbec/Cahors/Pressac
  iv Grenache/Tinto/Alicante
  v   Muscat/Frontignac/Moscato Bianco/Moscatel
5 i   Cherries
  ii Pears
  iii Apples
  iv Blackcurrants
6 Sparkling
7 None. Oxidation is a necessary part of the sherry-making process. Autolysis is the action of dead yeast cells, left in sparkling wine for several years after secondary fermentation, producing a 'bready' or 'biscuity' flavour in fine champagne. Carbonization is the addition of carbon dioxide to produce cheap sparkling wine and other fizzy drinks. *Botrytis cinerea* is a benign fungus that shrivels ultra-ripe grapes, concentrates their flavour and produces the world's finest sweet wines, for example, Sauternes and Beerenauslese.
8 Fining (clarifying and stabilizing wine)

21 Who was who

1	Cliff Richard	6	Tony Curtis
2	Bob Dylan	7	Fred Astaire
3	W. C. Fields	8	Dean Martin
4	Cary Grant	9	Tina Turner
5	Rock Hudson	10	Julie Andrews

22 The name's Smith

1 14
2 *Casino Royale*
3 *Chitty Chitty Bang Bang*
4 True, in *Never Say Never Again*
5 Q
6 *Tomorrow Never Dies*
7 *Goldfinger*
8 A steel-rimmed bowler hat
9 *Tomorrow Never Dies* starred Teri Hatcher, television's Lois Lane
10 Bond married her

23 It's a great part

Hair of Cher
Eyes of Liza Minnelli
Nose of Gerard Depardieu
Mouth of Julia Roberts
Chin of Arnold Schwarzenegger
Body of Marilyn Monroe
Legs of Mr Bean (Rowan Atkinson)

24 Relatively close

1 Humphrey Bogart
2 Whitney Houston
3 Carrie Fisher
4 Janet Leigh
5 Jamie Lee Curtis
6 Warren Beatty
7 Debbie Reynolds
8 Francis Ford Coppola
9 Nicolas Cage
10 Dionne Warwick
11 Lauren Bacall
12 Shirley Maclaine

1 is the husband of 11
2 is the cousin of 10
3 is the daughter of 7
4 is the mother of 5
6 is the brother of 12
8 is the uncle of 9

25 Marvellous mammals

1 Aardvark
2 Whales, dolphins and porpoises, i.e., mammals that live entirely in water
3 Sloth
4 Polar bear
5 Marsupial
6 Sheep
7 Tiger
8 Koala bear
9 Bat
10 Raccoon

26 Dinoquiz

1 Plants (they were vegetarian)
2 Michael Crichton
3 Tyrannosaurus rex
4 Birds
5 That a giant meteorite had struck the Earth
6 *On the Town*
7 Thunder
8 The Cretaceous period
9 Canada (Alberta)
10 Lizard

27 In your garden – and beyond

1 Cactus
2 Golden Rod
3 Rose
4 Botany
5 Carnation
6 Herbs
7 Mistletoe
8 Globe artichoke[1]
9 Breadfruit
10 Heather
[1] Strictly speaking, Jerusalem artichokes are a completely different plant

28 Woofers and mousers

1 Edinburgh
2 Calvin Coolidge
3 St Bernard
4 15
5 Bloodhound
6 Stretch
7 False: females bite more often
8 Sylvester
9 Butch or Spike[1]
10 False

[1]In the early episodes the bulldog was named Butch. It was not until 1952 that he became known as Spike.

29 Doctor, doctor

1 The leg
2 Jonas Edward Salk
3 German measles
4 Osteopathy
5 The brain
6 The stethoscope
7 Smallpox
8 Clavicle
9 Hypnosis
10 The cardiac pacemaker

30 Pluses and minuses

1 Pi (π)
2 Bertrand Russell
3 12
4 August Ferdinand Möbius (the Möbius strip)
5 Boolean
6 Lewis Carroll
7 Pierre de Fermat (Fermat's Last Theorem)
8 Euclid
9 John Napier (Napier's bones)
10 Blaise Pascal

31 Technical pursuit

1 Hans Geiger (the Geiger counter)
2 Polaroid
3 Laptop computer
4 Al Jolson in *The Jazz Singer* (1927)
5 The electric light bulb
6 Frank Whittle
7 Karl Benz
8 Guglielmo Marconi
9 The world wide web
10 Radar

32 In the stars

1 Sputnik I
2 The Sea of Tranquillity
3 Nicolaus Copernicus
4 Asteroids
5 Saturn
6 Edwin Hubble
7 Magellan
8 Jupiter
9 Hale-Bopp
10 Sirius (the dog star)

33 In the pipeline

A connects with D
B connects with E
C connects with F

34 Trivia trail

Correct route:
South Korea
Easter
The **North** Star
George **East**man
South Sea Bubble
The **South** Island
Clint **East**wood
Northern Ireland
North Dakota
The **North** Sea
South Africa
Southpaw
The Wise Men of the **East**
East Germany
South Pole
West Side Story
Southern Lights
Vivienne **West**wood
West Point
North Atlantic Treaty Organization (NATO)
Mae **West**
Southern Cross
West Bank
Robert **South**ey
Eastings
New **South** Wales
Eastern
South America
The boxes '17th-century politician'
and 'Former republic of France'
were not visited during the route.

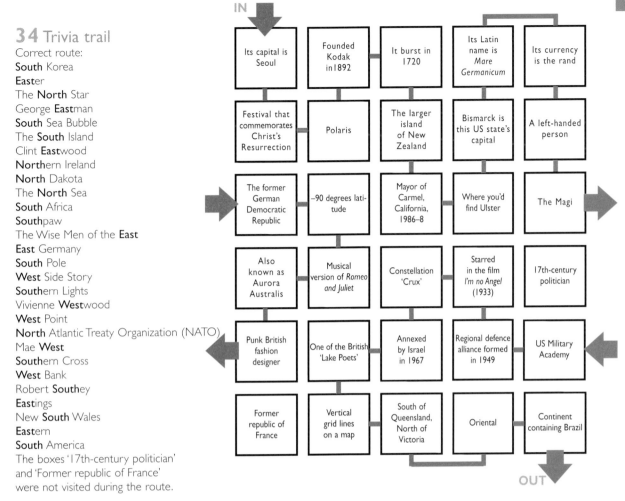

IN

Its capital is Seoul	Founded Kodak in 1892	It burst in 1720	Its Latin name is *Mare Germanicum*	Its currency is the rand
Festival that commemorates Christ's Resurrection	Polaris	The larger island of New Zealand	Bismarck is this US state's capital	A left-handed person
The former German Democratic Republic	−90 degrees latitude	Mayor of Carmel, California, 1986–8	Where you'd find Ulster	The Magi
Also known as Aurora Australis	Musical version of *Romeo and Juliet*	Constellation 'Crux'	Starred in the film *I'm no Angel* (1933)	17th-century politician
Punk British fashion designer	One of the British 'Lake Poets'	Annexed by Israel in 1967	Regional defence alliance formed in 1949	US Military Academy
Former republic of France	Vertical grid lines on a map	South of Queensland, North of Victoria	Oriental	Continent containing Brazil

OUT

35 Place these names

1 Mexico, Luxembourg
2 Zambia and Zimbabwe
3 Idaho, Illinois, Indiana, Iowa
4 Ran (France), wed (Sweden), run (Brunei) and had (Chad)
5 Republic of Ireland, Greece, Finland

36 Watch your language

6 Hungary
7 Brazil
8 Four: German, French, Italian, Romansch
9 Canada, Cameroon
10 Cantonese

37 Neighbours

11 Denmark, The Netherlands (Holland), Belgium, France, Switzerland, Austria, Czech Republic, Poland and Luxembourg
12 USA and Canada
13 Pakistan
14 The Gambia is almost completely surrounded by Senegal
15 USA–Mexico – nearly 500 million crossings a year

38 Common places

16 They are all rivers in North America
17 They are all lakes in Africa
18 They are the highest mountains in their respective continents: North America, South America, Africa, Australia
19 They are all capital cities of Caribbean countries (Barbados, Trinidad, St Lucia, Haiti, Jamaica)
20 They are all islands in the Mediterranean

39 Biggest, smallest, tallest

21 Russia
22 Canada
23 Venezuela
24 Mauna Loa on Hawaii
25 The State of the Vatican City
26 Lake Superior
27 Mount Elbrus
28 It's the deepest point of the Earth's oceans
29 The Great Australian Desert
30 Alabama, Wyoming

40 Movie locations

1 Argentina
2 Poland
3 Brazil
4 Russia
5 Morocco
6 Mexico
7 Ireland
8 China
9 France
10 Australia

41 Map file

1 Corsica
2 South Africa
3 France
4 Poland
5 Iceland
6 Italy
7 Peru
8 New Zealand
9 Mexico

42 Take your pick

1	c	Michelangelo	9	b	Picasso	17	b	Violin	25	a	As a jackal
2	a	'La Gioconda'	10	a	Constable	18	c	Animals	26	c	A bird
3	b	Frans Hals	11	c	Puccini	19	a	Conductor	27	b	Robin Goodfellow
4	b	Salvador Dalì	12	b	Nine	20	b	Slowly	28	b	Valhalla
5	a	Edvard Munch	13	b	Woodwind	21	a	Chimera	29	c	Sir Lancelot
6	c	A seashell	14	c	Methuselah	22	b	Ireland	30	b	Mandrake
7	b	Andy Warhol	15	c	British	23	a	The Eve of May Day			
8	c	Turner	16	a	Tchaikovsky	24	b	Cerberus			

43 Treasure hunt

Correct routes:

START 1 leads to the brown cross
START 2 leads to the light green cross
Explanations for FALSE answers:
1 In radio, AM stands for 'amplitude modulation'.
2 The Pyramid of the Sun is in Mexico.
3 An otter's habitation is called a holt.
4 The sternum is the breast bone.
5 In Buddhism, enlightened souls enter Nirvana.
6 Libya's flag is pure green.
7 In the TV show 'Happy Days', the Fonz's first name was Arthur.
8 *Ultra vires* means 'beyond one's powers.'
9 The dodo became extinct in 1681.
10 A scalene triangle has no identical angles.
11 The word 'pizza' means 'pie'

The correct versions of the false answers of the unused questions:
The title *A Man for All Seasons* refers to Sir Thomas More.
The Joshua Tree is an album by U2.
Homer wrote the poem *The Odyssey*.
Aries is the Zodiac sign of the ram.
Hans Christian Andersen was Danish.

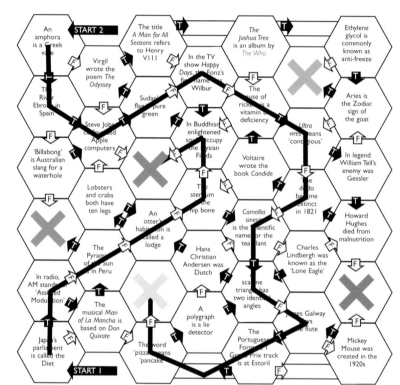

44 Images of Britain

1 The Angel of the North
2 Lincoln Cathedral
3 Castle Howard
4 Blackpool Tower
5 Canary Wharf
6 Ironbridge
7 The Royal Pavilion
8 Caernarfon Castle
9 The Bridge of Sighs
10 The Vale of the White Horse
11 Eilean Donan Castle
12 Clifton Suspension Bridge

45 Location finder

Gateshead
Lincoln
North Yorkshire
Blackpool
London
Coalbrookdale
Brighton
Gwynedd
Cambridge
Uffington
Loch Duich
Bristol

46 Dates to remember

1997
1400¹
1726
1894
1991
1779
1822
late 13th century
1831
c. 3000 BC
c. 1260
1864

¹The foundations were built in 1280 and the distinctive western towers were built in 1400

47 Who?

LEVEL 1

1 St David.
2 The Prime Minister. In fact, the inscription 'First Lord of the Treasury' appears on the door of No. 10 Downing Street.
3 Wallis Simpson. The quotation comes from Edward VIII's abdication speech.
4 Tom Jones.
5 Margaret Thatcher.
6 Geri Halliwell (Ginger Spice).

LEVEL 2

7 Florence Nightingale.
8 The Tolpuddle Martyrs (Tolpuddle being the Dorset village where this took place).
9 Billy Bragg.
10 Graham Greene.
11 Charles Rennie Mackintosh.

LEVEL 3

12 Terry Farrell.
13 Felons, holders of public office, the insane, members of the Armed Forces, peers and priests.

48 What?

LEVEL I

1 The Stone of Destiny (or 'Stone of Scone').
2 His pipe and his bowl and his fiddlers three.
3 England: rose; Ireland: shamrock;
  Scotland: thistle; Wales: daffodil.

LEVEL 2

4 Allotments.
5 A man on foot, carrying a red flag – hence the Red Flag Act of 1865. This act was later applied to cars.

LEVEL 3

6 Anything made out of sterling-quality silver, gold or (more recently) platinum. These are the hallmarks used by the four assay offices (London, Birmingham, Sheffield and Edinburgh respectively).
7 An obituary for 'English Cricket' was published, after a heavy defeat by Australia at the Oval. It went on to say that 'The body will be cremated and the ashes taken to Australia', which gave rise to 'The Ashes' test match.

49 Why?

LEVEL I

1 Because he could not write – he did, however, make his mark.
2 As a protest against taxes imposed by her husband on the townspeople.
3 Fishing rights in Icelandic waters.
4 Because it was assumed that the 'Princes in the Tower' – Edward V and his younger brother Richard – were murdered there.

LEVEL 2

5 The act allowed the authorities to release suffragettes who had become ill through hunger strikes and force feeding. They were re-arrested to serve out their sentence as soon as they had regained their strength. This bizarre law was known as the Cat and Mouse Act.
6 It was the subject of the first ever photographic negative. Lacock Abbey was the home of Fox Talbot, an early pioneer in photography.

LEVEL 3

7 His stories were sold as weekly or monthly parts, and were written as episodes in an ongoing story with cliffhanger endings at the end of each part. The later chapters were written after the first ones had been published.
8 '£' is a stylized version of 'L', which stands for 'Libra', the Latin word for pound.

50 Where?

LEVEL I

1 The English and Scottish parliaments, thus creating the Kingdom of Great Britain.
2 Bradford.
3 Portmeirion.
4 Aberystwyth.

LEVEL 2

5 Croydon.
6 Llangollen.

LEVEL 3

7 Oxford.
8 Nottingham.
9 Milton Keynes.

51 Matchmakers

Bottle labelled 'Drink Me'	*Alice in Wonderland*
Golden Fleece	*Jason and the Argonauts*
Apple	*William Tell*
Sword named 'Excalibur'	*Legend of King Arthur*
Submarine named Nautilus	*20,000 Leagues Under the Sea*
Albatross	*Rime of the Ancient Mariner*
Persian slipper	*Adventures of Sherlock Holmes*
Pieces of eight	*Treasure Island*
Glass slipper	*Cinderella*
Handbag	*The Importance of Being Earnest*

52 Famous first lines

1 *Richard III* – William Shakespeare
2 *The Trial* – Franz Kafka
3 *Rebecca* – Daphne du Maurier
4 'Ode to Autumn' – John Keats
5 *A Tale of Two Cities* – Charles Dickens
6 *A Passage to India* – E. M. Forster
7 *A la Recherche du Temps Perdu* (Remembrance of Things Past) – Marcel Proust
8 *Jabberwocky* – Lewis Carroll
9 *Captain Corelli's Mandolin* – Louis de Bernières
10 *Lord of the Rings* – J. R. R. Tolkien

53 What's in a name?

REAL NAMES	PEN NAMES
Samuel Clemens	Mark Twain
Hiraoka Kimitake	Yukio Mishima
Eric Blair	George Orwell
Francois-Marie Arouet	Voltaire
Alexei Maximovich Peshkov	Maxim Gorky
Catherine Cookson	Catherine Marchant
Charlotte Brontë	Currer Bell
Agatha Christie	Mary Westmacott
Mary Ann Evans	George Eliot
Rev'd Charles Dodgson	Lewis Carroll

54 Famous last lines

1 *Heart of Darkness* – Joseph Conrad
2 *The Name of the Rose* – Umberto Eco
3 *Animal Farm* – George Orwell
4 *Around the World in Eighty Days* – Jules Verne
5 *An Inspector Calls* – J. B. Priestley
6 'The Old Vicarage, Grantchester' – Rupert Brooke
7 *The Strange Case of Dr Jekyll and Mr Hyde* – R. L. Stevenson
8 *If* – Rudyard Kipling
9 *Macbeth* – William Shakespeare
10 *Nineteen Eighty-Four* – George Orwell

55 Who said it?

1 Juliet – William Shakespeare
2 Uriah Heep – Charles Dickens
3 The Three Musketeers – Alexandre Dumas
4 Owl – Edward Lear
5 Don Quixote – Miguel de Cervantes
6 Miss Jean Brodie – Muriel Spark
7 Robinson Crusoe – Daniel Defoe
8 Philip Marlowe – Raymond Chandler
9 Jane Eyre – Charlotte Brontë
10 Mowgli – Rudyard Kipling

56 Children's favourites

1 Never Never Land – J. M. Barrie
2 His nose grows longer – G. Lorenzini
3 Kansas – Frank Baum
4 By feeling the pea through all the beds, she proved she was a real princess – Hans Christian Andersen
5 Injun-Joe – Mark Twain
6 Narnia – C. S. Lewis
7 Hansel and Gretel – Brothers Grimm
8 Gaul/France – Goscinny & Uderzo
9 Hogwarts – Joanna Rowling
10 A seagull – Richard Adams

57 Whose line
1 'Auld Lang Syne' – Robert Burns
2 'The Elephant' – Hilaire Belloc
3 'Divine Comedy' (or 'Inferno') – Alighieri Dante
4 'Hiawatha' – Henry Longfellow
5 'The Soldier' – Rupert Brooke
6 'In Memoriam' – Alfred Lord Tennyson
7 'The Rubaiyat of Omar Khayyam' – Translated by Edward Fitzgerald
8 'Elegy in a Country Churchyard' – Thomas Gray
9 'Not Waving but Drowning' – Stevie Smith
10 'The Cow' – Ogden Nash

58 Fictional females
1 Miss Marple – Agatha Christie – *Murder in the Vicarage* et al
2 Elizabeth Bennett – Jane Austen – *Pride and Prejudice*
3 Tinker Bell – J. M. Barrie – *Peter Pan*
4 Eliza Doolittle – George Bernard Shaw – *Pygmalion*
5 Alice – Lewis Carroll – *Alice in Wonderland*
6 Daisy Buchanan – F. Scott Fitzgerald – *The Great Gatsby*
7 Lady Chatterley – D. H. Lawrence – *Lady Chatterley's Lover*
8 Mrs Proudie – Anthony Trollope – *Barchester Chronicles*
9 Emma Bovary – Gustave Flaubert – *Madame Bovary*
10 Sethe – Toni Morrison – *Beloved*

59 Hit the headlines
1 1858. Visions of Christ were seen at Lourdes in France.
2 1985. The *Oprah Winfrey Show* was born. Winfrey also starred in the film *The Color Purple* in 1985.
3 1859. Blondin walked over Niagara Falls – in later crossings, he did so blindfold and on stilts!
4 1961. Hammarskjöld was Secretary General of the United Nations for eight years.
5 1979. Louise Brown was the world's first 'test-tube baby'.
6 1868. This was the first recorded hole-in-one in golf.
7 1903. Gillette invented the first razor with disposable blades.
8 1978. Karol Wojtyla is better known as Pope John Paul II.
9 30 BC. Cleopatra. A Shakespeare play later put forward the theory that she was bitten by an asp.
10 1969. Paul McCartney, of Liverpool pop group *The Beatles*, got married.
11 1922. *Reader's Digest* was founded.
12 1898. Marie and Pierre Curie isolate radium. Marie Curie died of radiation exposure.
13 1930. The first football World Cup.
14 1913. The world's first modern crossword puzzle is printed.
15 1783. The first manned hot-air balloon flight takes place.

60 Battle stations
1 (a) Battle of Hastings   (b) 1066
2 (a) Battle of Agincourt   (b) 15th century (1415)
3 (a) Battle of Trafalgar   (b) 1805
4 (a) Waterloo   (b) 1815
5 (a) The Alamo   (b) 1830s (1836)
6 (a) Battle of the Little Bighorn (b) 1870s (1876)
7 (a) Pearl Harbor   (b) December 1941
8 (a) D-Day   (b) June 1944
9 (a) Goose Green   (b) May 1982
10 (a) Operation Desert Storm   (b) January 1991

61 Those were the days
1 1929
2 Benito Mussolini
3 John Logie Baird
4 Charles Lindbergh
5 Greta Garbo
6 1939
7 The Reichstag
8 The Long March
9 Orson Welles
10 *Mallard*
11 1948
12 Leon Trotsky
13 Glenn Miller
14 Clement Attlee
15 George Orwell
16 1956
17 Roger Bannister
18 Dwight D. Eisenhower
19 Nikita Khrushchev
20 Edmund Hillary and Sherpa Tensing
21 1961
22 Edwin 'Buzz' Aldrin
23 Brian Epstein
24 *A Man for All Seasons*
25 Dr Christiaan Barnard
26 1977
27 General Idi Amin
28 Captain Mark Phillips
29 John Betjeman
30 Ayatollah Khomeini
31 1987
32 Nicolae Ceausescu
33 *The Last Emperor*
34 Boris Becker
35 Peter Wright
36 1990
37 Lisa-Marie Presley
38 Paula Jones
39 Barcelona
40 'Candle in the Wind' by Elton John

62 They made history
1 Suleiman the Magnificent
2 Alexander the Great
3 Joan of Arc
4 Catherine the Great
5 Peter the Great
6 John F. Kennedy
7 Golda Meir
8 Otto von Bismarck
9 Julius Caesar
10 Louis XIV
11 Yasser Arafat
12 Mao Zedong
13 Genghis Khan
14 Elizabeth I
15 Henry II (Plantagenet)
16 Martin Luther King
17 Mahatma Gandhi
18 Winston Churchill

Alexander the Great was tutored by Aristotle.

63 Wet afternoon medley
It Keeps Rainin'	Fats Domino 1961
Crying in the Rain	The Everly Brothers 1962
Tell it to the Rain	The Four Seasons 1967
Don't Let the Rain Come Down	Ronnie Hilton 1964
Raindrops Keep Falling on my Head	B. J. Thomas 1970
I Can't Stand the Rain	Tina Turner 1985
Rain Rain Rain	Frankie Laine 1954
Laughter in the Rain	Neil Sedaka 1974
Just Walkin' in the Rain	Johnnie Ray 1956
Rainy Night in Georgia	Randy Crawford 1981

64 Summer songs
The Sun Ain't Gonna Shine Anymore	The Walker Brothers 1966
Sunny Afternoon	The Kinks 1966
Summer is Over	Frank Ifield 1964
Summertime Blues	Eddie Cochran 1958
House of the Rising Sun	The Animals 1964
Summer Holiday	Cliff Richard 1963
Sunshine of Your Love	Cream 1968
Don't Let the Sun Go Down on Me	Elton John 1974
Summer Wind	Frank Sinatra 1966
You are the Sunshine of My Life	Stevie Wonder 1973

65 Rainbow rhapsody
Yellow Submarine	The Beatles
Green, Green Grass of Home	Tom Jones
Red Red Wine	UB40
Blue Monday	New Order
Black Velvet	Alannah Myles
White Christmas	Bing Crosby
Pink Cadillac	Natalie Cole
Silver Dream Machine	David Essex
Golden Brown	The Stranglers
Orange Crush	REM

66 War effort

The White Cliffs of Dover   Vera Lynn (Burton/Kent)
Run Rabbit Run   Flanagan and Allen (Kennedy/Carr)
Wish Me Luck   Gracie Fields (Parr-Davies)
Boogie Woogie Bugle Boy   The Andrews Sisters (Raye/Prince)
Lili Marlene   Marlene Dietrich (Leip/Scultze)
I'll Be Seeing You   Dinah Shore (Kahal/Fain)
In the Mood   Glenn Miller (Glenn Miller)
Sentimental Journey   Doris Day (Green/Brown/Homer)
One For My Baby   Frank Sinatra (Mercer/Arlen)
Don't Let's Be Beastly to   Noël Coward (Noël Coward)
the Germans

67 Technicolor test

Red Hot Chilli Peppers   Give it Away
Pink Floyd   Another Brick in the Wall
Yello   The Race
Deacon Blue   Real Gone Kid
Black Sabbath   Paranoid
Barry White   You're the First the Last My Everything
Bobby Goldsboro   Honey
Al Green   Let's Stay Together
Bobby Brown   Two Can Play That Game
Hot Chocolate   You Sexy Thing

68 Classical oddities

LEVEL 1
1 The 1812 Overture.
2 In theory, the whole piece happens 840 times.
3 John Cage.
4 Earth was deliberately missed out, and Pluto was not discovered until 1930.

LEVEL 2
5 He paid them to faint.
6 He didn't use any musical scores – he always conducted the orchestra from memory.
7 Tchaikovsky.
8 Schubert.

LEVEL 3
9 George Antheil.
10 A circus elephant.

69 It's instrumental

LEVEL 1
1 Harp.
2 Piccolo.
3 Oboes and bassoons.
4 Plectrum.

LEVEL 2
5 Gamelan.
6 Calliope.
7 Ocarina.
8 Only three.

LEVEL 3
9 The American composer John Sousa is the man behind both: he invented the sousaphone (a large tuba) and wrote *The Liberty Bell*, which was used as the theme music for *Monty Python*.
10 Violoncello. Pianoforte is the full name of the piano, in the same way that violoncello is the full name of the cello.

70 The works

LEVEL 1
1 *The Bridal Chorus* ('Here comes the bride...').
2 Because it was the first ever symphony to use a chorus of singers.
3 *Aida*.
4 They were all works that were left unfinished by the composer. In addition, all four have since been 'completed' by other composers.

LEVEL 2
5 3rd symphony (*Eroica*).
6 *The Marriage of Figaro* (Mozart) and *The Barber of Seville* (Rossini).
7 *Bolero*.
8 *The Nutcracker* (during 'Dance of the Sugar Plum Fairy').

LEVEL 3
9 *The Rite of Spring* (later performances were somewhat better received).
10 Haydn.

Testers

Many thanks to the following people, who gave their time to test the puzzles in this book.

Helen Aitchison   Rosie Anness   Adrian Bew   Janet Bew   Karen Bew   Philip Bew   Donald Binney   Roy Butcher   Cortina Butler   Alison Candlin   Andrew Chapman   Gabriel Colyer   Jordan Colyer   Martin Colyer   Liz Edwards   Matthew Edwards   Alison Ewington   Simon Hemelryk   Kathleen Hennessy   Phil Holden   Jessica Howard   Paul Howard   Richard Hudson   Deborah Hutchings   Mark Kermode   John Lister   Peter Mason   Catherine Messenger   Leslie Miller   Susan Miller   Christine Noble   Francesca Parenti   Keith Parker   Nick Perry   Jon Plumb   Jenny Rathbone   Barry Rockall   Lynda Rockall   Nadia Schwartzmann   Robert Shelley   Amy Smith   David Smith   Lucy Smith   Jill Steed   Lorraine Taylor   Martin Thompson   Sophie Thompson   Rachel Warren Chadd   Rachel Weaver

Puzzle contributors

Contributors are listed next to the numbers of the puzzles they compiled. Any puzzles not listed were created by Book Creation Services.

Mind mazes

Guy Campbell and Paul Moran:
3, 7, 9, 10–13, 15, 17, 54–63

Anna Nilsen:
14, 16, 18

Justin Scroggie:
19, 20

David Bodycombe:
21–53, 72–77, 83, 85, 86, 88

Philip Carter:
64–71

Word power

David Bodycombe:
1–4, 11, 12, 17–20, 27, 41–43, 47, 48, 79–83, 98

Philip Carter:
5

Brainwarp:
7–10, 28, 36, 37, 39, 40, 72, 76

Probyn Puzzles:
13–16, 24, 25, 73, 78, 99

Michael Mepham:
22, 23, 30

Jeffery Pike:
26, 31, 32, 44, 58, 74, 75, 96

Guy Campbell and Paul Moran:
29, 38, 70, 71, 77, 97

Justin Scroggie:
33–35, 60–69

C. J. Jones:
46, 53, 54

Brian Greer:
50

Chris Maslanka:
51, 52, 55–57, 104–127

Puzzlemakers:
59

Alan Simmons:
84–90

Thinks.com Ltd:
45, 49, 91, 92, 95, 100–103

Smart solutions

Puzzlemakers:
1–11

Philip Carter:
12–19, 25–31, 47–52

Michael Mepham:
20

David Bodycombe:
21–23, 34–44

Justin Scroggie:
24, 32, 33

Guy Campbell and Paul Moran:
45, 46

Chris Maslanka:
53

Figure it out

David Bodycombe:
1, 3, 8, 20–28, 36–39, 71–74, 81–85, 89, 90

Chris Maslanka:
2, 9–16, 101

Justin Scroggie:
4–7, 19, 67–70, 102–112

Guy Campbell and Paul Moran:
17, 18, 34, 35, 86–88

Erwin Brecher:
29–33, 91–95

Ken Russell and Philip Carter:
40–65

Philip Carter:
75–80

Puzzlemakers:
96–100

Think sideways

David Bodycombe:
1–6, 20–26, 51

Chris Maslanka:
1 (question 10), 3 (questions 6, 7), 7–19, 27–50, 52–56

Lloyd King:
57–71

Train your brain

Guy Campbell and Paul Moran:
1–13, 91–93

David Bodycombe:
15–18, 94–97

Ken Russell and Philip Carter:
19–90

Justin Scroggie:
100–103

Tricky trivia

David Bodycombe:
1–3, 23, 24, 33, 34, 43–50, 59, 64, 66, 68–70

Michael Mepham:
6–13

Guy Campbell and Paul Moran:
14, 16, 17, 21, 22, 28, 40, 63, 65, 67

Justin Scroggie:
15, 51–58

Aileen Hall:
18–20

Philip Carter:
25–27, 29–32

Jeffery Pike:
35–39, 42, 60, 61

Feature material supplied by: Brian Augarde; David Bodycombe; Don Manley (Quixote); Justin Scroggie.

Illustration credits

Guy Campbell and Paul Moran: Contents, p. 6; Mind mazes puzzles 3, 7, 9–13, 15, 17, 54–63; Smart solutions puzzles 45, 46; Figure it out puzzles 34, 35; Train your brain puzzles 1–13, 93

Darren Walsh: Mind mazes puzzle 8

Anna Nilsen: Mind mazes puzzles 14, 16, 18

Justin Scroggie: Mind mazes puzzles 19, 20; Figure it out puzzles 81–85

Flag Institute Enterprises Ltd, Chester: Mind mazes puzzles 38, 39

Helen Backhouse: Contents, p. 7; Smart solutions puzzle 24; Figure it out puzzles 96, 97; Think sideways puzzles 19, 27–37, 50, 53–56, 69, 70

All other illustrations by Book Creation Services.

Answers (page 98)

1 Man; who crawls on all fours as a baby, then walks upright on two legs, then leans on a stick when he is old.

2 A floppy disk.

Answers (page 127)

'An apple a day keeps the doctor away.' (Each letter has been moved on two places in the alphabet.)

'Russia is a riddle wrapped in a mystery inside an enigma.' (Winston Churchill. Each letter is encoded with the one at the opposite end of the alphabet: A=Z, B=Y, and so on.)

Picture credits

10 Corbis-Bettmann/UPI

17 AKG London, Corbis, Corbis-Bettmann, Corbis-Bettmann/UPI, Getty One Stone; background art by Helen Backhouse

20 Angelo Hornak/Corbis (Indus Maze Games); Mimmo Jodice/Corbis (Minotaur); Ancient Art & Architecture Collection (Chartres Cathedral)

21 Jason Hawkes/Getty One Stone (Longleat maze – background), Skyscan Photolibrary (Hever Castle and Bickton Park Foot Maze), E&E Picture Library/Geraldine Evans (Watts Chapel Angel)

54 AKG London

55 M. C. Escher's *Relativity* © Cordon Art B.V. – Baarn – The Netherlands. All rights reserved AKG London.

56 © Salvador Dali – Foundation Gala – Salvador Dali/DACS 2000 (Salvador Dali, *Swans Reflecting Elephants*, 1937)/AKG London

57 © ADAGP, Paris & DACS, London 2000 (Viktor Vasarely, *Toroni-Nagy*, 1969)/AKG London

61 Getty One Stone, except 3 and 6 (AKG London)

63 Robert Harding Picture Library

98 Sylvain Grandadam/Getty One Stone

99 The Art Archive

100–101 SCRABBLE ® is a registered trademark of J. W. Spear & Sons, Leicester LE3 2WT, England

126 Bettmann-Corbis (Julius Caesar), The Art Archive (Colossus), AKG London (Enigma Machine)

127 The Art Archive (Rosetta Stone)

136–137 AKG London

145 Rex

146 Tim Davies/Getty One Stone (Tiger) G. Ryan & S. Beyer/Getty One Stone (full sunflower), George Bernard/Science Photo Library (seed head of sunflower)

147 Claude Nuridsany & Marie Perennou/Science Photo Library (Nautilus shell), Mehau Kulyk/Science Photo Library (snowflake), Dr Fred Espenak/Science Photo Library (fractal background), Adam Hart-Davis/Science Photo Library (tap) Getty One Stone/Coneyl Jay (waterdrop)

184 Arcaid/Paul Raferty

185 David Reed/Corbis (Edward de Bono), The Art Archive (Sherlock Holmes), Rex (Trevor Bayliss)

212 Secchi-Lecaque/Roussel-Uclef/CNRI/Science Photo Library (neuron), Andrew Olney/Getty One Stone (baby)

213 Nick Vedros/Getty One Stone (smiling man)

214–215 Photographer Andrew Sydenham

221 Getty One Stone

224–225 Getty One Stone

230–231 Rex

232 Mel the dog appears courtesy of Dan and Joan Adams

238 'Double Your Money' (Hughie Green)/Ronald Grant Archive

239 Freud Communications

242 Getty One Stone, except 1 (Martin Jones/Arcaid) and 6 (Richard Waite/Arcaid)

248–249 AKG London

Book Production Manager Fiona McIntosh
Pre-Press Manager Howard Reynolds
Pre-Press Technical Analyst Martin Hendrick

Origination Studio One, London, England
Paper Townsend Hook Ltd, Snodland, England
Printing and binding Brepols Graphic Industries NV, Turnhout, Belgium

400-012-02

READER'S DIGEST COMPENDIUM OF
PUZZLES & BRAIN TEASERS

WITH OVER 1000 PUZZLES

Keep your brain fit ● **Test your word power** ●
Improve your knowledge ● **Sharpen your memory** ● **Have hours of fun**

Entertaining!
Compelling!

Stimulating!
Challenging!

**FREE pen and acetate sheet
so you can do the
puzzles again
and again**

ISBN 0-276-42449-2

ISBN 0 276 42449 2
£26.99

9 780276 424496